UNIVERSITY OF EDINBURGH

Pfizer Medical Monographs

6

This volume
comprises the papers read
at the sixth Symposium of
the Pfizer Foundation of the
Postgraduate Medical School,
University of Edinburgh, 1970.
Further volumes will
be published
annually

Pfizer Medical Monographs 6

# CONTROL OF GONADAL STEROID SECRETION

EDITORS
DAVID T. BAIRD AND J. A. STRONG

EDINBURGH
*at the University Press*

EDINBURGH UNIVERSITY PRESS
22 George Square, Edinburgh

ISBN 0 85224 204 2

Printed in Great Britain by
Western Printing Services Ltd
Bristol

¶WHEN the proposal for a Pfizer Symposium on reproductive endocrinology was being developed, the need to concentrate on a single theme led naturally to the series of subjects embraced within the title ultimately adopted, namely control of gonadal steroid secretion. The Trustees have reason to be pleased that almost without exception, the invitations issued on their behalf were accepted. Although limitations of various kinds were inevitable in planning the meeting, it was possible to assemble a range of authoritative speakers on each of the topics chosen.

This volume includes the substance of the papers delivered and the discussion which followed during the Sixth Pfizer Symposium held in Edinburgh on 13th, 14th and 15th May, 1970. We hope that the participants will be satisfied with the record of their efforts which this monograph represents. We are confident that it will be of interest and great value to very many others who could not be present.

In addition to a debt of gratitude to the participants for their collaboration in preparing manuscripts for the press, we are also particularly indebted to a number of personal friends among the participants who very generously agreed to help with the editorial task by preparing the transcript of the discussions after each session. This not only lightened our burden but we hope will be rewarded by considerably earlier publication than would otherwise have been possible.

We would like to thank Professor Eric C. Mekie, Director of the Edinburgh Postgraduate Board for Medicine, for providing the facilities and organisation for the meeting, Mrs M. Deuchars, Secretary to the Board, and the other members of staff who helped in many ways.

Finally, we are especially indebted to Miss Martha Mackenzie of the University Department of Medicine, Miss Jean Burnie of the University Department of Obstetrics and Miss Christine Matheson who together grappled with the task of transcribing the recording of the discussion.

The recorders referred to who edited the transcript were as follows: Session I, Dr K.P.Bland; Session II, Dr R.D.Bulbrook; Session III, Dr K.Fotherby; Session IV, Dr B.A.Cooke; Session V, Professor M.C. Macnaughton; Session VI, Dr A.I.Klopper.

Unfortunately we were unable to persuade Professor Harris to allow us to publish the transcript of his paper with which the Symposium opened, and on which so much that followed was based.

DAVID T. BAIRD

J. A. STRONG

Dr A. Aakvaag, Oslo
Dr K. D. Bagshawe, London
Dr D. T. Baird, Edinburgh
Dr K. P. Bland, Edinburgh
Dr H. Braunsberg, Edinburgh
Dr J. B. Brown, Melbourne
Dr R. D. Bulbrook, London
Dr W. R. Butt, Birmingham
Dr B. A. Cooke, Glasgow
Mr C. S. Corker, Oxford
Dr M. G. Coyle, Dundee
Dr A. C. Crooke, Birmingham
Dr N. Deshpande, London
Dr B. T. Donovan, London
Dr F. Dray, Paris
Prof. K. B. Eik-Nes, Los Angeles
Dr D. Exley, Oxford
Dr K. Fotherby, London
Dr P. Franchimont, Liège
Prof. C. Gemzell, Uppsala
Dr E. P. Giorgi, Glasgow
Dr J. K. Grant, Glasgow
Dr H. Gregory, Macclesfield
Dr K. Griffiths, Cardiff
Dr R. A. Harkness, Edinburgh
Prof. G. W. Harris, Oxford
Dr B. M. Hobson, Edinburgh
Prof. E. W. Horton, Edinburgh
Dr W. M. Hunter, Edinburgh
Dr W. J. Irvine, Edinburgh
Dr A. A. A. Ismail, Edinburgh
Prof. V. H. T. James, London
Dr S. L. Jeffcoate, London
Dr E. D. B. Johansson, Uppsala
Dr A. I. Klopper, Aberdeen
Dr P. Leymarie, Paris
Dr J. A. Loraine, Edinburgh
Prof. P. C. MacDonald, Dallas
Dr A. McLaren, Edinburgh
Prof. M. C. Macnaughton, Glasgow
Dr G. D. Matthew, Edinburgh
Mrs E. A. Michie, Edinburgh
Prof. I. H. Mills, Cambridge
Dr R. W. Morris, Sandwich
Dr F. Naftolin, Oxford
Dr J. Newton, London
Dr R. E. Oakey, Leeds
Prof. W. D. Odell, California
Prof. L. M. Pickford, Edinburgh
Prof. F. T. G. Prunty, London
Dr P. M. Stevenson, Edinburgh
Dr S. R. Stitch, Leeds
Dr P. B. Stones, Sandwich
Prof. J. A. Strong, Edinburgh
Dr H. J. van der Molen, Rotterdam
Dr A. Vermeulen, Ghent
Dr D. Y. Wang, London
Dr L. Wide, Uppsala

# The Extra-Hypothalamic Control of Gonadotrophin Secretion

B. T. DONOVAN

Department of Physiology, Institute of Psychiatry
De Crespigny Park, London

¶ A VARIETY of neural structures, besides the hypothalamus, contribute to the neuroendocrine mechanisms concerned with the control of gonadotrophin secretion. These include the amygdaloid nuclei, hippocampus, and brain stem reticular formation, as well as the afferent systems mediating the sensations of sight, smell, hearing and touch. The role of such exteroceptive factors and extra-hypothalamic structures in the regulation of pituitary function has been reviewed on a number of occasions recently [1–5], so that the present paper will be concerned only with some particularly intriguing aspects of the subject.

The clinical information available on the effect of brain damage or disease on gonadotrophin secretion has not contributed greatly to the understanding of the processes involved. Disorders of sexual function were most common in a series of fourteen clinical cases of intracranial extra-sellar lesions studied from an endocrine viewpoint [6], but the hypothalamus appeared to be affected in all. Lesions of the thalamus produced surgically in the treatment of disorders of involuntary movement did not elicit endocrine changes [7]. Temporal lobe seizures in children have been associated with precocious, or delayed, puberty [8], but many patients with comparable seizures show no signs of gonadal dysfunction. Disturbances in menstrual rhythm were found in monkeys after temporal lobectomy, but the nature of the changes produced is not clear [9].

In view of the importance of psychological factors in the genesis of reproductive disorders such as amenorrhoea, dysfunctional uterine bleeding, dysmenorrhoea, psychogenic infertility and spontaneous abortion [10], it is perhaps surprising that so little is known of the role of the cerebral cortex in the control of gonadotrophin secretion. Much of the brain of the rabbit, including the neocortex, fornix, septum, lateral amygdala and dorsal thalamus, can be removed without preventing ovulation, while in the rat regular oestrous cycles and normal pregnancies have continued after complete removal of the neocortex [11]. Involvement of the cerebral cortex in the control of gonadotrophin secretion in the male has been indicated by the work of Soulairac and Soulairac [12] who associated testicular atrophy in the rat with damage to the cerebral cortex. However, the act of coitus is now known to promote gonadotrophin secretion in the male [13–16], so that any deficiency in sexual behaviour occurring after cortical lesions may secondarily depress testicular function. Signs of luteinizing hormone (LH) release in rats upon stimulation of the cortex by the local injection of hypertonic saline were observed by Taleisnik, Caligaris and de Olmos [17]. The effect could be prevented by the addition of procaine to the fluid but no specially effective locus of stimulation was found.

More direct information on the extra-hypothalamic control of gonadotrophin secretion has come from study of the exteroceptive factors involved, especially that of environmental lighting [1, 3, 18]. Under normal conditions the stimulus of light is transduced into neural activity by the retina, but the pathway between the optic nerves and hypothalamus has proved difficult to identify. Much attention has been given to a direct route between the optic chiasma and hypothalamus, but this has not been established anatomically [19, 20]. More roundabout routes exist, in that visual stimuli may be relayed through the tegmentum of the midbrain without necessarily traversing the superior colliculi. Although sunlight has been shown to penetrate to the hypothalamus of the sheep, dog, rabbit and rat [21], and light directed to the suprachiasmatic region of blinded rats brought about changes in the vaginal cycle [22], visual radiation is not believed to act physiologically in this way.

Over the years there have been many suggestions that the pineal gland may be involved in the transmission of photic stimuli to the hypothalamus and pituitary, but it is only recently that an experimental basis for this view has been provided. The significant experiments involved the blinding of hamsters or the exposure of the animals to but one or two hours of light daily. Gonadal atrophy quickly ensued, but if the animals were pinealectomized the gonads did not regress. Removal of the superior cervical ganglia also prevented gonadal degeneration, and if blinded animals with small reproductive organs were subjected to pinealectomy or ganglionectomy slow gonadal enlargement occurred [23]. The pineal gland contains the indole melatonin, which is formed from N-acetylserotonin by the enzyme hydroxyindole-methyl transferase (HIOMT), present only in the organ. Both the concentrations of melatonin and HIOMT fluctuate in the course of 24 hours, with that of melatonin being low during the day but reaching a peak at the onset of darkness. HIOMT activity in the pineal gland of rats is inhibited by exposure to constant light, rises in animals kept in the dark, and also rises in animals kept in constant light but subjected to superior cervical ganglionectomy [24, 25]. Interruption of the major projections from the eyes, by interference with the optic tracts, did not block the effect of light upon HIOMT activity, so that an alternative pathway, perhaps involving the medial forebrain bundle, seems to be used. Lesions in the medial forebrain bundle inhibit the response to continuous illumination in rats and are believed to act by severing the inferior accessory optic tract running from the optic chiasma to the rostral midbrain tegmentum [26, 27]. It is suggested that a projection runs from the medial terminal nucleus of the inferior accessory optic tract (the nucleus of Bochenek) down the spinal cord to supply the sympathetic outflow in the thorax, and, in turn, the superior cervical ganglia, which innervate the pineal gland. This is a long, complicated, and indirect route that, while accounting for the comparable effects of superior cervical ganglionectomy or medial forebrain bundle lesions on light-induced vaginal changes in the rat, leaves several matters unresolved. As yet the evidence for pineal gland involvement in the control of gonadotrophin secretion is indirect and largely inferential [25, 28] and it is by no means clear how any pineal gland factor reaches the hypothalamus or hypophysis. Diffusion across the thalamus may occur, but appears unlikely. On the other hand it is fair to add that both superior cervical ganglionectomy and pinealectomy delay the onset of light-induced oestrus in the ferret [29]. The physiological function of melatonin also remains to be established, for the role of this compound in gonadal physiology remains equivocal, although the implantation of melatonin into the reticular formation or median eminence reduced the pituitary content and plasma level of LH in castrated male rats [23, 30–32].

Implicit in most discussions of the effect of light on endocrine activity is the idea that photic energy acts as a stimulus. This is an over-simplification, for little is known of the effects exerted by photic energy beyond the retina. Alongside the stimulatory action of light in advancing puberty or accelerating the onset of oestrus in seasonally breeding species [33], exposure to long days can inhibit gonadotrophin secretion [34–36]. This effect has been demonstrated in animals kept under conditions involving long days from the middle of summer, as well as in animals exposed to different regimes of light and darkness, where a greater acceleration of oestrus occurred in ferrets provided with sixteen hours of light daily, than in animals kept under constant illumination [37, 38]. It may help to explain why the breeding season of ferrets, normally geared to the increasing length of day in the spring, ends in midsummer, when the days are still long.

The neural mechanism upon which light acts remains unknown. However, photic stimuli unquestionably can reach and interact with the mechanism controlling the circadian fluctuations in hormone secretion, as is well seen in rats, where constant illumination quickly brings the oestrous cycle to a halt and persistent vaginal oestrus ensues [11]. Not all species respond in this way, for the oestrous rhythm of the guinea-pig and hamster is not affected by changes in the length of day. It has proved difficult to demonstrate any effect of environmental lighting on the menstrual cycle of the monkey [39], although circadian rhythms in deep body temperature and locomotor activity alter with changes in photoperiods [40], while the information available for the human differs from that obtained experimentally. Zacharias and Wurtman [41] concluded that blind children had an earlier menarche than normal girls, but there was no difference in the age at menarche of groups of blind and non-blind children studied by Thomas and Pizzarello [42]. Subsequently, Zacharias and Wurtman [43] analyzed the information collected from 524 blind and 436 non-blind girls and showed that blind girls lacking light perception experienced menarche an average of seven months earlier than non-blind controls. This effect is the opposite of that observed in rats and ferrets, where light promotes gonadotrophin secretion and ovarian activation [1, 3].

Olfactory stimuli, too, can be influential in modifying sexual function. The chemical agents involved are called pheromones, and can trigger sexual behaviour in male and female, affect the timing of oestrus, or block an expected pregnancy [44]. Sexual arousal in male rhesus monkeys can be elicited by pheromones produced in the perineal region of females under the influence of oestrogen [45]. While removal, or blockade, of the olfactory bulbs prevents such responses, the neural pathways mediating them have not been defined, largely because many routes are open to olfactory stimuli. From the olfactory tracts significant information can be channelled to the amygdaloid nuclei, the piriform lobe, the septal area and, indirectly, to the hippocampus [46], as well as directly to the hypothalamus [47]. Projections from the primary olfactory cortex – the piriform cortex – of the rabbit have been traced to the amygdaloid nuclei, the entorhinal area, and the entire rostrocaudal extent of the hypothalamus. Agenesis of the olfactory lobes in man has been associated with gonadal malfunction [48], and removal of the olfactory bulbs in rabbits [49, 50], mice [51,] and pigs [52] has had similar consequences. Vaginal opening was delayed in rats rendered anosmic in infancy [53] although the oestrous rhythm of adult rats or guinea-pigs was not disturbed [54, 55]. Stimulation of the olfactory bulbs in the cat has caused ovulation [56].

There is no doubt that the amygdaloid nuclei in the temporal lobes of the brain influence gonadotrophin secretion. Anatomical and electrophysiological studies indicate that the amygdala project to a wide subcortical region extending from the septum through the preoptic area and hypothalamus to the midbrain tegmentum, and that the two nuclear complexes within the amygdala use separate pathways for this purpose. The stria terminalis acts for the corticomedial and the basolateral nuclei, whereas a ventral amygdalofugal system, taking a sublenticular and subcapsular course, serves the basolateral group. Both systems project to the same tuberal hypothalamic region, but differing responses on the part of hypothalamic cells have been observed. Impulses travelling along the ventral amygdalofugal pathway first activate and then inhibit neurones in the ventromedial nuclei, while impulses conveyed by the stria terminalis simply inhibit ventromedial cells [57, 58].

The input to the amygdaloid nuclei comes from a variety of sources. Olfactory fibres end in the corticomedial group of nuclei, the piriform cortex connects with the basolateral group, and projections from the hypothalamus, thalamus and neocortex have also been made out. It is thus not surprising that the electrical activity of the basolateral nuclear group, for example, is altered by a range of sensory stimuli [46], and, in turn, that stimulation of the amygdaloid nuclei has elicited ovulation in rabbits [59, 60], cats [59, 61] and rats [62, 63]. In the recent work of Velasco and Taleisnik [64], electrochemical stimulation involving irritation from the electrolytic deposition of iron, and chemical stimulation by the local application of carbachol, were used and the ovulatory response was blocked by transection of the stria terminalis, but not by interference with the ventral amygdalofugal pathway. The concentration of follicle-stimulating hormone (FSH) and LH in the plasma of oestrogen-treated spayed rats rose with stimulation of the amygdaloid complex, but the LH level of intact males, or of castrated males primed with oestrogen or testosterone propionate, was not elevated. Stimulation of the preoptic area in male rats, as well as in females, increased the output of LH. The onset of puberty in infant rats has been delayed by stimulation of the amygdaloid nuclei [65].

Lesions of the amygdaloid nuclei, as well as interruption of the stria terminalis, accelerate sexual development in female rats [66]. Seemingly, only lesions of the corticomedial nuclear complex have this effect, and it is important that, once sexual maturity is reached, the ability to run completely normal vaginal cycles, to respond to constant illumination, and to mate, become pregnant and rear litters is retained [67]. On this basis the effect of amygdaloid lesions is transient and could be due to irritation of the brain at the periphery of the lesion. However, the delay in puberty observed, with electrical stimulation of the amygdala [65], argues against this view. Testicular function in adult rats and cats [69] suffering amygdaloid damage has been reported to be depressed, whereas lesions in the basolateral nuclei of male and female deermice appear to raise the output of LH [70–72].

On the basis of the results just outlined, the amygdaloid nuclei appear to be involved in the inhibition of gonadotrophin secretion in infancy and to exert a facilitatory action on hormone release in the adult. Critchlow and Bar-Sela [67] drew attention to the fact that the animals in which ovulation had been induced by electrical stimulation of the amygdala had been either primed with oestrogen (rabbit and cat) or were in persistent oestrus (rat), so that the hormonal background could be significant in determining the kind of response observed. Thus, the prevailing level of oestrogen might determine the nature of the responses of hypothalamic units to any influence derived from the temporal lobe. It is also possible that the inhibitory influence apparent in infancy is transient and lost upon sexual maturation, or that sexual maturation occurs as a consequence of the loss of inhibition. However, there is evidence for the existence of a cyclic drive towards gonadotrophin secretion long before puberty, and the cyclic mechanism can be speedily activated by oestrogen [73, 74].

Together with the amygdala, the hippocampus forms part of the rhinencephalon and was thought to be concerned with the sense of smell; bût this view is no longer tenable [46, 75]. There is no relationship between the size of the hippocampus and the development of the olfactory sense, while human individuals lacking olfactory bulbs and tracts do not also suffer loss or reduction of the hippocampus.

Electrical or chemical stimulation of the hippocampus frequently has been associated with grooming, licking of the genitalia, erection, and signs of pleasure [75]. In rabbits, electrical stimulation of the hippocampus has caused ovulation, with the response being blocked by interruption of the fornix, the projection from the hippocampus to the hypothalamus [76]. The timing of puberty in rats was not affected by electrical stimulation of the hippocampus in infancy [65], whereas in adults, electrochemical stimulation of the hippocampus during prooestrus prevented ovulation in a high proportion of cases, and was also able to block the ovulation expected upon stimulation of the amygdala or preoptic area [64].

Delay in the onset of puberty after lesions in the hippocampus has been suggested [77], but not confirmed [78]. Decreases in ovarian weight after the placement of hippocampal lesions in infant rats has been noted [79], but vaginal opening was not delayed, nor testicular weight affected. Lesions in the anterior ventrolateral hippocampus have prevented the precocious puberty normally induced with testosterone treatment [80].

The functional relationship between the hippocampus and amygdala in the control of gonadotrophin secretion poses complex problems. Kawakami, Seto, Terasawa and Yoshida [81] examined the interplay between the two structures in a variety of experiments on rabbits and concluded that an inverse relationship existed, with the excitability of the hippocampus being low during oestrus, and that of the amygdala being raised. Treatment of spayed rabbits with progesterone increased the amplitude and frequency of hippocampal electrical activity, while reducing the amplitude of that of the amygdala. Ovulation could be induced by electrical stimulation of the dorsal hippocampus but was blocked by bilateral lesions in the fornix. Although ovulation also followed electrical stimulation of the amygdala, the formation of progesterone in the ovaries was less enhanced. Kawakami and his colleagues [82] consider that progesterone and LH exert a positive feedback action on hippocampal activity, and a negative feedback action upon the amygdala. When progesterone or oestradiol was implanted in the hypothalamus or limbic structures of rabbits and ovarian steroidogenesis followed, a variety of effects emerged [82]. Progesterone implanted in the arcuate nuclei facilitated progesterone and oestrogen formation by the ovary, whereas placement of the steroid in the ventro-medial nucleus of the hypothalamus inhibited the formation of progesterone and facilitated that of oestrogen. Implants of progesterone in the hippocampus, but not in the amygdala, enhanced progesterone synthesis. Oestrogen implants in the hypothalamus suppressed oestrogen production and favoured that of progestin, while those in the amygdala depressed both oestrogen and progestin formation. Hippocampal implants of oestradiol accelerated the production of oestrogen. This intricate interaction is difficult to interpret in terms of changes in gonadotrophin secretion, but points to opposite effects on the amygdala and hippocampus. It is also difficult to reconcile these findings with those of Velasco and Taleisnik [64], which indicate that the hippocampus can inhibit the release of LH. To some degree, species differences may be involved, in that the rat runs oestrous cycles while the rabbit does not. The rising levels of oestrogen at prooestrus in the rat may also facilitate the effect.

In assessing the significance of the information summarized earlier, it is important that while the amygdaloid nuclei and hippocampus can alter the output of gonadotrophin, the hypothalamus possesses a high degree of autonomy. This is illustrated by studies of the functional capacity of hypothalamic islands, which show that while there is little gonadal atrophy in male and female rats, ovulation stops in the female [83]. Our own work [84, and unpublished] indicates that the presence or absence of the suprachiasmatic nuclei in the island determines the response observed. Vaginal cycles stopped and the animals remained in dioestrus when small hypothalamic islands which excluded the suprachiasmatic nuclei were prepared, whereas if these nuclei formed part of the island the rats remained vaginally oestrous for long periods. Severance of the anterior connections of the hypothalamus, by making an arc-shaped cut which incorporated the suprachiasmatic nuclei in the peninsula of tissue connected to the pituitary stalk, also led to persistent cornification of the vagina, but when the nuclei were excluded from the peninsula, by locating the cut posterior to them, oestrous cycles and ovulation continued. These results may be taken to indicate that the suprachiasmatic area promotes the secretion of the complex of gonadotrophic hormones necessary for follicular growth in the ovaries and oestrogen secretion, for disconnection of the area from the median eminence depresses gonadotrophin release, perhaps by reducing the supply of luteinizing hormone releasing factor [85]. It also appears that the suprachiasmatic area is normally subject to inhibition through the preoptic region, for only when preoptic afferents are cut off does persistent vaginal cornification develop. This study further indicates that the posterior connections of the hypothalamus may be significant in the control of ovulation in the rat. Although division of these connections by making a cut in the posterior hypothalamus did not disturb ovarian function, it is noteworthy that oestrous cycles continued in animals in which frontal cuts were made caudal to the suprachiasmatic nuclei with the connections to the posterior hypothalamus remaining intact. Thus, the posterior input to the hypothalamus may, in the absence of a drive from the preoptic area, provide sufficient drive to the medio-basal hypothalamus to cause ovulation. Kordon [86] has suggested that a mechanism stimulating the secretion of LH is to be found in the premamillary region. Massive damage to midbrain structures has blocked ovulation in the rat [87] possibly by destruction of fibres passing forward to the hypothalamus in the neighbourhood of the mamillary peduncles. However, complete transection of the peduncles did not affect reproductive function in males or females [88].

Isolation of the hypothalamus in guinea-pigs has given slightly different results to those observed in the rat [84, and unpublished]. Persistent oestrus occurred, as in rats, when islands which included the suprachiasmatic nuclei were prepared, or when frontal cuts were made in the hypothalamus anterior to these nuclei. However, when the anterior border of the island was located posterior to the suprachiasmatic nuclei vaginal cycles continued. Irregular cycles were also sustained in animals in which frontal cuts were placed in the hypothalamus caudal to the suprachiasmatic area. Since the oestrous cycle in the guinea-pig extends over sixteen days, as compared with four or five days in the rat, sufficient time may have been available for the diffusion of enough neurotransmitting agent for ovulation from the suprachiasmatic area across the cut to the median eminence region, while the suprachiasmatic drive towards the oversecretion of gonadotrophin was depressed.

Analysis of the extra-hypothalamic control of gonadotrophin secretion underlines the high importance of inhibitory mechanisms in the control of gonadotrophin secretion. Indirect evidence for the existence of such mechanisms has been available for some time [89], but only now is precise information coming to hand. This indicates that inhibitory processes can originate in the amygdala and hippocampus, and raises the general question of the role of these structures in endocrine activity; for the secretion of ACTH appears to be promoted by stimulation of the amygdala and to be inhibited by excitation of the hippocampus [see 90]. It may be that the amygdala and hippocampus are involved in the genesis of the circadian rhythm of release of gonadotrophin and ACTH. The implantation of cortisol into the hippocampus or midbrain of cats has disrupted the diurnal pattern of adrenal activity, without suppressing the adrenal reaction to stress [91]. Fundamentally, the secretion of gonadotrophin is a cyclic process in both sexes, with the rhythm being depressed in the developing male by an action of androgen on the brain [92, 93]. It may be significant that the stimulation of the amygdala of male rats failed to enhance LH output, in contrast to the positive responses of females [63]. However, it is to be emphasized that oestrous cycles continue in females after damage to the amygdaloid nuclei, so that this neurogenic influence is not indispensable, perhaps because cycles of endocrine function can be driven through the reticular formation. It is also important to recall that cyclic ovarian activity is compatible with complete isolation of the hypothalamus.

Much of the material available on the role of extra-hypothalamic structures in the control of gonadotrophin secretion has been based on changes in gonadal function ensuing after stimulation or damage. The few studies in which changes in hormone secretion have been followed directly, by hormone assay, have yielded information of great interest. More will be welcomed.

## REFERENCES


[1] Amoroso, E.C. and Marshall, F.H.A. In *Marshall's Physiology of Reproduction*, vol. 1, Part 2, p. 707. Ed. A.S. Parkes. London: Longmans Green, 1960.

[2] Davidson, J.M. In *Neuroendocrinology*, vol. 1, p. 565. Eds. L. Martini and W.F. Ganong. New York: Academic Press, 1966.

[3] Donovan, B.T. In *The Pituitary Gland*, vol. 2, p. 49. Eds. G.W. Harris and B.T. Donovan. London: Butterworths, 1966.

[4] Flerkó, B. In *Neuroendocrinology*, vol. 1, p. 613. Eds. L. Martini and W.F. Ganong. New York: Academic Press, 1966.

[5] Harris, G.W. and Campbell, H.J. In *The Pituitary Gland*, vol. 2, p. 99. Eds. G.W. Harris and B.T. Donovan. London: Butterworths, 1966.

[6] Kahana, L., Lebovitz, H., Lusk, W., McPherson, H.T., Davidson, E.T., Oppenheimer, J.H., Engel, F.L., Woodhall, B. and Odom, G., *J. clin. Endocr. Metab.*, **22**, 304, 1962.

[7] Odell, W.D., Van Buren, J.M. and Hertz, R., *J. clin. Endocr. Metab.*, **22**, 1262, 1962.

[8] Anastasopoulos, G., Diakoyiannis, A. and Routsonis, K., *J. Neuropsychiat.*, **1**, 65, 1959.

[9] Wada, J.A. and Erikson, L.B., *Science*, **135**, 46, 1962.

[10] Gibbons, J.L. In *Modern Trends in Endocrinology*, 2nd Series, p. 201. Ed. H. Gardiner-Hill. London: Butterworths, 1961.

[11] Everett, J.W., *Physiol. Rev.*, **44**, 373, 1964.

[12] Soulairac, A. and Soulairac, M.-L., *C. r. Soc. Biol.*, **152**, 921, 1958.

[13] Endröczi, E. and Lissák, K., *Acta physiol. Hung.*, **21**, 203, 1962.

[14] Taleisnik, S., Caligaris, L. and Astrada, J.J., *Endocrinology*, **79**, 49, 1966.

[15] Saginor, M. and Horton, R., *Endocrinology*, **82**, 627, 1968.

[16] Haltmeyer, G.C. and Eik-Nes, K., *J. Reprod. Fert.*, **19**, 273, 1969.

[17] Taleisnik, S., Caligaris, L. and de Olmos, J., *Am. J. Physiol.*, **203**, 1109, 1962.

[18] Hammond, J., *Vitam. Hormones*, **12**, 157, 1954.

[19] Kiernan, J., *J. comp. Neurol.*, **131**, 405, 1967.

[20] Nauta, W.J.H. and Haymaker, W. In *The Hypothalamus*, p. 136. Eds. W. Haymaker, E. Anderson and W.J.H. Nauta. Springfield: Thomas, 1969.

[21] Ganong, W.F., Shepherd, M.D., Wall, J.R., Van Brunt, E.E. and Clegg, M.T., *Endocrinology*, **72**, 962, 1963.

[22] Lisk, R.D. and Kannwischer, L.R., *Science*, **146**, 272, 1964.

[23] Reiter, R.J. and Fraschini, F., *Neuroendocrinology*, **5**, 219, 1969.
[24] Wurtman, R.J., Axelrod, J. and Kelly, D.E., *The Pineal*. New York: Academic Press, 1968.
[25] Wurtman, R.J. and Anton-Tay, F., *Recent Prog. Hormone Res.*, **25**, 493, 1969.
[26] Moore, R.Y., Heller, A., Wurtman, R.J. and Axelrod, J., *Science*, **155**, 220, 1967.
[27] Moore, R.Y., Heller, A., Bhatnager, R.K., Wurtman, R.J. and Axelrod, J., *Arch. Neurol.*, **18**, 208, 1968.
[28] Donovan, B.T., *Mammalian Neuroendocrinology*. London: McGraw-Hill, 1970.
[29] Herbert, J., *J. Endocr.*, **43**, 625, 1969.
[30] Motta, M., Fraschini, F. and Martini, L., *Proc. Soc. exper. Biol. Med.*, **126**, 431, 1967.
[31] Fraschini, F., Mess, B. and Martini, L., *Endocrinology*, **82**, 919, 1968.
[32] Debeljuk, L., *Endocrinology*, **84**, 937, 1969.
[33] Donovan, B.T. and van der Werff ten Bosch, J.J., *Physiology of Puberty*. London: Arnold, 1965.
[34] Donovan, B.T. In *The Effects of External Stimuli on Reproduction*. Ciba Foundation Study Group no. 26, p. 43. Eds. G.E.W. Wolstenholme and M. O'Connor. London: Churchill, 1967.
[35] Donovan, B.T., *J. Endocr.*, **39**, 105, 1967.
[36] Thorpe, D.H. In *The Effects of External Stimuli on Reproduction*. Ciba Foundation Study Group no. 26, p. 53. Eds. G.E.W. Wolstenholme and M. O'Connor. London: Churchill, 1967.
[37] Hart, D.S., *J. exp. Biol.*, **28**, 1, 1951.
[38] Hammond, J., *J. agric. Sci.*, **42**, 293, 1952.
[39] Erikson, L.B., *Fert. Steril.* **15**, 352, 1964.
[40] Winget, C.M., De Roshia, C.W. and Hetherington, N.W., *Comp. Biochem. Physiol.*, **30**, 621, 1969.
[41] Zacharias, L. and Wurtman, R.J., *Science*, **144**, 1154, 1964.
[42] Thomas, J.B. and Pizzarello, D.J., *Obstet. Gynec.*, **30**, 507, 1967.
[43] Zacharias, L. and Wurtman, R.J., *Obstet. Gynec.*, **33**, 603, 1969.
[44] Bruce, H.M., *Br. med. Bull.*, **26**, 10, 1970.
[45] Michael, R.P. and Keverne, E.B., *Nature*, **218**, 746, 1968.
[46] Brodal, A., *Neurological Anatomy in Relation to Clinical Medicine*. 2nd edn. London: Oxford University Press, 1969.
[47] Powell, T.P.S., Cowan, W.M. and Raisman, G., *J. Anat.*, **99**, 791, 1965.
[48] Gauthier, G., *Acta Neurovegetativa*, **21**, 345, 1960.
[49] Franck, H., *C. r. Soc. Biol.*, **169**, 389, 1966.
[50] Franck, H., *C. r. Soc. Biol.*, **160**, 863, 1966.
[51] Whitten, W.K., *J. Endocr.*, **14**, 160, 1956.
[52] Orbach, J. and Kling, A., *Brain Res.*, **3**, 141, 1966.
[53] Signoret, J.P. and Mauleon, P., *Ann. Biol. Anim. Biochem. Biophys.*, **2**, 167, 1962.
[54] van Beugen, L. and van der Werff ten Bosch, J.J., *Acta Endocr.*, **37**, 470, 1961.
[55] Donovan, B.T. and Kopriva, P.C., *Endocrinology*, **77**, 213, 1965.
[56] David, R., Thiery, G., Bonvallet, M. and Dell, P., *C. r. Soc. Biol.* **146**, 670, 1952.
[57] Cowan, W.M., Raisman, G. and Powell, T.P.S., *J. Neurol. Neurosurg. Psychiat.*, **28**, 137, 1965.
[58] Dreifuss, J.J., Murphy, J.T. and Gloor, P., *J. Neurophysiol.*, **31**, 237, 1968.
[59] Koikegami, H., Yamada, T. and Usui, K., *Folia psychiat. neurol. Jap.*, **8**, 7, 1954.
[60] Hayward, J.N., Hilliard, J. and Sawyer, C.H., *Endocrinology*, **74**, 108, 1964.

[61] Shealy, C.N. and Peele, T.L., *J. Neurophysiol.*, **20**, 125, 1957.
[62] Bunn, J.P. and Everett, J.W., *Proc. Soc. exper. Biol. Med.*, **96**, 369, 1957.
[63] Velasco, M.E. and Taleisnik, S., *Endocrinology*, **84**, 132, 1969.
[64] Velasco, M.E. and Taleisnik, S., *Endocrinology*, **85**, 1154, 1969.
[65] Bar-Sela, M.E. and Critchlow, V., *Am. J. Physiol.*, **211**, 1103, 1966.
[66] Elwers, M. and Critchlow, V., *Am. J. Physiol.*, **198**, 381, 1960.
[67] Critchlow, V. and Bar-Sela, M.E. In *Neuroendocrinology*, vol. 2, p. 101. Eds. L. Martini and W.F. Ganong. New York: Academic Press, 1967.
[68] Yamada, T. and Greer, M.A., *Endocrinology*, **66**, 565, 1960.
[69] Kling, M.D., Orbach, J., Schwartz, N.B. and Towne, J.C., *Arch. gen. Psychiat.*, **3**, 391, 1960.
[70] Eleftheriou, B.E. and Zolovick, A. J., *J. Reprod. Fert.*, **14**, 33, 1967.
[71] Eleftheriou, B.E., Zolovick, A.J. and Norman, R.L., *J. Endocr.*, **38**, 469, 1967.
[72] Eleftheriou, B.E., Desjardins, C. and Zolovick, A.J. *J, Reprod. Fert.*, **21**, 249, 1970.
[73] McCormack, C.E. and Meyer, R.K., *Proc. Soc. exp. Biol. Med.*, **110**, 343, 1962.
[74] Strauss, W.F. and Meyer, R.K., *Science*, **137**, 860, 1962.
[75] Green, J.D., *Physiol. Rev.*, **44**, 561, 1964.
[76] Kawakami, M., Seto, K. and Yoshida, K., *Jap. J. Physiol.*, **16**, 254, 1966.
[77] Riss, W., Burstein, S.D. and Johnson, R.W., *Am. J. Physiol.*, **204**, 861, 1963.
[78] Gellert, R.J. and Ganong, W.F., *Acta Endocr. Copnh.*, **33**, 569, 1960.
[79] Kling, A., *Am. J. Physiol.*, **206**, 1395, 1964.
[80] Zarrow, M.X., Naqvi, R.N. and Denenberg, V.H., *Endocrinology*, **84**, 14, 1969.
[81] Kawakami, M., Seto, K., Terasawa, E. and Yoshida, K., *Prog. Brain Res.*, **27**, 69, 1967.
[82] Kawakami, M., Seto, K., Yoshida, K. and Miyamoto, T., *Neuroendocrinology*, **5**, 303, 1969.
[83] Halász, B. In *Frontiers in Neuroendocrinology*, p. 307. Eds. W.F. Ganong and L. Martini. New York: Oxford University Press, 1969.
[84] Butler, J.E.M. and Donovan, B.T., *J. Endocr.* **43**, xx, 1969.
[85] Schneider, H.P.G., Crighton, D.B. and McCann, S.M., *Neuroendocrinology*, **5**, 271, 1969.
[86] Kordon, C., *Rev. Eur. Endocr.*, **4**, 91, 1967.
[87] Critchlow, V., *Endocrinology*, **63**, 596, 1958.
[88] Pekary, A.E., Davidson, J.M. and Zondek, B., *Endocrinology*, **80**, 365, 1967.
[89] Donovan, B.T., *Mem. Soc. Endocr.*, **9**, 1, 1960.
[90] Mangili, G., Motta, M. and Martini, L. In *Neuroendocrinology*, vol. 1, p. 297. Eds. L. Martini and W.F. Ganong. New York: Academic Press, 1966.
[91] Slusher, M.A., *Exp. Brain Res.*, **1**, 184, 1966.
[92] Harris, G.W., *Endocrinology*, **75**, 627, 1964.
[93] Barraclough, C.A. In *Advances in Reproductive Physiology*, vol. 3, p. 81. Ed. A. McLaren. London: Logos Press, 1968.

*Discussion of paper by Dr B. T. Donovan*

*Odell* You have suggested that the suprachiasmatic area may be involved in whatever stimuli increased oestrogen secretion in the persistent-oestrous rat. The very fact that these animals have developed and retained large pre-ovulatory follicles may be the reason that they are secreting large amounts of oestrogens. One may not have to postulate hypersecretion of LH and/or FSH. It has been suggested that the development of the follicle from the initiation of growth to the pre-ovulatory stage may be, at least partly, independent once it is initiated by the FSH surge. It is possible, therefore, to suggest that the suprachiasmatic area may be involved in the development of the follicle, but that the high oestrogen production may be independent of a continued hypersecretion of gonadotrophin.

*Donovan* I was being deliberately vague. I did not want to say that this area favours the secretion of FSH more than LH, because we do not know what the ratio of the two hormones is and which is the more effective; that is why I spoke in terms of the gonadotrophic complex that stimulates oestrogen secretion. Certainly, if you cut off the hypothalamus from the anterior inflow from the preoptic area, the switch for ovulation seems to be disconnected. Now the switch for ovulation is generally thought to reside in the preoptic area, anterior to the suprachiasmatic nuclei, but we find that in animals which have anterior cuts which don't necessarily incorporate the suprachiasmatic nuclei, ovulation can occur. Yet we have cut off this preoptic area. It may be that a caudal inflow, shall we say, involving the reticular formation, is important in providing an alternative trigger for ovulation but that is still speculative.

*Odell* Drs Ramaley and Gorski have shown that this same anterior hypothalamic cut causes precocious puberty in rats. However it is not the anterior lesion or tumour that causes precocious puberty in humans, but the posterior lesion. Can you tie these two findings together in some way?

*Donovan* This is certainly an intriguing paradox. The only thing that I can say is that all the experimental work implicates the anterior hypothalamus in the acceleration of sexual maturity. The clinical data do not fit, but then the clinical studies are never very precise. The pathological changes within the brain are generally widespread and it is hard to say that the anterior hypothalamus is not involved. It would be nice to have studies carried out on infant monkeys but this has not been done.

*Harris* There is one type of clinical case in which the lesion is very localized, the small hamartoma tumours which often lie behind the pituitary stalk. These would cause a very localized lesion by pressure on the posterior part of the tuber cinereum.

*Donovan* But do such appendages to the hypothalamus necessarily cause a lesion? I am not sure. It is often argued that the hypothalamus is normal and also suggested that the hamartoma is producing releasing factor which is reaching the portal vessels. However there is no experimental evidence for this idea.

*Naftolin* Vaginal opening earlier than is usual may not signify puberty in the classical sense. In collaboration with Drs Brown-Grant and Munck we have measured plasma and pituitary LH levels in adult androgen-sterilized Lister rats; these are not elevated above the levels in normal male or dioestrous female rats.

*Donovan* It is true that vaginal opening by itself should not be taken as an index of puberty, but I think the androgen-sterilized rat is a strange creature anyway. In much of the work on the acceleration of puberty the ovaries have been checked at the time of vaginal opening, and corpora lutea found, so that in these particular well-defined circumstances vaginal opening is a good index of puberty.

*Corker* You make the point about the elevated oestradiol levels, or oestrogen levels, in these constant oestrous rats. In fact during the oestrous phase of the cycle the oestradiol level is very low and is not elevated. There appears to be no difference in the oestradiol levels of rats with a cornified or a non-cornified vagina. We have looked at a few constant oestrous rats and their levels are also very low.

*Harris* It is clear that there may be a considerable latent period between the increase in blood oestrogen and the effects it causes. For example, Dr Richard Michael found a long latent period between the administration of oestrogen and the onset of sexual behaviour in the ovariectomized cat. It seems to me therefore that there may not be an immediate effect of oestrogen on the vagina, but that oestrogen may trigger some process which involves a considerable time lag before the effect is mediated.

*Baird* Is it wise to equate oestrogen with oestradiol? There is fairly good evidence from bioassays that oestrone is relatively more potent at inducing vaginal cornification than in other bioassays for oestrogens. Failure to detect a high level of oestradiol in rats with constant vaginal cornification may only imply that a high level of another oestrogen is present.

*Donovan* This is an extremely important point. We have argued in a variety of ways that during infancy there is a feedback action of oestrogen on the brain. We have no idea which oestrogen it is, and we are uncertain whether it can be equated with oestradiol.

# The Chemistry of the Releasing Factors

H. GREGORY

I C I Pharmaceuticals Division
Macclesfield, Cheshire

¶ ALTHOUGH the existence of agents regulating the release of the gonadotrophins has been known for some time, progress towards full chemical characterization has been rather slow. This may reasonably be attributed to the extremely small amounts of purified material which can be isolated. At the present state of knowledge it is perhaps realistic to refer to impressions of the nature of the releasing factors.

Opinions vary as to whether or not luteinizing hormone releasing factor (LRF), follicle stimulating hormone releasing factor (FRF) and the other known factors all belong to a similar class of compounds chemically [1, 2]. This point will presumably be resolved only by the eventual synthesis of the various factors. Meanwhile, as our efforts so far have been devoted exclusively to LRF, I will refer mainly to this particular entity.

## ISOLATION

It is obviously of prime importance to have efficient test systems for studies on the isolation of such substances, and several systems have been described for the releasing factors [3]. In our work, two methods have been used to assess LRF activity. In the first of these, samples were infused directly into the anterior pituitary of isolated rabbits in oestrus [4] and in the second, samples were administered i.v. to androgen-sterilized 'constant oestrus' rats [5]. The latter test enabled large numbers of fractions to be scanned rapidly. In both cases the release of LH was shown by ovulation. As the source of the luteinizing hormone releasing factor, we used ovine stalk median eminence fragments.

The initial extraction was carried out more or less according to published methods [6]. Acetone dried tissues were extracted with hot aqueous acetic acid and the extract was lyophilyzed. This material was triturated with glacial acetic acid, and inert protein was reprecipitated using acetone. Treatment with ether produced an active precipitate amounting to about 2·5 g per 1000 median eminence fragments. The procedure we have adopted to provide LRF of high specific activity from the crude extract is summarized in Table 1. This sequence of purification stages evolved from the examination of a wide variety of chromatographic methods.

The yields at stages 4 to 6 are not recorded by weight. No attempt was made to weigh the small amounts of material obtained and the stage 7 value was, in fact, obtained by weighing about 40 μg of material. In spite of all the precautions taken this value must be subject to considerable error. Quantities at the other stages were determined in terms of peptide content – small samples were subjected to amino-acid analyses, which may or may not be relevant measurements.

The biological assay systems did not lend themselves to ready quantification although this was established in broad terms by endeavouring to find

TABLE 1. Purification steps involved in preparing LRF of high specific activity from ovine stalk median eminence fragments

| Stage | Procedure | Yield (% Crude) |
|---|---|---|
| 1. Solvent Extraction | 0·5N Acetic acid<br>(a) Isopropanol<br>(b) Petroleum ether | 21% |
| 2. Gel Filtration | Sephadex G-25<br>0·3N Acetic acid | 15% |
| 3. Partition Chromatography | Sephadex G-25<br>n-Butanol, pyridine<br>acetic acid, water | 0·13% |
| 4. Partition Chromatography | Sephadex G-25<br>2-Butanone, pyridine<br>acetic acid, water | |
| 5. Electrophoresis | Sephadex G-25<br>Pyridine, acetic acid<br>water pH 6·5 | |
| 6. Cellulose Chromatography | Cellulose<br>n-Butanol, acetic acid<br>water | |
| 7. Gel Filtration | Sephadex G-15<br>50% pyridine, water | 0·0008% |

a threshold dose to cause ovulation. However, it can be said that material from stage 3 would reliably induce ovulation in 'constant oestrus' rats at doses of 25 μg i.v. whereas considerably less than 1 μg of stage 7 material was required.

The methods of isolation do give some indications of the nature of LRF and may be considered in a little more detail. Stage 1 involved the removal of inert proteinaceous material and provided an extract suitable for gel-filtration. During the latter process, the column effluent was monitored at 280 mμ and this served as a measure of column performance and also allowed the region of activity to be identified. The LRF was appreciably retarded (between 1·6 and 2·2 × Vo) but appeared somewhat earlier than the nonapeptide vasopressin.

Purification was carried on by partition chromatography rather than the ion-exchange processes favoured by other groups [1, 2], and the systems developed proved to be efficient methods of enhancing the quality of the LRF preparation. It was necessary to use polar solvents to obtain suitable partition coefficients for the active entity and in this respect it behaved in a similar manner to a variety of small peptides including both the basic bradykinin and the acidic gastrin. The elution pattern was established by submitting aliquots to the Folin-Lowry reaction after which biological activity was found to be in a region of low colour yield. Beyond this stage the amount of material was so small that biological activity was the only reliable scanning method. Electrophoresis was carried out on thin layers of Sephadex G-50 equilibrated with pyridine acetate buffer at pH 6·4. The active material moved to the cathode at about 0·4 times the mobility of the basic dye methylene blue. At pH 3·5 the movement was similar to that of bradykinin. The behaviour of LRF has been studied previously on thin layers of cellulose [7]. This was developed into a column chromatography process and the active material was significantly retarded when elution was carried out with a solvent derived from n-butanol, acetic acid and water. This product was then subjected to gel-filtration on Sephadex G-15 and emerged at about 1·25 × Vo.

This and other procedures which have been applied to the agents regulating gonadotrophin release have made use of methods applied extensively to polypeptide purification. At each point LRF behaves in a manner compatible with polypeptide structure but this does not, of course, exclude other types of structure. The behaviour on Sephadex, which can be misleading, would indicate a molecular weight of 1,000 – 1,500. FRF from several species [1, 2] and PIF [1, 8] gave similar indications of molecular size. Chromatography on carboxymethyl cellulose did not separate porcine LRF and FRF but preparative electrophoresis did so successfully [1]. FRF appears to be even more basic than LRF. Impure samples of the latter are not retarded by diethylaminoethyl Sephadex [9] but this is not so with more refined material. This may indicate the existence of some acidic functional group or it may be an adsorption effect. Adsorption appears to be the most likely explanation of the observation that highly purified LRF can be completely retained on Sephadex G-25 in aqueous solution [9]. However, the isolation methods do convey the impression that LRF and FRF are basic, water soluble compounds of molecular weight 1,000 – 1,500.

Earlier studies on the releasing factors provided partially purified material which contained amino-acids [10, 11] and our most highly purified samples do contain them. However, it was reported recently that a highly purified LRF sample contained only minute amounts of amino-acids [12] and similar doubts have been expressed regarding FRF. Moreover, it was reported that five polyamines isolated from porcine hypothalamic extracts could account for most of the follicle-stimulating hormone-depleting activity of the crude extracts [13]. It appears subsequently that the releasing factor is a separate entity to these amines [14].

The great difficulty of making reliable physical measurements upon such small quantities can be illustrated by reference to recent work on the thyrotrophin releasing factor. Reports that amino-acids represented a minor component of highly purified TRF [15, 16] have been followed by further reports that a tripeptide structure represented the TRF molecule [17 – 19]. Incidentally, TRF from different species appears close to both LRF and TRF on Sephadex G-25 chromatography [1].

### ACTION OF ENZYMES

Different groups studying the releasing factors have looked at the effect of enzymes. Earlier work indicated that LRF activity was destroyed by the action of trypsin and pepsin [7, 20, 21] but more recently it has been suggested that this was not so [1]. Inactivation of FRF by enzymatic action has also been reported [22]. In our studies both trypsin and chymotrypsin reduced the activity of an LRF preparation to a level below that which would induce ovulation. These different results cannot readily be interpreted but the conditions of incubation used by the various workers are obviously critical.

There does, however, appear to be agreement that chymotrypsin will effectively deactivate LRF. This is a peptidase with a high specificity although this is somewhat less than that of trypsin. Additionally, both have esterase activity but the same stereochemical considerations apply [23]. Pepsin does not have simple esterase activity [23] and if deactivation of LRF is fully authenticated then the presence of peptide bonds may be inferred. When large enzyme quantities are used in relation to the substrate, then factors such as adsorption or contamination with other enzymes may play a part. With small amounts of enzyme or short incubation times, the rate of cleavage of particular bonds may be slow, and meaningful control experiments are not easily constructed.

Table 2 shows the action of four enzymes upon a partially purified LRF

TABLE 2

| | Enzyme | | Activity of product |
|---|---|---|---|
| 1 | Pepsin | pH 2·5 | Active |
| 2 | Control | pH 2·5 | Active |
| 3 | Thermolysin | pH 8·0 | Inactive |
| 4 | Trypsin | pH 8·0 | Inactive |
| 5 | Chymotrypsin | pH 8·0 | Inactive |
| 6 | Control | pH 8·0 | Active |

sample (ca. 5 μg/rat). The enzyme substrate ratio was 1:20 in terms of weight of enzyme to the 'peptide' weight of the LRF sample; incubation was at 25° for 3 hours. In each experiment the weight of sample was the same and was at least four times the amount required to induce ovulation. Thus samples 3, 4 and 5 certainly had less than 25 per cent of the activity remaining. The efficacy of the enzyme preparations was shown by their action upon synthetic peptides under identical conditions.

### STRUCTURE INVESTIGATIONS

Experiments with enzymes can be conveniently carried out on a small scale in that the end point is a biological measurement. Chemical investigations are influenced to a greater extent by the amount of material available – in this case about 1 mg per 50,000 hypothalamic fragments. It is not feasible, for example, to carry out the detailed chromatographic examinations that have been applied in polypeptide chemistry. Nor is it convenient to use a wide variety of spray reagents to obtain structural information, or to use the normal spectroscopic methods of organic chemistry. A sample of material prepared via an earlier process [9] (active at ca. 2 μg/rat) was examined by ultraviolet absorption and mass spectrometry but these were uninformative. The amino-acid composition of this material was in broad agreement with a total nitrogen value obtained microanalytically. The absence of sulphur containing amino-acids was in keeping with the observation that thioglycollate did not affect the activity [10, 21].

The stability of LRF was examined under a variety of conditions and these are summarized in Table 3. Of necessity, each of these experiments

TABLE 3

| | Activity retained | Activity reduced |
|---|---|---|
| 1 | Formic acid, −10°, 2·5 hrs. | + Performic acid |
| 2 | 0·005 N HCl, 25°, 3 hrs. | |
| 3 | Phosphate buffer, pH 7·7, 25°, 3 hrs. | + 2:4-Dinitro-1-fluorobenzene |
| 4 | 50% Aqueous pyridine, 45°, 3 hrs. | + Phenylisothiocyanate |
| 5 | Sec. Butanol : Aqueous ammonia pH 10·5 4°, 20 hrs. | |
| 6 | N-Ethylmorpholine : HCl buffer, pH 8·0 Dimethylformamide, 25°, 16 hrs. | + 2:4:5-Trichlorophenyl acetate |

was carried out using a small number of test animals. It cannot be said that activity was destroyed but rather that it fell below the level that would reliably induce ovulation in the constant oestrus rats. The results indicated that the preparation was susceptible to mild oxidation and to reagents commonly known to react with polypeptides. It is noteworthy that activity was not readily lost by keeping a sample at pH 10·5. Bearing in mind the action of chymotrypsin and possible esterase action, it is probable that some amino-acid esters would undergo hydrolysis by such treatment.

Treatment with 2:4:5-trichlorophenyl acetate, under conditions whereby peptides are acylated, caused a loss of biological potency, and the formation of an acetyl derivative was inferred. Consequently use was made of $^{14}C$ acetate to give radioactive derivatives which could be readily identified in further chromatographic processes. Although LRF loses biological activity, labelled material can be recovered and manipulated without the losses associated with spray reagents. This process was found to be quite satisfactory using different synthetic peptides.

Initial investigations were carried out with partially purified material (ca. 5 μg/rat) from 1,000 SME fragments [9]. This was treated under the appropriate conditions to give a radioactive product which was subjected to thin-layer electrophoresis on kieselguhr at pH 3·5. A series of bands was observed and these were purified further by two-dimensional chromatography on silica gel thin layers. This provided several components with differing radioactive intensities. The level of detection was such that small peptides could be readily observed in quantities of 1 μg. Amino-acid analyses indicated that peptide quantities of 1 to 10 μg were associated with the detectable components and these values corresponded broadly to the intensity of the spots, although this was not precisely quantified.

These experiments lent some encouragement to the concept that LRF was peptidic and it seemed possible that further structural information could be obtained using the dansyl Edman technique [24]. This requires the presence of a free N-terminus in a given peptide structure. Experiments with various synthetic peptides showed that although the phenylthiocarbamoyl peptides were less stable than the acetyl derivatives it was possible to carry out similar separation procedures.

Partially purified LRF (from 2000 SME) was treated with $^{14}$C phenylisothiocyanate and the products separated by thin-layer electrophoresis (pH 6·4) and chromatography. Again several radioactive derivatives were observed, several of which were known to be side products of the reaction. Based on the acetylation experiments, initial efforts were devoted to spots containing basic amino-acids. However, when the Edman degradation was attempted the results were at best inconclusive.

Further attention was then devoted to the purification process and a product of higher specific activity was obtained (Table 1) amounting to about 20 μg per 1000 SME fragments. A portion of the product was analyzed for amino-acid content and this gave values of 16 μg per 1,000 SME. Whilst these figures are by no means accurate they do indicate that peptide material can account for a large portion of the purified extract. It is of course conceivable that the active entity may be a minor component at this point. Nevertheless, similar amounts of lysine, arginine, serine, glutamic acid, glycine, leucine, tyrosine and phenylalanine were observed together with smaller amounts of other acids – aspartic acid, alanine and valine. The presence of basic and aromatic amino-acids indicates that the potential exists for the action of trypsin and chymotrypsin.

When this material was reacted with dansyl chloride and hydrolyzed, the only fluorescent products observed were the ε-lysine and O-tyrosine derivatives. Thus it would appear that the peptidic material present does not exhibit detectable free α-amino groups. This may well be the explanation for the inconclusive $^{14}$C phenylisothiocyanate experiments. A considerable number of biologically active peptides are now known to have a blocked N-terminus. Indeed the tripeptide structure proposed for TRF [17–19] possesses an N-terminal pyroglutamic acid residue. Work is proceeding upon our LRF preparation still based on the premise that the active entity is a peptide.

As has been mentioned above, the manipulation of micro amounts raises many problems and this is a particular problem with peptides. Contamination from non-hypothalamic sources can be quite serious; for example a single fingerprint on a glass surface will provide more amino-acids (but different ratios!) than can be obtained from the purified LRF from over 1000 SME fragments. This level of working explains why some of the conclusions which have been drawn regarding the structure of the releasing factors based upon indications at one time, have become less acceptable in the light of further experimentation.

ACKNOWLEDGEMENT

I would like to express my gratitude to Mrs E. Tidswell for the great care with which she has carried out a large part of the experimental work described above.

## REFERENCES


[1] Schally, A.V., Arimura, A., Bowers, C.Y., Kastin, A.J., Sawano, S. and Redding, T.W., *Recent Prog. Hormone Res.*, **24,** 497, 1968.

[2] McCann, S.M., Dhariwal, A.P.S. and Porter, J.C., *Ann. Rev. Physiol.*, **30,** 589, 1968.

[3] Schally, A.V., Arimura, A., Muller, E.E., Saito, T., Bowers, C.Y., White, W.F., Cohen, A.I. and Corbin, A. In *Pharmacology of Reproduction*, p. 41. Ed. E. Diczfalusy. New York: Pergamon Press, 1968.

[4] This was carried out in the Department of Human Anatomy, Oxford under the direction of Professor G.W. Harris with whom we are collaborating on this work.

[5] This testing was carried out at I.C.I. Pharmaceuticals Division under the direction of Dr A.L. Walpole.

[6] Guillemin, R., Schally, A.V., Lipscomb, H.S., Anderson, R.N. and Long, J.M., *Endocrinology*, **70,** 471, 1962.

[7] Fawcett, C.P., Reed, M., Charlton, H.M. and Harris, G.W., *Biochem. J.*, **106,** 229, 1968.

[8] Grosvenor, C.E., Flavio, M., Dharival, A.P.S. and McCann, S.M., *Endocrinology*, **81,** 1021, 1967.

[9] Gregory, H., Walpole, A.L., Charlton, H.M., Harris, G.W. and Reed, M.M., *Pharmacology of Hormonal Polypeptides and Proteins*, p. 123. Eds. L. Martini and R. Paoletti. New York: Plenum Press, 1968.

[10] Guillemin, R., *Recent Prog. Hormone Res.*, **20,** 89, 1964.

[11] Schally, A.V. and Bowers, C.Y., *Endocrinology*, **75,** 608, 1964.

[12] Schally, A.V., Bowers, C.Y., White, W.F. and Cohen, A.I., *Endocrinology*, **81,** 77, 1967.

[13] White, W.F., Cohen, A.I., Dippel, R.H., Strong, J.C. and Schally, A.V., *Endocrinology*, **82,** 742, 1968.

[14] Kamberi, I.A. and McCann, S.M., *Endocrinology*, **85,** 815, 1969.

[15] Schally, A.V., Redding, T.W., Bowers, C.Y. and Barrett, J.F., *J. biol. Chem.*, **244,** 4077, 1969.

[16] Guillemin, R., Burgus, R., Sakiz, E. and Ward, D.N., *C. r. Acad. Sci., Paris*, **262,** 2278, 1966.

[17] Boler, J., Enzman, F., Folkers, K., Bowers, C.Y. and Schally, A.V. *Biochem. Biophys. Res. Commun.*, **37,** 705, 1969.

[18] Burgus, R., Dunn, T.F., Desiderio, D., Vale, W. and Guillemin, R., *C. r. Acad. Sci., Paris*, **269,** 226, 1969.

[19] Nair, R.M.G., Barrett, J.F., Bowers, C.Y. and Schally, A.V., *Biochemistry*, **9,** 1103, 1970.

[20] Jutisz, M., De La Llosa, P., Sakiz, E., Yamazaki, E. and Guillemin, R., *C. r. Soc. Biol. Paris*, **157,** 235, 1963.

[21] McCann, S.M. and Ramirez, V.D., *Recent Prog. Hormone Res.*, **20,** 131, 1964.

[22] Dhariwal, A.P.S., Watanake, S., Antunes, Rodrigues J. and McCann, S.M., *Neuroendocrinology*, **2,** 294, 1967.

[23] *The Enzymes*, vol. 4. Eds. P.D. Boyer, H. Lardy and K. Myrback. New York: Academic Press, 1960.

[24] *Methods in Enzymology*, vol. II, p. 469. Ed. C.H.W. Hirs. New York: Academic Press, 1967.

*Discussion of paper by Dr H. Gregory*

*Butt* You mentioned two or three examples where you used certain reagents to reduce the activity of your preparation. Have you tried the t-butyloxycarbonyl group as a reagent because with this you could remove it again and recover your activity?
*Gregory* We intend to use both this and the benzyloxycarbonyl group. Another reagent, which can be reacted with amino groups, is maleic anhydride. The derivative is stable at pH 6 but by lowering the pH the blocking group can be removed again. We are trying this at the moment with radioactive maleic anhydride.
*Butt* Have you tested your LRF preparation for any other releasing activity?
*Gregory* No, we have not.
*Odell* How good is your evidence that there are either nine or ten amino-acids in LRF? You have indicated that TRF (a tripeptide) emerges from the Sephadex columns in about the same tube number as LRF. Could you in fact be dealing with a three or four amino-acid substance?
*Gregory* Yes, it is possible. My conclusions are based on its behaviour, on Sephadex, under a variety of conditions compared with other polypeptides. I do not understand at the moment how TRF at the cruder stages is travelling ahead of vasopressin and yet is apparently that much smaller.
*Odell* I believe that the structure of TRF may have been elucidated by taking the possible combinations of tripeptides composed of the three amino-acids, glutamine, histidine and proline, and studying them for activity, i.e., a polypeptide with potent TRF activity was finally synthesized. Is it possible that native TRF is actually larger than a tripeptide and that this is a small fragment with biological activity like the active tetrapeptide part of gastrin?
*Gregory* It is well established that a glutamine residue as the N-terminal acid of a peptide can cyclize to give a pyroglutamyl residue. There have been suggestions that if there is a glutamine in the middle of a polypeptide, then the same process could take place. I do not know of any evidence which has actually established this, but, if it did take place, then the polypeptide could break and conceivably leave an active fragment.
*Harris* I think that all the possible combinations of the three amino-acids in TRF were synthesized some years ago. However, it was not until the terminal groups were blocked that the releasing factor activity became apparent.
*Gregory* The published work ties the physicochemical evidence in with the tripeptide structure but I think it is true that the synthetic peptide work showed the way.

*Harris* Would it be possible chemically to detect the TRF molecule in portal vessel blood? It seems to me that this would be the final and necessary test of a particular molecule as the physiological entity.
*Gregory* It would be extremely difficult chemically. There is nothing unusual about the components of TRF; the only specific sort of test one can use is the Pauly reaction for the histidine part. This would not be specific for TRF though and I think a chemical reaction on such a small scale would be extremely difficult.
*Odell* The measurement of releasing factors in portal blood will probably be relatively easy when competitive protein binding techniques are available. Now that TRF is available, immunoassays will shortly be forthcoming and will make the job relatively easy.
*Naftolin* Are you suggesting that there may be a neurophysin-like material involved? Dr George Fink (D.Phil. Thesis, Oxford 1967) worked out a method to separate LH from LRF in portal blood. Does portal plasma LRF run on Sephadex G-25 follow the same elution pattern as your purified material? The portal plasma LRF is a potent material that has been through the 'capillary filter' and may thus have lost its carrier material.
*Gregory* I do not think there would be any carrier protein which would put the active material in this molecular range on Sephadex G-25. The purification used by Dr Fink gave two active regions on Sephadex chromatography and my own belief is that the second of these could well be explained by an adsorption effect. There could be adsorption of some semipurified material then the salt peak coming along behind could release it; apparently producing two regions of activity.
*Odell* If I recall correctly, at the recent Atlantic City Meeting evidence was presented that neurophysin is actually released into the blood stream and circulates, thus size may be unrelated to whether a substance passes through the capillary barrier.
*Donovan* Has work been done on the testing of mixtures of shortchain synthetic polypeptides for LRF activity?
*Gregory* We are not doing it yet. I think we have sufficient information of one sort or another to start making peptide structures soon. We are fairly experienced in polypeptide synthesis. With our radioactive phenylisothiocyanate experiments we had hoped to determine the sequence of a number of polypeptides, but the lack of reaction prevented this.

## SESSION I. GENERAL DISCUSSION

*Klopper* As a point of common interest, can anybody say if FSH and LH midcycle peaks in women coincide?

*Odell* The data are a little contradictory, but in over 60 per cent of the patients we studied, the LH and FSH peaks coincide at midcycle (*Proc. Endocr. Soc.*, 1967, p. 61; *Radioisotopes in Medicine; In vitro studies*, 1968, p. 165; *J. clin. Invest.*, **47**, 2551, 1968). If I recall correctly, in over three-quarters of the patients which Dr Ross et al. (*Recent Prog. Hormone Res.* (**26**, 1, 1970) and Drs Midgley and Jaffe (*J. clin. Endocr. Metab.*, **28**, 1699, 1968) studied independently, the LH and FSH peaks coincided. In the measurements of Drs Faiman and Ryan (*J. clin. Endocr. Metab.*, **27**, 1711, 1967) there has been a less frequent coincidence of the LH and FSH peaks. In those instances where they do not coincide, the FSH peak usually precedes the LH peak in the patients we have studied.

*Loraine* Bioassay of FSH in the human menstrual cycle is mainly restricted to urinary levels and the data are contradictory. Stevens et al. (*Recent Research on Gonadotrophic Hormones*, Ed. E.T.Bell and J.A.Loraine, p. 227, E. & S. Livingstone, London 1967) mainly found the FSH peak during menstruation or the early follicular phase, whereas other data, including our own, reveal the positioning of the FSH peak to be very variable. If the peaks of FSH and LH activity are occurring simultaneously at midcycle as most radioimmunoassays would suggest, what then is the function of the FSH?

*Odell* One is not only ignorant of what this midcycle FSH surge is doing but also whether it is required for ovulation or setting the stage for later events.

*Mills* I wonder whether the critical point is not the question of when the peak of these hormones is to be found, but the time at which their level begins to rise?

*Ismail* In a recent report by the Louvain group (Thomas et al., *J. clin. Endocr. Metab.*, **30**, 269, 1970) they demonstrated a biphasic peak of LH and some of the data at this meeting also show a biphasic peak for oestrogen. Maybe the FSH peak coincides with either one of these LH peaks.

*Naftolin* We have looked at one patient every six hours and have seen a biphasic peak of plasma LH, similar to that reported by the Louvain group. For some time it has been apparent that certain patients have a sort of rebound after their alleged peak, i.e., a day later they have a secondary peak. It may be that this is important in the development of a functional corpus luteum.

*Johansson* Dr Wide has been doing the LH measurements and we have only two patients with samples taken every six hours, but in these cases we have not been able to find a biphasic LH peak. As Dr Wide has said several times, the biphasic peak may not be a biological phenomenon, it could be that, if one has a less specific method, the antisera could pick up some metabolites of LH and so a broad peak would be obtained. It may thus be wiser not to look at the peaks of secretion but at the time when the hormone level first shows a significant rise.

*Grant* I wonder if Dr Donovan would comment on the question of pheromones. Could these possibly be acting as primary triggers?

*Donovan* They could be acting as a primary trigger on the olfactory epithelium just as light acts on the retina but what happens from then on I do not know.

*Naftolin* In a collaborative study with Dr R. Short and Mr C. B. Katongale we found that in two bulls there was a clear rise in plasma LH prior to serving but after they had seen/smelled the cow.

*Eik-Nes* In the rabbit we find from crude measurement of plasma testosterone that information is needed by the male rabbit in order to promote testosterone secretion.

*Horton* May I just raise the suggestion that pheromones might not just be acting via the olfactory apparatus but that they might be absorbed into the circulation and act as hormones?

*Donovan* The brain or other receptor within the organism would have to be extremely sensitive.

*Corker* Do lesions of the amygdala prevent the pregnancy-block induced by the introduction of a strange male mouse?

*Donovan* This has not been studied.

*Harris* Dr Brown-Grant removed the olfactory bulbs from mice to see if he could prevent the pregnancy-block induced by a strange male. The difficulty he encountered was that oestrous cycles were either absent or very irregular after the operation.

*Oakey* I think there is some circumstantial evidence that the foetus can produce LH. How could LH production be controlled in the foetus?

*Harris* I do not know. The work of Professor Jost in Paris indicates of course that pituitary gonadotrophins are released in the foetus. Whether this foetal secretion is under hypothalamic control is another matter. Some workers believe that since the hypophysial portal system may not be present in foetal forms, hypothalamic control cannot be envisaged. However it seems to me that the hypothalamus could affect pituitary activity in these very small organisms by a process of chemical diffusion rather than by blood carriage. There is an analogy for this suggestion in the fact that diffusion of some testicular hormone seems to exert a direct excitatory effect on the Wolffian duct and an inhibitory effect on the Müllerian duct.

*Donovan* The hypothalamus is, of course, very poorly developed in foetal life and in many species nuclear differentiation occurs postnatally.

*Harris* I do not know whether Dr Donovan would agree, but it seems to me that the hypothalamus or the diencephalic region is the main control centre for hormone release, which is then played upon and modulated by amygdaloid, hippocampal and other influences in the brain.

*Donovan* I would agree with this; the very fact that ovulation can occur in animals in which the hypothalamus has been isolated from the rest of the brain is significant in this regard.

*Odell* Dr Grumbach et al. (1970) have published both foetal blood concentrations and pituitary concentrations of FSH. (LH measurement is complicated in the human because of the presence of HCG.) FSH appeared in rather large concentrations in the pituitary, and progressively increased in the blood beginning somewhere around two months of foetal age. Dr Fisher and co-workers in our hospital have been studying TSH during foetal development and find a very similar picture, namely that TSH increases in parallel with thyroxine concentration during foetal development, beginning at about two months.

*Oakey* What was the condition of the foetal ovaries in the females examined? Were they relatively quiescent even in the presence of these large quantities of FSH?

*Odell* I am not sure I can answer that. In the prepubertal human it is clear that LH and FSH are present in the blood. The concentrations of FSH and LH are slightly below those of the adult and these levels do not lead to stimulation of the gonads in the sense that we are talking about. I think we are talking about a dose-response relationship between the amounts of hormone circulating and the sensitivity of the end organ. Both these factors may be important.

*Cooke* The only evidence I know of concerning LH and the foetus is that published by Jaffe, Lee and Midgley (*J. clin. Endocr. Metab.*, **29**, 1281, 1969). They used a radioimmunoassay which distinguishes between LH and HCG and found that the gonadotrophic activity in cord blood could be accounted for by HCG and not LH. The only other evidence is histochemical and shows that cells which look like LH-producing cells appear in the pituitary about midterm.

*Odell* The studies of Wurtman and Axelrod (*Science*, **143**, 1328–30, 1963) indicate that cervical sympathectomy affects the level of the enzyme system synthesizing melatonin in the pineal gland. Does cervical sympathectomy abolish the effect of light on reproductive physiology in the context you were talking about?

*Donovan* The short answer is that the cervical sympathetics play a very minor part in the perception of visual stimuli. If you take normal adult rats and remove the cervical sympathetics there is no effect on cyclic activity. The way in which the sympathetic system has been implicated here is in the rather special circumstances of taking rats, or hamsters, and putting them in the dark, then the testes regress. If while they are in the dark the cervical sympathetic ganglia are removed, then the testes enlarge much faster than they do without cervical sympathectomy. This is a very special circumstance. It has also been argued that the cervical sympathetics are involved in the response of the ferret to environmental illumination. Exposure of an anoestrous ferret to long days in winter induces oestrus. Remove the cervical sympathetic ganglia and it takes longer for the animal to come into oestrus. This has been attributed to the reduction of the amount of light entering the eye because of the standard Horner's syndrome effects. However, the work of Dr Herbert in Birmingham, referred to in my paper, casts a little doubt on this interpretation; he is of the view that the pineal gland is involved.

# Pituitary–Gonadal Interrelations

WILLIAM D. ODELL
RONALD S. SWERDLOFF
GUY E. ABRAHAM
HOWARD S. JACOBS
*and* PATRICK C. WALSH

Division of Endocrinology
Harbor General Hospital, Torrance, California

¶ In the past five years the development and widespread use of sensitive and precise competitive binding methods for quantifying polypeptide and steroid hormones has led to the rapid acquisition of a considerable body of data. Discussion of pituitary-gonadal interrelationships as an isolated subject is difficult, for gonadal control mechanisms operate as a functioning integrated unit consisting of the central nervous system, pituitary, and the gonad. In fact, one of the clearest pictures to be extracted from recent data is the extensive interdependence of this system. Figures 1 and 2 schematically present the integrated unit in males and females. As the figures indicate, the hypothalamic centres appear to be functionally different in men and women. Previous discussants have presented the details of the central nervous system control of pituitary gonadotrophin secretion. We shall discuss the pituitary-gonadal interrelationships in three portions: (1) prepuberty and puberty, (2) the adult female, and (3) the adult male.

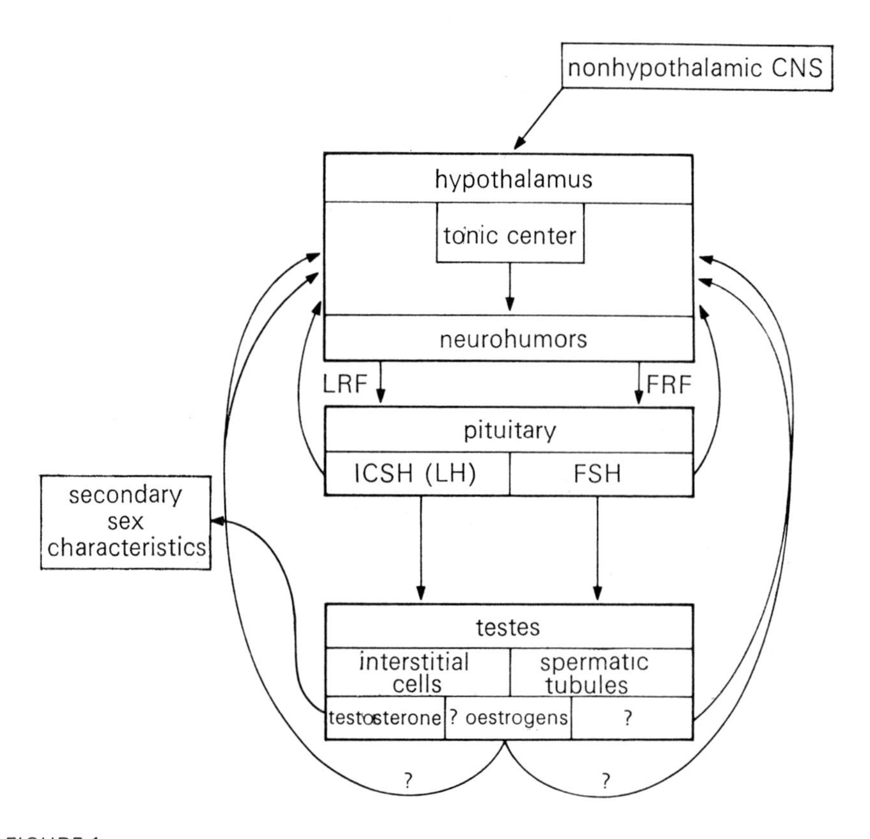


FIGURE 1
Schematic presentation of the central nervous system-hypothalamic-pituitary-testicular interrelationships in males. (Reproduced with permission from *Reproductive Physiology*, by W. D. Odell and D. Moyer, C.V. Mosby & Co., St. Louis, in press, 1971.)

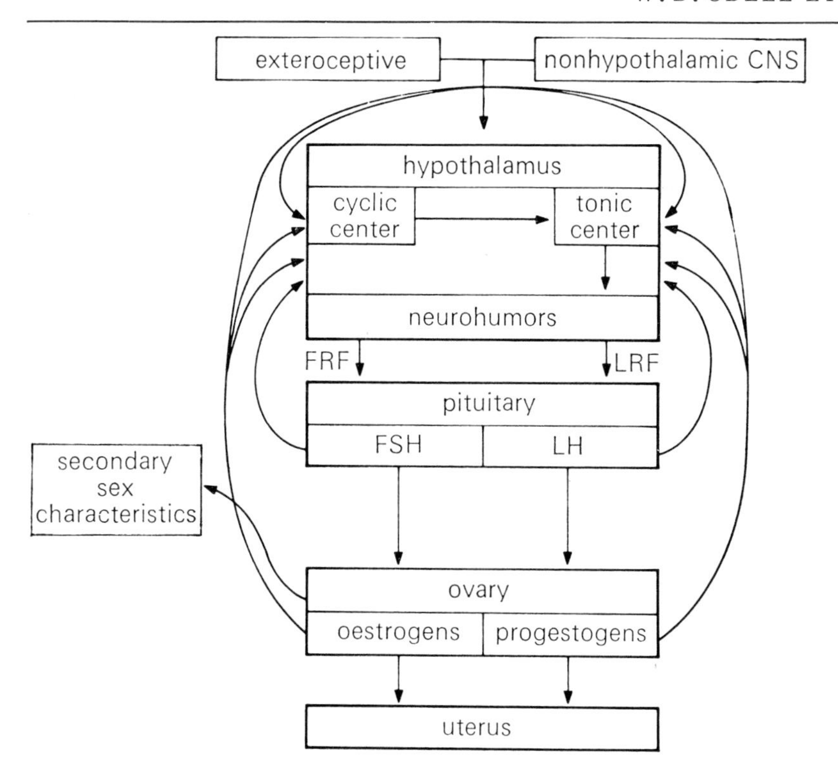


FIGURE 2
Schematic presentation of the central nervous system-hypothalamic-pituitary-ovarian interrelationships in females. (Reproduced with permission from *Reproductive Physiology*, by W. D. Odell and D. Moyer, C. V. Mosby & Co., St. Louis, in press, 1971.)

The measurements of follicle stimulating hormone (FSH), luteinizing hormone (LH), and the gonadal steroids have been made using either radioimmunoassays (FSH, LH, oestradiol) or similar competitive binding assays in which the binder is a tissue binding protein (oestradiol, oestriol), or a circulating blood protein (progesterone, 17-hydroxyprogesterone). We do not discuss methods herein, but obviously questions of specificity, sensitivity, and precision are important when we deal with physiological concepts. Thorough understanding of recent data is possible only if the problems of specificity, sensitivity, and precision are understood. For details of the parameters, we suggest referral to the recent workshops [1–3] on methods, previous publications from our laboratory and from other laboratories on assay methods [4–12], and additional references given throughout the discussion.

## I. PREPUBERTAL PITUITARY–GONADAL INTERRELATIONS

Until recently most clinical endocrinologists believed that the pituitary gland of the prepubertal child did not secrete gonadotrophins and that puberty was initiated and developed concomitant with the initiation of gonadotrophin secretion. In a popular pediatric-endocrine text published in 1965, a paragraph entitled 'Hormonal Control of Sexual Development' began with the following: 'The development of secondary sexual characteristics depends upon the secretion of gonadotrophins by the anterior pituitary. Although these may be present in the pituitary during early childhood, they are not released until adolescence' [13]. However, some thirty-six years earlier experimental studies in rats had revealed that gonadotrophins were secreted prepubertally and that a dynamic central nervous system-pituitary-gonadal interrelationship existed. In 1929, Kallas studied prepubertal gonadotrophin secretion by means of parabiotic sexually immature female rats [14]. When one partner of the parabiotic pair was castrated, the other showed signs of precocious puberty indicating that castration had resulted in increased gonadotrophin secretion which in turn led to stimulation of gonads in the intact partner.* Kallas made the following conclusion: 'In the infantile rat weighing 15 to 20 grams, precocious puberty may be produced by parabioses with an infantile castrated rat of the same age. The changes appear several days after the onset of the parabioses; the ovaries, the uterus, the vagina, and the vaginal plate correspond to those that are observed in an infantile animal after injection of the anterior pituitary. It follows that the anterior pituitary of the infantile animal is already capable of producing the regulatory hormones and of transmitting them via the blood. Our studies demonstrate that the infantile ovaries are held under the dependence of the pituitary.'

While at the present time we would substitute central nervous system-hypothalamus for pituitary, in other respects this conclusion remains true today. In 1951, Byrnes and Meyer, using the same parabiotic preparation studied by Kallas, found that, if tiny doses of oestrogens were injected into the immature castrated parabiont, gonadotrophin secretion could be suppressed [15]. Doses of oestrogen could be selected that were so small that no effects on secondary sex characteristics, as judged by uterine weight, were observed, and yet suppression of gonadotrophin secretion occurred. Table 1 presents an example of the data obtained by Byrnes and Meyer. More recently Johnson has parabiosed intact prepubertal rats to hypophysectomized prepubertal rats and observed stimulation of the gonads in the hypophysectomized parabiont adding further support to the conclusion of Kallas [16]. Using ovarian follicular development and the human

* It appears that polypeptide hormones freely cross the parabiotic union, but that steroid hormones do not. The reasons for this phenomenon are unknown.

TABLE 1. Effects of oestradiol on gonadotrophin secretion from parabiotic immature rats

| Group | Treatment | Dose μg/day | Number pairs | Ovarian weight/mg | Uterine weight/mg |
|---|---|---|---|---|---|
| Intact–Intact | None (Non-castrated controls) | 0 | 5 | 17 | – |
| Castrate–Intact | None | 0 | 23 | 160 | 52 |
| Castrate–Intact | Oestradiol administered to castrate | ·0032 | 2 | 146 | 47 |
| | | ·0065 | 2 | 122 | 60 |
| | | ·0065 | 1 | 15 | 43 |
| | | ·009 | 2 | 16 | 45 |
| | | ·012 | 3 | 25 | 51 |
| | | ·020 | 3 | 20 | 65 |
| | | ·025 | 3 | 25 | 135 |
| | | ·050 | 2 | 29 | 168 |

Modified from [15]. *Immature* female rats were joined in parabiotic union; the ovaries averaged 17 mg in weight. One partner was castrated, the ovarian weight increased from increased gonadotrophin secretion and averaged 160 mg. Varying doses of oestradiol were administered to the castrate partner. Inhibition of pituitary gonadotrophin secretion, without stimulation of uterine weight, occurred when doses of ·0065 to ·020 μg/day of oestradiol were administered. Lower doses failed to inhibit pituitary secretion, higher doses inhibited pituitary secretion but also stimulated uterine weight. Intact–Intact = immature female rat joined by parabiosis to another immature female rat; castrate–intact = castrate immature female rat joined by parabiosis to intact immature female rat

chorionic gonadotrophin (HCG) augmentation reaction, he was able to show FSH was present; using prostate and seminal vesicle weight increase, he was able to show LH was present. With the development of sensitive radioimmunoassays for follicle stimulating hormone (FSH) [17] and luteinizing hormone (LH) [18] in rats, we have made direct measurements of LH and FSH concentrations in blood in the prepubertal rat [19]. Figures 3 and 4 illustrate these data from the male animal. This strain of rats is weaned at twenty-one days of age and achieves full spermatogenesis at approximately sixty-three days of age. Between the ages of twenty-one and forty-nine days, testicular weight increases rapidly. After forty-nine days, a slower rate of increase is observed. Prostate weight increases rapidly between twenty-one days and seventy-seven days, and thereafter the rate of increase falls. LH and FSH are detectable in serum from all animals between the ages of twenty-one and ninety-one days. LH concentrations increase from a mean of 35 mμg/ml at twenty-one days to 50 mμg/ml at ninety-one days of age.* These small changes appear to occur progressively and are presumably responsible for the increasing testosterone

* We have not discussed methods in this manuscript. Consideration in detail of specificity of the assay system used indicates that the LH concentrations could be slightly lower prepubertally, since the *elevated* FSH produces small amounts of cross-reaction in the LH assay. For details the reader is referred to our publication which discusses this assay system [19].

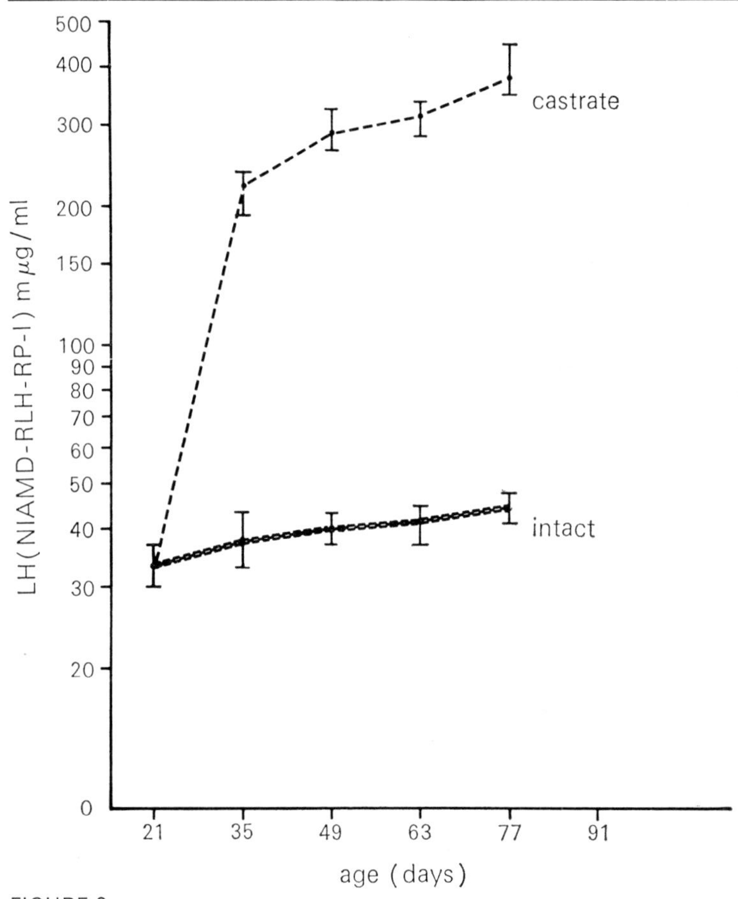


FIGURE 3
Serum LH concentrations in male rats between the ages of weaning and 91 days. In the intact rat, LH concentrations increase progressively with age. Castration at 21 days of age results in prompt increase in serum LH concentrations. The brackets enclose 1 S.E.M. (modified from [19])

secretion, evidenced by the changes in prostate weight. FSH concentrations are higher at twenty-one days (average 866 ± 79 (SEM) mμg/ml) than they are in the sexually mature animal (average 490 ± 58 mμg/ml). FSH concentrations appear to be highest at thirty-five days of age and to fall gradually to adult concentrations by sixty-three days. Castration at twenty-one days of age results in a marked increase in LH and FSH concentrations, and the magnitude of this increase appears to be similar to that observed in the sexually mature animal.

Let us now turn to a second animal model, the cow. Sexual maturity, in the cattle studied, occurs at about thirteen months of age when the first oestrus cycle is usually observed. We have developed a radioimmunoassay for bovine LH and studied LH concentrations during pubertal

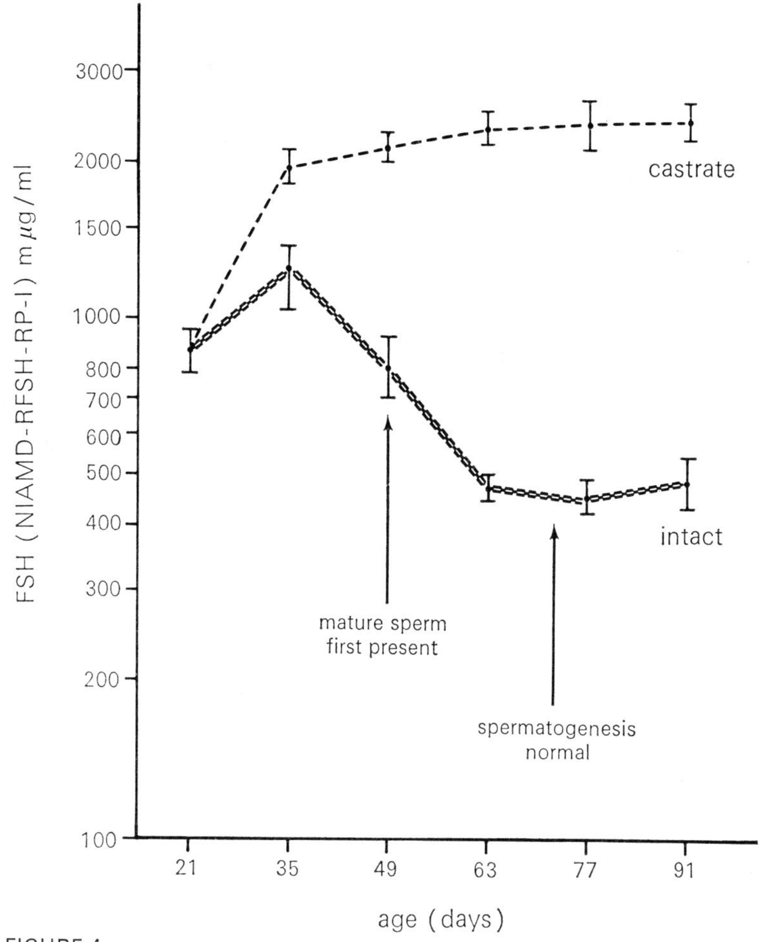


FIGURE 4
Serum FSH concentrations in male rats between the ages of weaning and 91 days. Note that FSH is higher in prepubertal rats than it is in sexually mature rats and *falls* to adult levels as spermatogenesis becomes normal. Spermatogenesis is normal beginning at 63 days of age. Castration of the weanling rat results in prompt increase in FSH concentrations. Brackets enclose 1 S.E.M. (modified from [19])

changes [20]. Figure 5 illustrates LH concentrations in single specimens obtained from cattle between the ages of fifteen days through sexual maturity. Considerable day-to-day variation occurs in cattle, and average concentrations at one month to four months of age are only slightly lower than those occurring in sexually mature cattle. The differences in the average concentration in sexually immature and sexually mature cattle are not significantly different, but the overall pattern is similar to that in the rat. When daily determinations are made, it can be shown that castration at all ages over one month results in significant increase in LH concentrations. Figures 6 and 7 illustrate such data and Figure 8 summarizes the study from

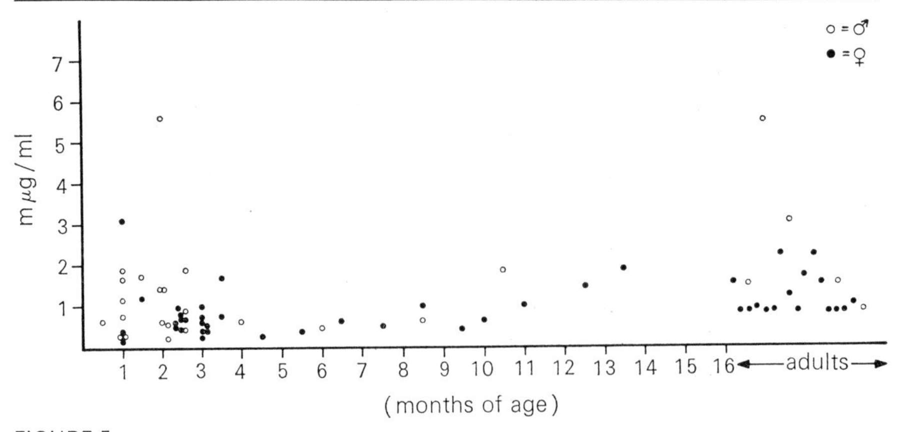


FIGURE 5

Scattergram of LH determined on samples randomly obtained from cattle of different ages. All samples were measured within a single assay to permit comparison of different age groups. Although the data suggest a small rise in LH with advancing age, this rise is not statistically significant with this relatively small population (reproduced with permission from [20])

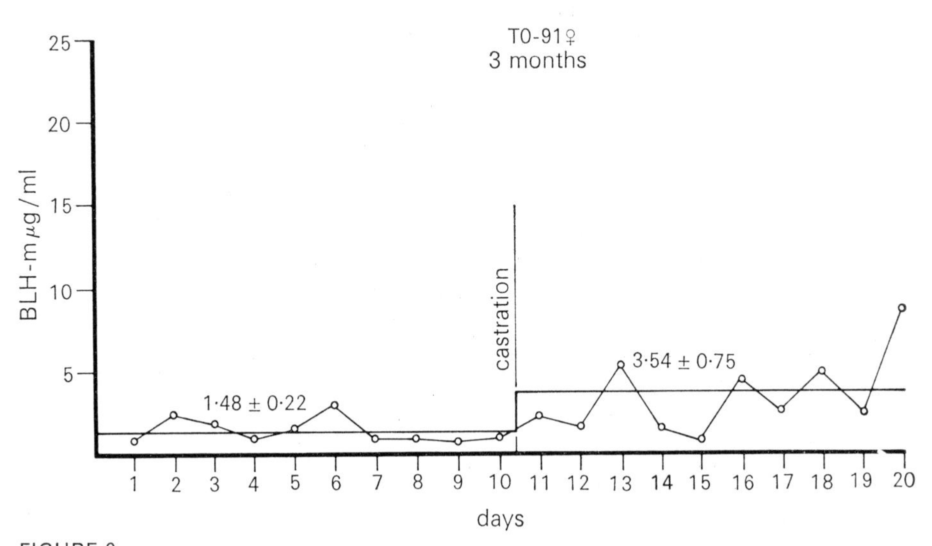


FIGURE 6

Daily determinations of serum LH in a three-month-old heifer before and after castration on day ten. Mean ± SE is indicated by the numbers and the mean before and after castration is shown by the solid line (reproduced with permission from [20])

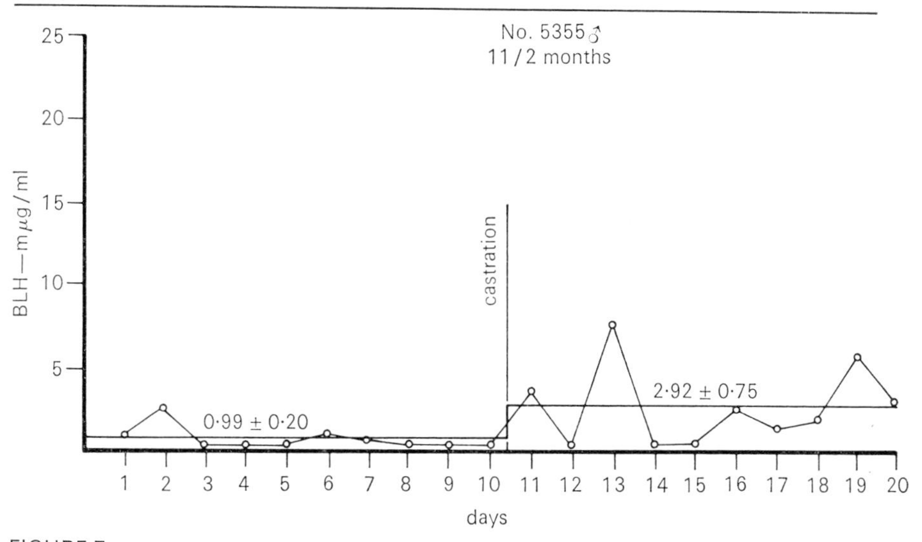


FIGURE 7
Daily determinations of serum LH in a three-month-old bull before and after castration on day ten. Mean ± SE is indicated by the numbers and the mean before and after castration is shown by the solid line (reproduced with permission from [20])

eleven animals castrated prior to four months of age. Castration of sexually mature animals results in increases in LH of the same magnitude as those observed when immature animals are castrated. Lastly, when animals are castrated at less than four months of age and LH concentrations are measured weekly until thirteen or more months of age, no alterations in these concentrations are observed at the usual age of sexual maturation. Once the concentrations have reached maximal castrate levels (two to four weeks after castration) they appear to fluctuate about a mean throughout the periods of study. Figures 9 and 10 present exemplary data.

In summary, the studies in rats and cattle indicate that LH concentrations are only slightly lower in prepubertal animals than in sexually mature animals and in the case of the cow are not statistically different because of wide day-to-day variations. Presumably this small increment is sufficient to result in increased gonadal steroid secretion and in progression of secondary sex characteristics. While our data on FSH in the cow remain incomplete and are not reported herein, FSH concentrations in the rat fall as spermatogenesis develops. These data in these two species of animals may now be contrasted with available data in children.

In 1964 [21], we first described a radioimmunoassay for human chorionic gonadotrophin and, in 1966, modified this to permit assay of human LH [22]. During the early utilization of these assay systems, we were surprised to find that LH was detectable in the blood of all children

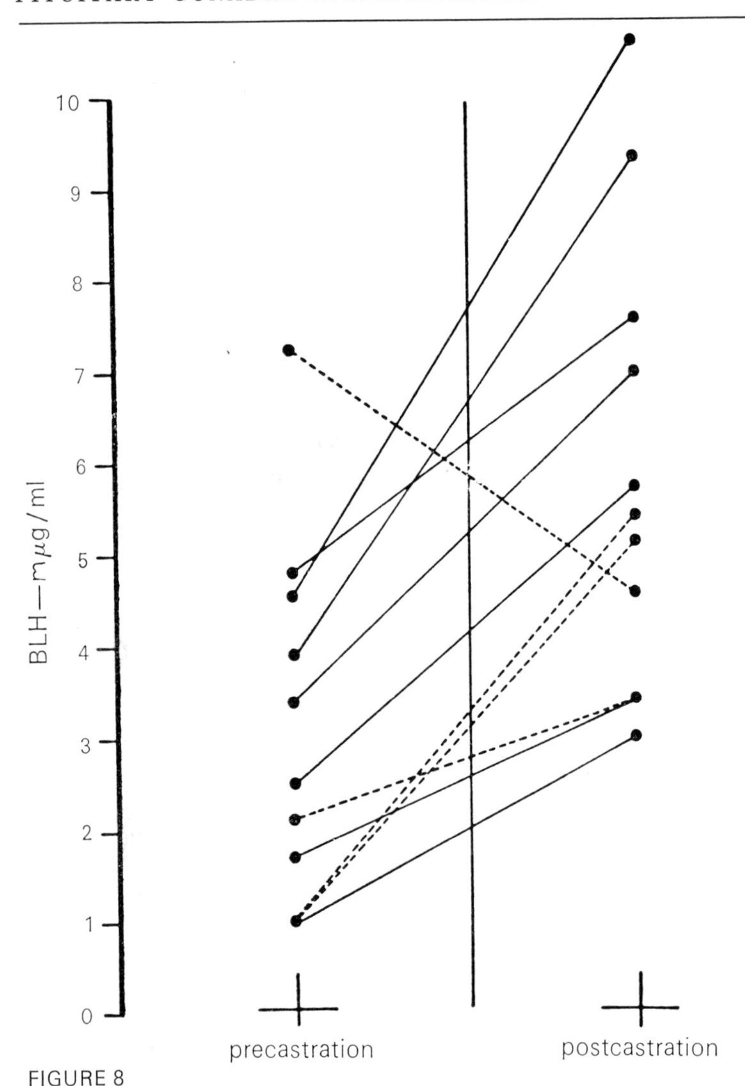


FIGURE 8
Average LH concentrations in cattle less than three months of age before and after castration. Each dot represents the average of 10 consecutive daily samples measured immediately pre and post castration. The solid lines represent females and the dotted lines represent males (reproduced with permission from [20])

over the age of one. Based upon these observations and consideration of the older studies in rats, we hypothesized that a dynamic central nervous system-pituitary-gonadal interrelationship probably existed in children before the age of puberty [23]. Bagshawe also reported that LH was detectable in urine from children by radioimmunoassay [24]. Subsequent studies from our laboratory using bioassays and pooled collections of urine from prepubertal children [25, 26], as well as numerous studies from others using radioimmunoassays for both FSH and LH, have verified and

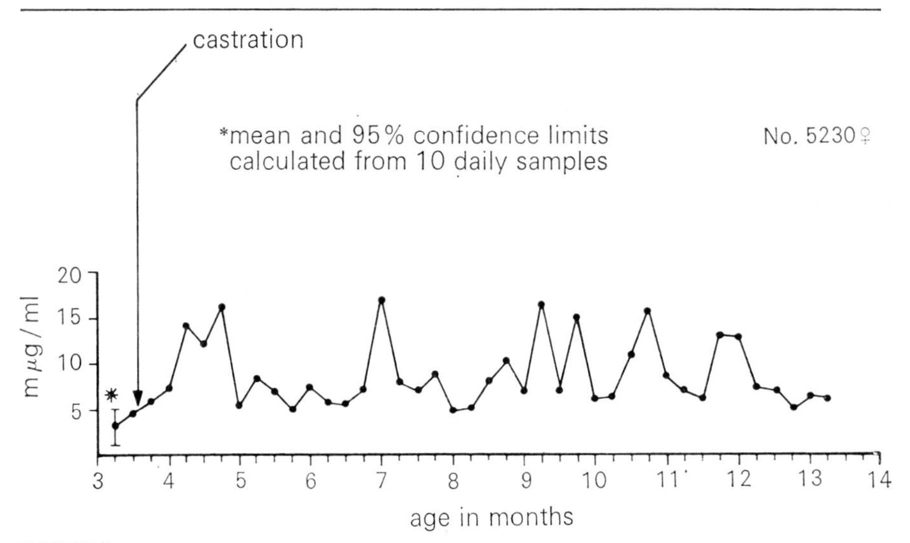


FIGURE 9
Weekly determinations of LH in a heifer castrated at $3\frac{1}{2}$ months of age. The mean and 95% confidence level of daily samples prior to castration is indicated by the brackets in the lower left-hand corner of the graph. Note that LH concentrations increase after castration and that the mean remains unchanging through the age of $13\frac{1}{2}$ months (reproduced with permission from [20])

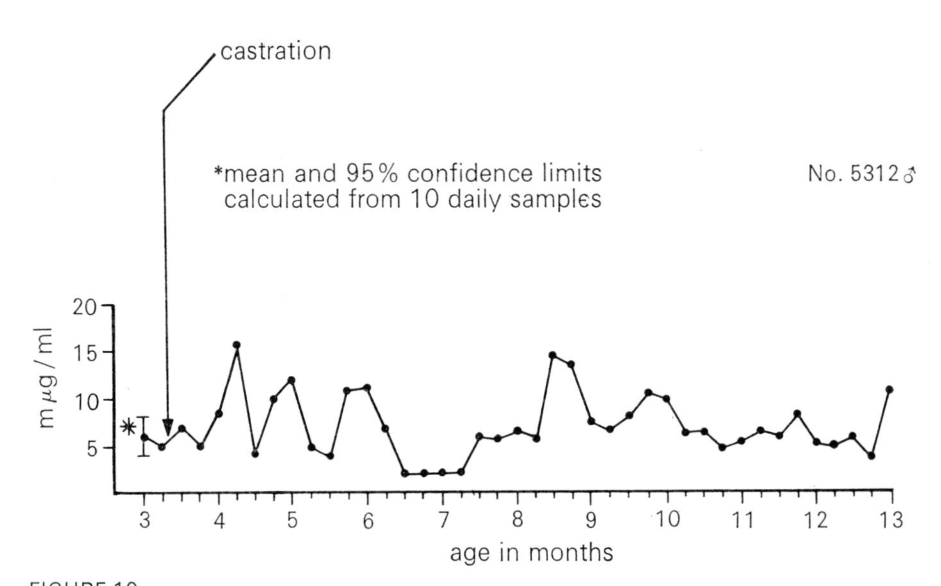


FIGURE 10
Weekly determinations of serum LH in a bull measured through 13 months of age. As in Figure 9, no increase in mean LH concentration was observed by the chronological age of normal sexual maturation (12 or 13 months) (reproduced with permission from [20])

amplified these observations. Studies from the laboratories of Drs Blizzard [27–31], Yen [32–34], and Grumbach [35, 36] have correlated serum LH and FSH concentrations with stages of sexual development in children. Table 2 illustrates these data for boys, and Table 3 for girls from the data of Blizzard et al. [31]. Concentrations of both LH and FSH increase slightly and progressively as one moves from sexual stage one, or the preadolescent stage, through stage three where early sexual hair and penile enlargement are present. After this, and through stages of full sexual maturity (stage five), LH appears to increase by small increments, but no significant changes in FSH are seen. Furthermore, if one plots population changes in serum LH and serum FSH against age in years, there is a progressive increase in concentrations of both hormones. Below the age of seven in both sexes of children, there appears to be a plateau of gonadotrophin concentration

TABLE 2
Serum FSH and LH concentrations in boys with different stages of sexual development and in adults*

| Stage of development | Serum FSH m i.u./ml Mean ± S.E. | Serum LH m i.u./ml Mean ± S.E. |
|---|---|---|
| I | 4·5 ± 0·2 | 3·9 ± 0·2 |
| II | 5·9 ± 0·3 | 6·8 ± 0·5 |
| III | 8·1 ± 1·0 | 8·5 ± 0·5 |
| IV | 8·5 ± 0·8 | 9·5 ± 0·6 |
| V | 7·1 ± 0·5 | 11·8 ± 0·6 |
| Adults | 7·4 ± 0·8 | 10·9 ± 0·7 |

*Stages of sexual development: I = preadolescent, II = beginning testicular enlargement and scrotal changes, III = early sexual hair and penile enlargement, IV = sexual hair visible on photograph and further penile and testicular enlargement, V = adult size genitalia. (Modified [31])

TABLE 3
Serum FSH and LH concentrations in girls during various stages of sexual development. Data from Penny et al. with permission [31]

| Stage of sexual development | Serum FSH m i.u./ml Mean ± S.E. | Serum LH m i.u./ml Mean ± S.E. |
|---|---|---|
| I | 4·2 ± 0·2 | 2·9 ± 0·2 |
| II | 5·5 ± 0·2 | 3·9 ± 0·8 |
| III | 8·0 ± 0·4 | 8·4 ± 0·6 |
| IV | 8·0 ± 0·5 | 11·3 ± 1·3 |
| Adults | (7·8)* | (12·7)* |
| Follicular Phase | 11·0 ± 0·4 | 15·6 ± 0·3 |
| Luteal Phase | 9·9 ± 0·4 | 11·7 ± 0·7 |

*The data of Penny et al. contained only 4 menstrual cycles. The data for adults is taken from our publications on FSH [6] and LH [49]. Stages of sexual development as on Table 2. (Modified [31])

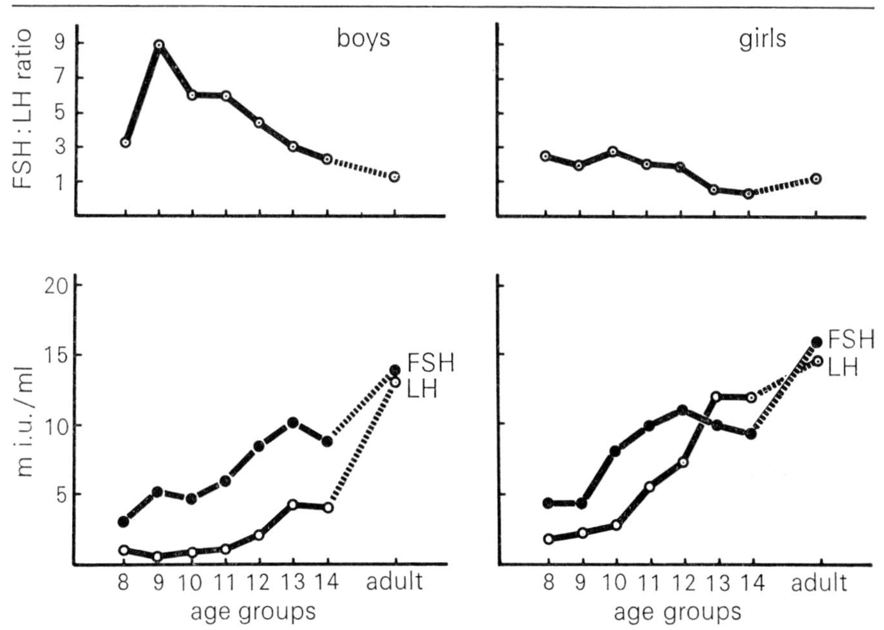


FIGURE 11
Serum FSH and LH in boys and girls between the ages of 8 and sexual maturity. Note that the ratio of FSH : LH is higher in prepubertal boys than prepubertal girls. These data have been previously published by Yen et al. [32–34] but have not been presented in this form. This figure was kindly sent to us by Dr Yen

which was not observed in either of the experimental animal models. After the age of eight or nine, and as sexual secondary sex characteristics develop, the concentrations of both hormones increase progressively. Yen et al. [32–34, 37] have reported that the ratio of FSH to LH is higher in boys between the ages of eight and fourteen than it is in girls of the same age. This finding is reminiscent of our findings in the rat, where FSH/LH ratios are high in males prior to the appearance of spermatogenesis, and the ratio falls as spermatogenesis is completed. However, the data of Yen are not in complete agreement with those of Blizzard et al. [27], and further studies are required to determine which observations are correct. As will be discussed later, these observations are pertinent to discussions of FSH control mechanisms in the male. Figures 11 and 12 show data from the publication of Yen et al. [32–34, 37].

Castration of prepubertal children is only rarely performed, and controlled studies such as we have performed in rats and cattle have not yet been made. Guyda et al. [28] and Blizzard et al. [30, 31] have reported concentrations of LH and FSH in girls with ovarian agenesis. They report that the mean concentrations of LH are significantly higher than in normal girls of the same age range, but less than those observed in sexually mature women. The LH concentrations in girls with gonadal agenesis do not lie

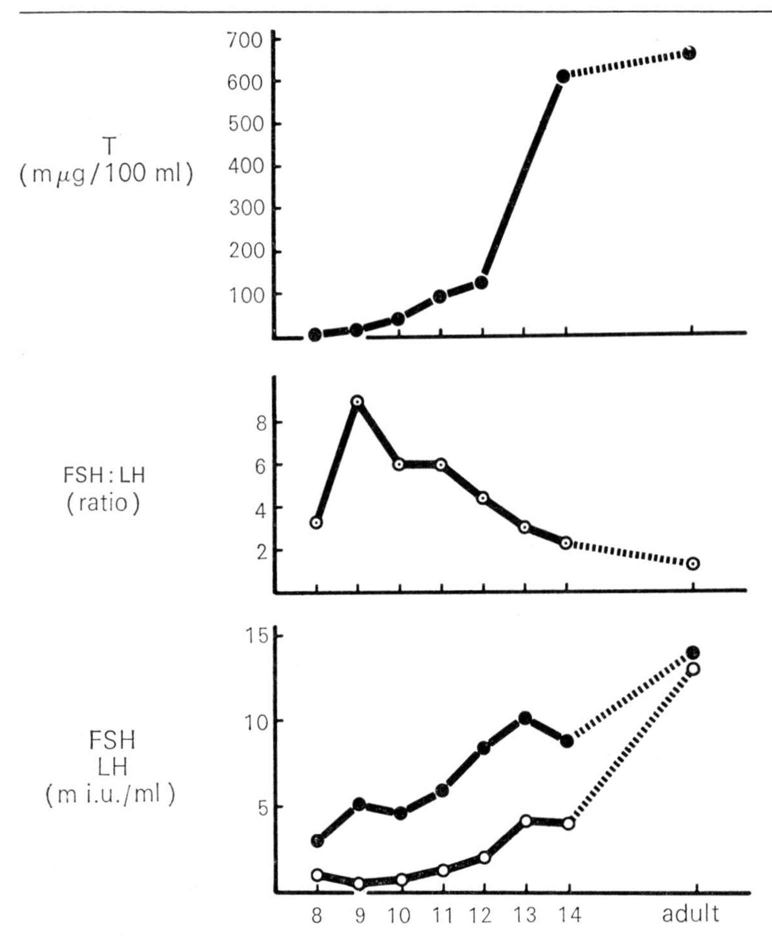


FIGURE 12
Serum LH and FSH, FSH : LH ratio and plasma testosterone in boys. Compare with Figure 4 (reproduced with permission from [33])

outside the range of LH concentrations found in normal girls. In contrast, however, serum FSH concentrations are generally increased above the range observed in age matched normal girls. It thus appears that in agonadal girls, FSH secretion increases earlier and to a greater extent than LH. At the usual age of sexual maturity both LH and FSH increase further to the high concentrations observed in castrate adult women or postmenopausal women. In addition, if ovarian agenesis patients* have the same alterations as children castrated prepubertally, this would indicate prepubertal castration does not result in as great an elevation in circulating gonado-

* These patients have karyotypic abnormalities, usually XO instead of normal XX sex chromosomes. Some patients have mosaic patterns and varying degrees of gonadal dysgenesis. Phenotypic abnormalities are frequently striking, and many patients may be diagnosed by such abnormalities as young children.

trophins as does castration of the sexually mature human. Table 4 summarizes these studies. These findings in girls contrast with those in the young castrated cow followed through the age of sexual maturity.

TABLE 4
Serum LH concentrations in girls without functioning ovaries and compared with eugonadal women and castrate or postmenopausal women.*

| Gonadal status | Age (years) | Serum LH m i.u./ml ± S.D. |
|---|---|---|
| Normal girls | 2 to 9 | 2·7 ± 0·3 |
| Girls with ovarian agenesis | 2 to 9 | 4·5 ± 0·3 |
| Normal women | 19 to 35 | 10·2 ± 0·8 |
| Women with ovarian agenesis | ⩾14 | 16 to 108 (range) |
| Castrated or postmenopausal women | ⩾20 | 30 to 150 (range) |

*Summarized from [30] and [23]

Kulin and Grumbach [37, 38] have utilized the antioestrogen, clomiphene, to study the sensitivity of the prepubertal control systems. In 1967, we reported that clomiphene in doses of 100 to 300 mg per day increases serum LH and FSH concentrations in normal men [23]. This drug has been extensively used to induce ovulation in infertile women [39–41]. We also showed that clomiphene treatment led to suppression of LH and FSH concentrations when it was administered to postmenopausal women, presumably due to an intrinsic weak oestrogen action [42]. Drs Kulin and Grumbach [37, 38] have shown that suppression also occurs in prepubertal children and, furthermore, that as little as one one-hundredth or less of the dose required to *stimulate* gonadotrophins in adult men or women will suppress gonadotrophins in prepubertal children. These data form the first demonstration that a more sensitive dynamic system exists in children.

In summary, in rats, cattle, and children, LH concentrations appear to increase progressively from prepuberty through puberty to sexual maturity and small changes would, therefore, be presumed to be responsible for the alterations in gonadal steroid secretion. In children, in contrast to rats and cattle, LH concentrations appear to be low and plateaued for a number of years prior to the increases observed with puberty. In children FSH concentrations are also lower before puberty than after puberty, whereas in the rat, FSH concentrations are higher prior to puberty than after puberty. Lastly, absence of gonads before puberty in children results in only small increases in circulating LH, whereas castration after puberty results in very large changes in LH. Thus fluctuations prepubertally in children appear to oscillate within a more tightly confined system than they do after sexual maturity. In contrast in cattle and rats, castration before puberty results in changes in FSH and LH of similar magnitude to those observed in the sexually mature castrated animal.

## II. PITUITARY–GONADAL INTERRELATIONS IN THE SEXUALLY MATURE FEMALE

In the sexually mature woman, LH and FSH concentrations fluctuate in blood in a rhythmic pattern related to ovarian function [6, 10, 23, 24, 43–57]. Figure 13 shows the mean concentrations observed in normal women throughout normal menstrual cycles from data collected in our laboratories. Small fluctuations in FSH are associated with major events in ovarian function. There is a small rise in FSH, which is initiated near the

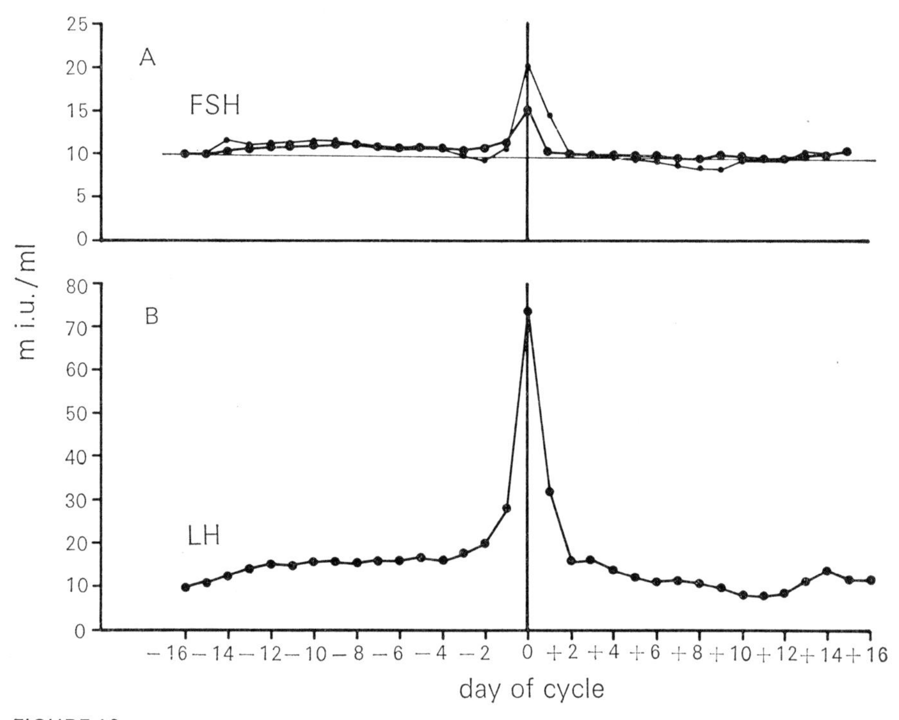


FIGURE 13

A. Mean FSH concentrations measured daily in 19 women (heavy line) throughout the menstrual cycle. Data drawn from [6]. For comparison the light line represents mean FSH concentrations redrawn from [47]. The solid horizontal line is drawn through the mean luteal phase FSH concentration to permit visualization of the small rise in follicular phase FSH concentrations

B. Mean LH concentrations measured daily in 10 women throughout the menstrual cycle. Redrawn from [23]. All data are centred about the midcycle LH peak. Onset of menses occurred variably on days −12–16 and +12 and +16

onset of menstrual bleeding and which continues through the first half of the follicular phase. In the latter half, FSH concentrations fall to slightly lower levels. Ross et al. [47] have found a sharp nadir just prior to the midcycle LH–FSH peak. In most women, a rise or peak in FSH occurs coincident with the LH ovulatory peak at midcycle. Afterwards, during the luteal phase, FSH falls to concentrations lower than those during any portion of the follicular phase and remains low until just prior to the onset of the next menses [6, 47]. Despite the fact that these changes represent only small alterations in FSH concentration, there has been fairly good agreement in the several publications describing fluctuations in serum FSH during the menstrual cycle [6, 42–47]. Thus although Saxena et al. [48] did not observe an early follicular phase rise or a lower luteal phase concentration, most other investigators have observed these changes [6, 42–47]. Faiman and Ryan [44] observed a midcycle FSH peak coincident with the LH peak in only three of ten subjects, but our studies [6, 53] and those of others [45, 46, 47] indicate that the FSH and LH peaks occur on the same day in most subjects.

LH concentrations are low at the onset of menses, but are slightly higher than the preceding luteal phase. Concentrations increase steadily throughout the follicular phase, and at midcycle, a sharp LH peak occurs which induces ovulation. Afterwards, LH concentrations fall again, and during the mid-luteal phase, concentrations are lower than during any other portion of the cycle [23, 49]. In general, these details have been found by most groups performing such studies using LH radioimmunoassays. The slight differences in luteal phase and follicular phase concentrations are consistently observed in our studies. Others [46, 47] have also found such differences, but in one study, follicular phase and luteal phase concentrations were similar [44].

Within the ovary another sequence of events is occurring. Near the onset of menses, a group of follicles begins to enlarge. From these follicles, one is selected (by unknown mechanisms) and continues to develop (presumably under stimulus of the small follicular phase increase in FSH), while the others regress in size. Through the first half of the menstrual cycle, growth of this follicle continues until the preovulatory follicle has been prepared. In response to the LH–FSH midcycle surge, ovulation follows and the follicle undergoes metamorphosis into a corpus luteum. The corpus luteum functions until near the subsequent menses. As depicted in Figure 14, these morphological changes are associated with major changes in steroid hormone secretion. Measurement of serum or plasma-oestradiol [55–58] reveals the following changes: At the beginning of the menstrual cycle, oestradiol concentrations are low; these concentrations slowly and progressively increase during follicle maturation. About one day

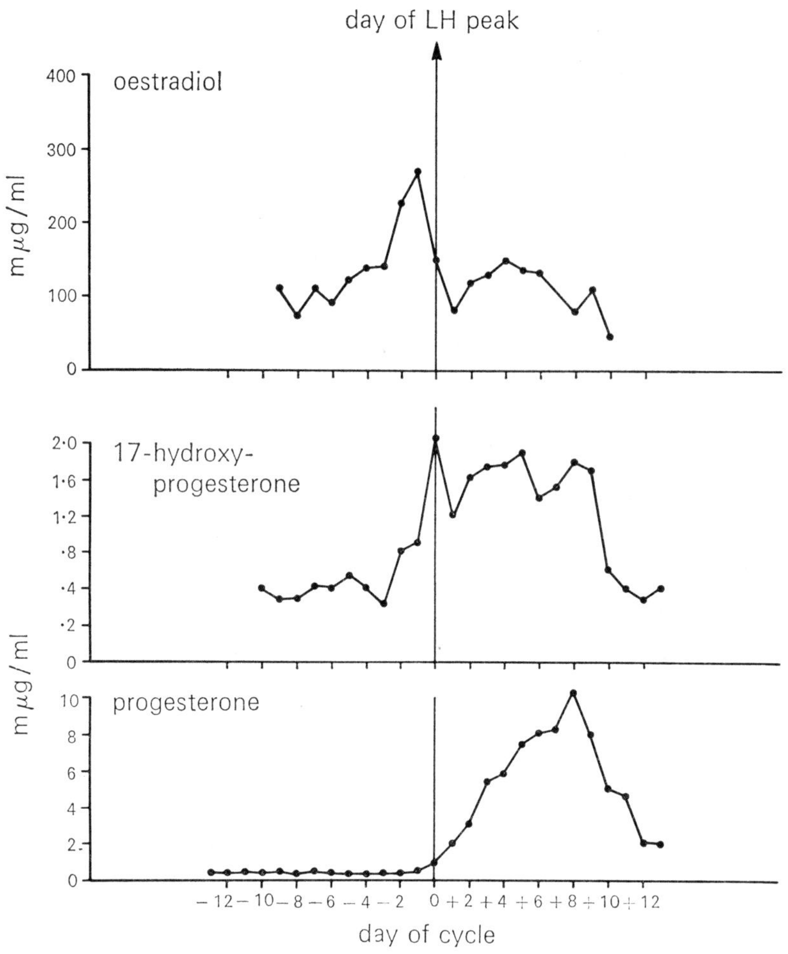


FIGURE 14
Mean concentrations of plasma progesterone from 10 women, 17-hydroxy-progesterone from 8 women, and oestradiol concentrations from 4 women measured daily throughout the normal menstrual cycle. Progesterone and 17-hydroxy-progesterone drawn from [47]. Oestradiol concentrations calculated from data of Abraham [55 & 56]

prior to, or coincident with, the LH–FSH ovulatory surge, a peak in oestradiol occurs. Oestradiol then falls to about fifty per cent of this value and rises again during corpus luteum function. Towards the end of the menstrual cycle, oestradiol concentrations fall just preceding the subsequent menses.

Progesterone concentrations remain low during the follicular phase, and probably remain at these levels until after the LH–FSH ovulatory peak. After ovulation, and during corpus luteum function, progesterone concentrations rise to high levels coincident with the highest secretion of oestradiol. They fall again in parallel with oestradiol. There is good agreement among several publications [9, 10, 47, 48] that progesterone concentrations remain less than two mμg/ml throughout the follicular phase. However, Saxena et al. [48], Neill et al. [10], and Runnebaum and Zander [59] found small preovulatory increases in progesterone. Yoshimi and Lipsett [9] and Ross et al. [47] found no such changes, and reported progesterone increased only after the LH–FSH surge.* Neill et al. reported that in the monkey, plasma progesterone concentrations increased about two days prior to ovulation [60]. Present methodology makes these small increments difficult to measure, but if they do exist, they are small and their physiological significance remains unknown. The concentration of 17-hydroxyprogesterone is also low at the onset of the menstrual cycle and, along with oestradiol, rises to a peak prior to, or coincident with, the LH–FSH peak. The 17-hydroxyprogesterone level then falls by about fifty per cent and rises again in parallel with oestradiol and progesterone during corpus luteum function [47, 61]. Oestrone concentrations appear to parallel those of oestradiol [54]. These steroid concentrations also fall dramatically near the end of the first menstrual cycle and as the next menstrual period begins.

Knowledge concerning the interdependence of the ovarian and pituitary secretions stems from a variety of observations in humans. Crooke et al. [62] have shown that infertile women with secondary amenorrhoea respond to a single injection of human FSH (which was impure and contained some LH activity) by a progressive increase in the urinary excretion of oestriol, reaching a peak ten to twelve days later. If HCG is administered nine days after the FSH injection, ovulation may occur. This sequence indicates either that FSH is bound in effective concentration within the ovary for this duration of time, or that once initiated, follicle growth continues spontaneously or under permissive low concentrations of endogenous FSH.

One might conjecture that, if FSH had a very long half-time of degradation (days), an increment at onset of follicular growth might permit continued elevations for the duration of follicular growth. However, the t-1/2 of disappearance is approximately three hours, which makes such a postulate unlikely [63]. In addition, in Dr Crooke's studies, the urinary excretion of FSH returned to control values while follicular growth continued [62].

After full follicular development has occurred, ovulation can usually be induced by treatment with human chorionic gonadotrophin, a hormone with LH-like properties, but one which has a much more prolonged half-time of disappearance from blood [64]. When a single injection of three to ten

* Follicular phase progesterone concentrations are low and quantification is difficult by existing methods. Small changes may be overlooked.

thousand units of HCG is administered to induce ovulation in infertile women, corpus luteum function, once initiated, may be completely normal [62, 65]. Because of this observation and the fact that in the sow, once ovulation occurs, hypophysectomy may be performed without effect on magnitude or duration of corpus luteum function [66], it was thought for some time that the corpus luteum functioned and ceased to function independently of pituitary secretion. However, Vande Wiele et al. [67] have shown that if human LH (which has a half-time disappearance of less than one hour [68]) is used to induce ovulation, continued treatment with small doses of LH are required after ovulation is induced to maintain corpus luteum function.

In 1968, we reported that when castrated or postmenopausal women were treated with oral oestrogens, the elevated serum LH and FSH were suppressed to concentrations similar to those seen in eugonadal women [69]. If oestrogen treatment was continued, LH and FSH concentrations remained low with slight day-to-day fluctuations. However, when progesterone or medroxyprogesterone treatment was instituted in these oestrogen suppressed women, an LH and FSH peak was observed which was self-limiting in spite of continuation of the progestogen. In terms of its height and duration, this LH–FSH surge was indistinguishable from the midcycle LH–FSH ovulatory peak. Figure 15 depicts data from our study. From these studies, we concluded in 1968 (before plasma and serum steroid measurements were available) that in women it was likely that an *ovarian steroidal signal* induced the ovulatory peak and that this signal might involve the secretion of a progestogen. Furthermore, we have shown that an oral synthetic oestrogen (mestranol) administered alone to eugonadal women increases serum LH, but not FSH [70]. Subsequently, oestradiol and 17α-hydroxyprogesterone concentrations were found to be elevated prior to the LH–FSH peak, and one or both of these steroidal hormones have been implicated as a signal for triggering the ovulatory peak. Progesterone *per se* may be low prior to the LH–FSH peak. Thus oestradiol in combination with a progestogen such as 17-hydroxyprogesterone, or even other oestrogens or progestogens, may constitute the ovarian signal.

Some studies in animals also amplify these studies in humans; both progestogens and oestrogens have been shown to facilitate ovulation. In 1940–43, Everett [71, 72] showed that ovulation could be induced in rats with a spontaneously occurring state of persistent oestrus. Later Greer [73] showed that progesterone would produce ovulation in rats with localized hypothalamic lesions causing persistent oestrus. Subsequently, Nallar et al. [74] and Redmond and Everett [75] demonstrated in normal cycling rats that progesterone administered in late dioestrus or in prooestrus resulted in elevated plasma LH and ovulation. Pfeiffer [76] re-

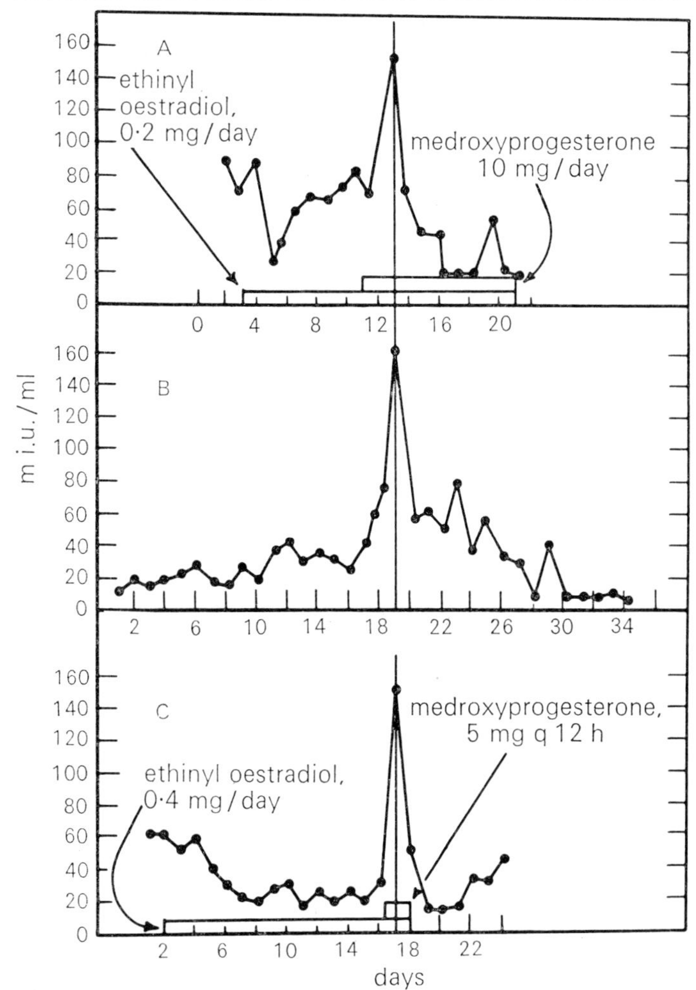


FIGURE 15
Induction of HLH peak by progestogen treatment in women. Part A depicts data obtained from a 58-year-old postmenopausal woman. Part B depicts, for comparison, data obtained by quantifying HLH daily in a eugonadal 23-year-old woman throughout a menstrual cycle. Part C depicts data obtained from a 58-year-old castrate woman. In the study depicted in Part A medroxyprogesterone was continued for 11 days. Note that after the LH surge induced at the onset of treatment, that LH fell and was lower than prior to progestogen treatment. In the study depicted in Part C, medroxy-progesterone was continued only for 2 days, LH peaked and fell during this treatment. The sample obtained on day 18 was drawn while the patient was still on medication (reproduced with permission from [69])

ported that progesterone treatment would cause ovulation in monkeys during the summer anovulatory periods. McCormack and Meyer reported that properly timed administration of progesterone to immature rats pre-treated with pregnant mare serum gonadotrophin markedly increased the percentage of rats which ovulated [77]. In follow-up of these studies, they also showed that in this experimental model, when administered under identical conditions, oestradiol-17β, corticosterone, or testosterone produced no effects on ovulation, but that 6-α-methyl-17α-hydroxyprogesterone or 20β-hydroxy-pregn-4-en-3-one increased the percentage of rats ovulating [78]. Administration of 20α-hydroxy-pregn-4-en-3-one was ineffective. It may well be that this is not an appropriate experimental model, since Goldman et al. have shown, in the rat, that the secretory rates of progesterone and 20α-hydroxy-pregn-4-en-3-one increased at least two hours prior to the LH ovulatory surge [79]. Kawakami and Sawyer demonstrated that single doses of progesterone administered to a rabbit lowered the threshold to arousal involving the brain stem reticular formation and the EEG 'after reaction threshold' involving the rhinencephalon and hypothalamus for a few hours [80]. Afterwards, the thresholds in both areas were elevated to supranormal levels. If applied to LH control centres, these studies could explain why progestogens may both stimulate and inhibit the secretion of LH as was shown by Caligaris et al. [81].

Oestrogens also induce ovulation. Everett [82] induced ovulation in pregnant rats by administration of oestrogen on day four of pregnancy. Brown-Grant [83] has recently reviewed much of the data on induction of ovulation during pregnancy in rats and reports that after day three, 6·25 to 100 μg of oestradiol benzoate will induce ovulation if competent follicles are present. Piper and Foote [84] reported that oestradiol treatment would induce ovulation in nonpregnant sheep. Goding et al., in further study of this model, infused 'Premarin' intravenously and noted LH discharge about thirty-six hours later [85]. This long lag period in triggering of LH is of interest. Shirley et al. [86], using a chemical oestrogen antagonist, showed that the anti-oestrogens will prevent ovulation in rats. Ferin et al. [87] showed that antibodies to oestradiol, administered on day two of dioestrus at least twelve hours prior to ovulation (but not if administered later), prevented the LH ovulatory surge and ovulation in rats. Ferrin et al. also showed that antibodies to progesterone failed to inhibit ovulation, although inhibition of other progestogens was not studied.

Palka et al. [88] implanted $H^3$-oestradiol in the median eminence area and pituitary. Median eminence implantation resulted in an increase in plasma LH and hypertrophy of the pituitary. Pituitary implantation was associated with no increase in plasma LH, but pituitary hypertrophy was still observed. These workers concluded that oestrogen stimulates pituitary release of LH by a central action on the median eminence but induces pituitary hypertrophy by a direct action on the pituitary cells. Ramírez has presented a number of studies in rats and discussed the nature of the positive and negative feedback systems in control of LH in females [89].

Treatment of infertile amenorrhoeic or oligomenorrhoeic women with clomiphene frequently results in ovulation, and pregnancy may result. Clomiphene is a synthetic compound with anti-oestrogen properties. We reported in 1967 that treatment of normal men with this drug led to an increase in serum LH [23]. Cargille et al. [90] amplified this observation and reported that both serum FSH and LH were increased when men were treated for five to seven days with clomiphene. FSH and LH also increase in serum when women are treated with this drug. Ross et al. [47] have studied nine ovulatory cycles produced by clomiphene treatment. Figure 16 shows

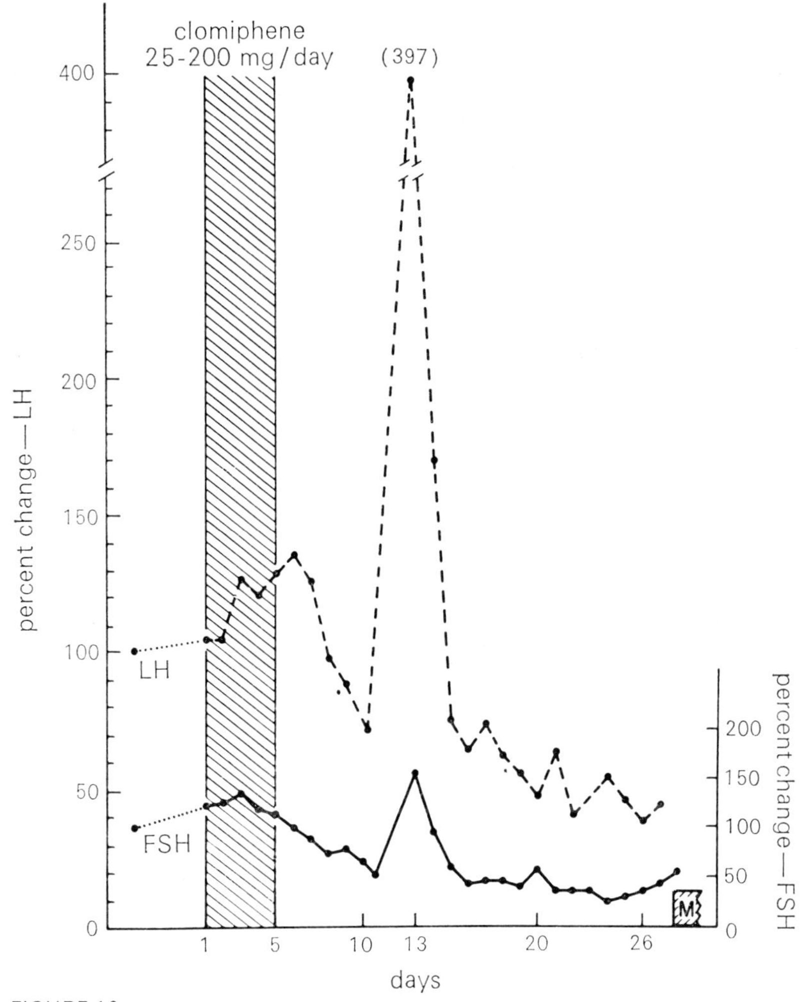


FIGURE 16
Changes in mean daily plasma LH (dash line) and FSH (solid line) concentrations during presumptively ovulatory cycles induced with clomiphene in 9 women with oligo-ovulatory or anovulatory infertility. Values on ordinate indicate the per cent of control values for LH (left) and FSH (right). Days 1–10 were synchronized on the day when treatment began but subsequent days were synchronized on the day of the LH midcycle peak (reproduced with permission from [47])

the rise in FSH and LH during treatment and also that, seven days after cessation of clomiphene treatment, a typical LH–FSH ovulatory peak is observed. Progesterone concentrations increase at midcycle in a fashion indistinguishable from a normal ovulatory cycle. The response to clomiphene assists in understanding events during the normal menstrual cycle. Presumably, clomiphene treatment results in an increase in serum FSH which starts the sequence of events. FSH stimulates follicle growth, which then proceeds to the preovulatory follicle spontaneously. A preovulatory steroidal surge triggers the LH–FSH release and ovulation follows. Abraham and Klaiber [55] have shown that an oestradiol peak preceded the LH–FSH ovulatory peak after clomiphene treatment. Figure 17 presents an example of such data. The follicle is transferred into the corpus luteum which survives autonomously or under control of low endogenous LH concentrations for its normal life span. The combined secretion of oestrogen and progestogen after ovulation acts as a powerful suppressor of LH and FSH. Thus the entire interlocking series of events during the clomiphene cycle and during

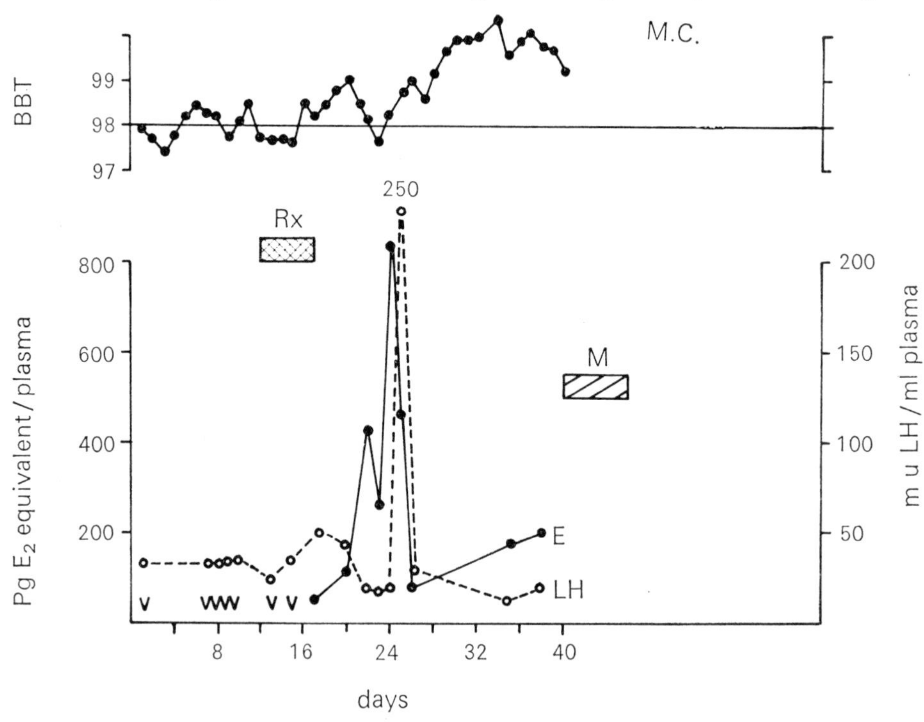


FIGURE 17
Plasma LH (dashed line) and oestradiol (solid line) measured in a woman with idiopathic secondary amenorrhoea, before and after treatment with clomiphene citrate, 50 mg daily for 5 days. 'M' indicates menses, Rx indicates treatment days, BBT indicates basal body temperature, and Pg $E_2$ indicates micro-micrograms (picograms) of oestradiol-17$\beta$. LH concentrations given in terms of 2nd IRP.HMG. (reproduced with permission from [55])

the normal menstrual cycle is initiated by the early rise in FSH. While clomiphene induces this rise in treated women, it is not known what induces the early FSH rise during the normal menstrual cycle. One might postulate that the dramatic fall in luteal steroids initiates the early follicular phase rise in FSH. However, clomiphene treatment does not initiate a series of menstrual cycles, but frequently results in normal corpus luteum function during the treatment cycle. Thus at least in this instance, the death of the functional corpus luteum is not associated with a subsequent FSH rise capable of initiating growth of another follicle.

## III. PITUITARY–GONADAL RELATIONSHIPS IN THE SEXUALLY MATURE MALE

In contrast to the female, LH and FSH concentrations remain relatively stable from day to day and from time of day to time of day in the male. In earlier publications we have reported that samples taken each two hours for twenty-four hours from men at bed rest or at normal activity showed no significant variations with time of day [91]. Most investigations have been in agreement concerning LH [51, 92, 93]. For FSH the data are conflicting. Saxena et al. [48] and Faiman and Ryan [94] have noted a diurnal variation in FSH. Franchimont [92], Peterson et al. [93], and we [91] have not noted diurnal variation.

It appears that LH concentrations are controlled via circulating testosterone concentrations. Administration of synthetic androgens orally to men results in lowering of serum LH and of plasma testosterone [95, 96]. Treatment of men with HCG, an 'LH-like' hormone, leads to prompt increases in plasma testosterone [96]. Testosterone treatment of male rats leads to a fall in LH [97]. Administration of LH to rats results in Leydig cell hypertrophy and increased testicular androgen production [98]. Thus LH and blood testosterone appear to be reciprocally related in a typical negative feedback system.

The control of FSH secretion is less clear. Castration of men results in increases in both serum LH and FSH [53]. Administration of androgens over two to four days does not suppress serum FSH but does suppress LH [94]. If testicular tubule function is fairly specifically inhibited by testicular irradiation in rodents [99, 100] and man [101–103] or cryptorchidism in rats [19, 104], FSH secretion increases, leaving Leydig cell function little affected, while LH secretion is affected slightly or not at all. Figures 18 and 19 depict the effects of cryptorchidism on FSH and LH concentrations in the immature male rat.* It thus appears likely that some

* Johnson [16] has published conflicting results. In his studies using parabiotic prepubertal rats, LH appeared to increase when one partner was made cryptorchid. The reason for this difference from our data, using radioimmunoassay, is not apparent. Johnson used slightly older animals of a different strain.

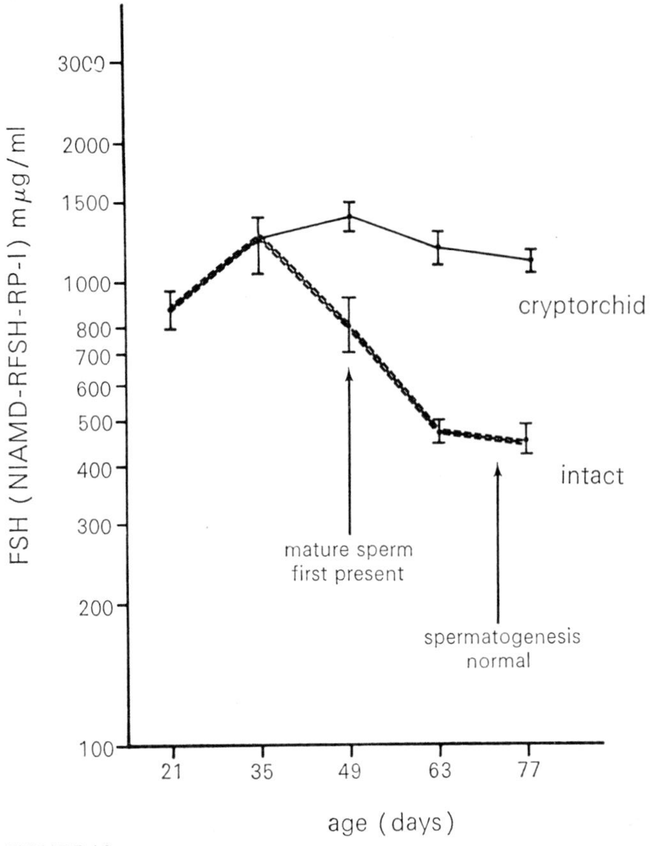


FIGURE 18

Effect of cryptorchidism on serum FSH in the rat between the ages of 21 days (weaning) and 77 days. Spermatogenesis is first normal at 63 days. FSH concentrations progressively fall as spermatogenesis is appearing in the tubules. Cryptorchidism prevents spermatogenesis and FSH concentrations remain elevated. Comparison with Figure 4 shows that cryptorchidism does not result in increase of FSH concentrations as high as is produced by castration (modified from [19]).

material elaborated by the testicular tubules or related to spermatogenesis acts to control FSH. Paulsen [101] has reviewed additional clinical pathophysiological data relating to this postulate. Klinefelter's syndrome is a relatively common disorder, characterized by varying degrees of impaired masculinization (Leydig cell failure) and infertility. When both Leydig cell and tubular function are severely impaired, both LH and FSH *excretion* are increased. In those subjects in whom plasma testosterone is nearly normal, LH may also be in the normal range, but FSH is increased. Another clinical syndrome, the Sertoli-Cell-Only syndrome, is characterized by normal testosterone levels and total absence of germ cells. In these patients LH levels are normal and FSH levels are increased. Thus these two clinical syndromes support the concept that a product related to spermatogenesis

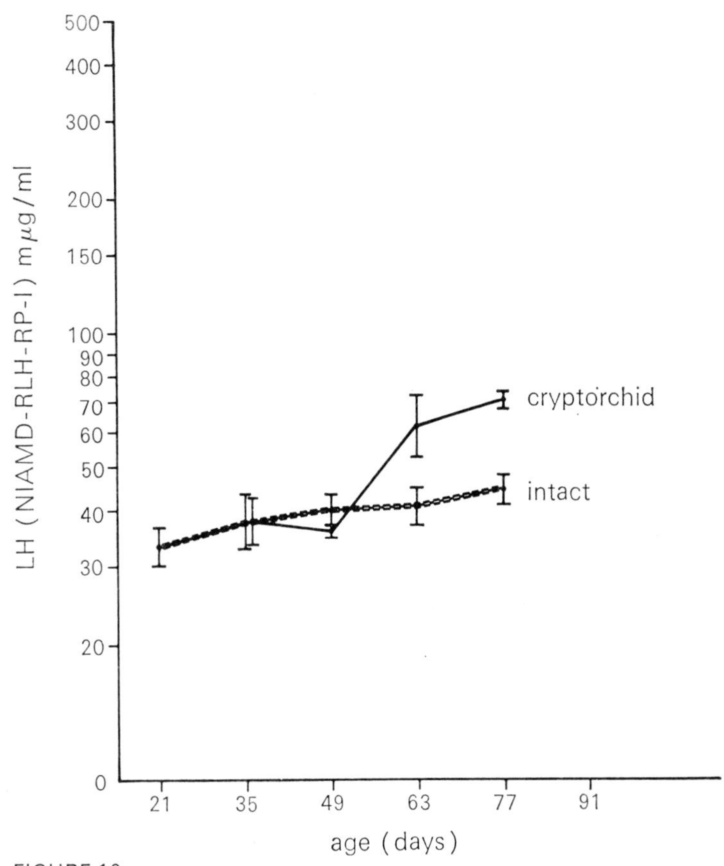


FIGURE 19
Effect of cryptorchidism on serum LH in the rat between ages of 21 days (weaning) and 77 days. Spermatogenesis is first normal at 63 days. Cryptorchidism did not affect LH concentrations until after 49 days of age (modified from [19])

acts to control FSH secretion. However, in contrast to what one might expect, patients with idiopathic oligospermia generally have normal FSH excretion.* These clinical states suggest the following hypotheses: (1) the tubular substance controlling FSH is secreted in such amounts that the postulated reduction in oligospermic men is not sufficient to increase FSH secretion, or (2) that primitive germ cells synthesize and secrete the postulated substance, and these are little affected in idiopathic oligospermia. It is even possible that the substance is synthesized by germinal epithelium and must be modified by some action of the Sertoli cell.

In addition, oestrogens suppress LH and FSH [95]. Blood oestradiol in men is derived from three different sources: (1) directly secreted oestradiol

* However, Dr S. Rosen has recently commented in discussion at American Federation Clinical Research, May 2, 1970, that many oligospermic men have slightly elevated FSH concentrations, with normal LH concentrations.

(about 20 per cent), (2) conversion of testosterone to oestradiol (about 50 per cent), and (3) conversion of oestrone to oestradiol (about 30 per cent) [105]. It is conceivable that oestradiol is the hormone controlling FSH, but no direct data exist. Lacy [106] has reviewed this subject in detail. Figures 20 and 21 demonstrate the effects on serum LH and FSH of oral treatment of men with oestrogen and androgen.

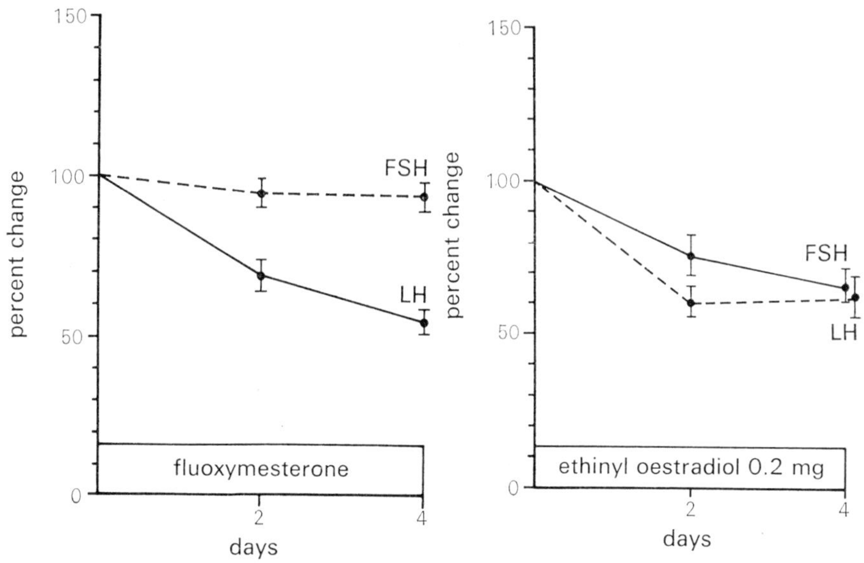


FIGURE 20 (left)
Changes in serum LH and FSH in sexually mature men treated with either 20 or 50 mg/day fluoxymesterone orally for 4 days. The brackets enclose 1 standard error of the mean (calculated from [95])

FIGURE 21 (right)
Changes in serum LH and FSH in sexually mature men treated with 0·2 mg/day ethinyl oestradiol orally for four days. The brackets enclose 1 standard error of the mean (calculated from [95])

The control of spermatogenesis is mediated by both LH and FSH. Administration of these two hormones to hypogonadotrophic hypogonadal men [107] or hypophysectomized rats [108] results in production of mature sperm. Lostroh [108], using highly purified LH and FSH to treat hypophysectomized rats, has shown that FSH plus testosterone will not restore spermatogenesis to normal in the atrophic testes. LH thus must act either to stimulate Leydig cell secretion of another steroid (or non-steroid) which acts with FSH on the tubule, or to augment FSH directly on the tubule. The picture is complicated however; testosterone treatment alone may *support* spermatogenesis in rats if administered immediately after hypophysectomy [109]. The reasons for the difference in restoration of spermatogenesis in the atrophic tubule versus maintenance are unclear. Additional studies are currently in progress in some laboratories to help clarify these points.

ACKNOWLEDGMENTS

We wish to express our gratitude to Mrs Sharyn Shaw, Miss Jayne High and Mrs Kay Moline for typing this manuscript, and to Mrs Marilyn Hescox and Sharyn Shaw for assistance in editing. We also wish to thank Drs Robert Blizzard, Sam Yen, Griff Ross and Charles Cargille for their kindness in sending us data from their laboratories for this manuscript.

## REFERENCES

[1] Diczfalusy, E. (Ed.) *Immunoassay of Gonadotrophins.* First Karolinska Symposia on Research Methods. Bogtrykkeriet Forum, Copenhagen, 1969.

[2] Diczfalusy, E. (Ed.) *Steroid Assays by Competitive Protein Binding.* Second Karolinska Symposia. Bogtrykkeriet Forum, Copenhagen, 1970.

[3] Peron, F.G. and Caldwell, B.V. (Eds.) *Immunological Methods in Steroid Determination.* New York : Appleton-Century-Crofts, 1970.

[4] Odell, W.D., Reichert, L.E. and Bates, R.W. In *Proteins and Polypeptide Hormones.* Excerpta Medica Foundation, Part I, p. 124. Ed. M. Margoulies. New York, 1968.

[5] Odell, W.D., Reichert, L.E., and Swerdloff, R.S. In *Gonadotropins 1968*, p. 401. Ed. E. Rosemberg. Los Altos, California: Geron-X, Inc., 1968.

[6] Odell, W.D., Parlow, A.F., Cargille, C. and Ross, G.T., *J. clin. Invest.*, **47**, 2551, 1968.

[7] Abraham, G. and Odell, W.D. In *Immunological Methods in Steroid Determination.* Eds. F.G. Peron and B.V. Caldwell. New York : Appleton-Century-Crofts, 1970. *Immunoassay of Gonadotrophins, Acta endocr., Copnh.*, Supp. **142**, p. 54.

[8] Odell, W.D., Abraham, G., Raud, H.R., Swerdloff, R.S. and Fisher, D.A. In *Immunoassay of Gonadotrophins, Acta endocr. Copnh.*, Supp. **142**, p. 54. Eds. E. Diczfalusy and A. Diczfalusy, 1970.

[9] Yoshimi, T. and Lipsett, M.D., *Steroids*, **11**, 527, 1968.

[10] Neill, J.D., Johansson, E.D.B., Datta, J.K. and Knobil, E., *J. clin. Endocr. Metab.*, **27**, 1167, 1967.

[11] Korenman, S.G., Perrin, L.E. and McCallum, T.P., *J. clin. Endocr. Metab.*, **29**, 879, 1969.

[12] Murphy, B.E.P., *Nature, Lond.*, **201**, 679, 1964.

[13] *The Diagnosis and Treatment of Endocrine Disorders in Childhood and Adolescence.* Eds. L. Wilkins, R.M. Blizzard and C.J. Migeon, 3rd ed., Springfield, Illinois: Charles C. Thomas Co., 1965.

[14] Kallas, H., *C. r. Soc. Biol., Paris*, **100**, 979, 1929.

[15] Byrnes, W.W. and Meyer, R.K., *Endocrinology*, **48**, 133, 1951.

[16] Johnson, D.C., *Acta endocr. Copnh.*, **51**, 269, 1966.

[17] Parlow, A.F., Daane, T.A. and Schally, A.V. In *Program of the 51st Meeting of The Endocrine Society*, p. 83. New York, 1969.

[18] Monroe, S.E., Parlow, A.F. and Midgley, A.R., Jr., *Endocrinology*, **83**, 1004, 1968.

[19] Swerdloff, R.S., Walsh, P.C., Jacobs, H.S. and Odell, W.D., *Endocrinology*, **88**, 120, 1971.

[20] Odell, W.D., Hescox, M.A. and Kiddy, C.A. In *Gonadotrophins and Ovarian Development*, p. 371. Eds. W. R. Butt, A. C. Crooke and M. Ryle. Edinburgh : E. & S. Livingstone, 1970.
[21] Paul, W.E. and Odell, W.D., *Nature, Lond.*, **203,** 979, 1964.
[22] Odell, W.D., Ross, G.T. and Rayford, P.L., *Metabolism*, **15,** 287, 1966.
[23] Odell, W.D., Ross, G.T. and Rayford, P.L., *J. clin. Invest.*, **46,** 248, 1967.
[24] Bagshawe, K.D., Wilde, C.E. and Orr, A.H., *Lancet*, **1,** 1118, 1966.
[25] Kulin, H.E., Rifkind, A.B., Ross, G.T. and Odell, W.D., *J. clin. Endocr. Metab.*, **27,** 1123, 1967.
[26] Rifkind, A.B., Kulin, H.E. and Ross, G.T., *J. clin. Invest.*, **46,** 1925, 1967.
[27] Johanson, A.J., Guyda, H., Light, C., Migeon, C.J. and Blizzard, R.M., *J. Pediat.*, **74,** 416, 1969.
[28] Guyda, H.J., Johanson, A.J., Migeon, C.J. and Blizzard, R.M., *Ped. Res.*, **3,** 538, 1969.
[29] Raiti, S., Johanson, A. J., Light, C., Migeon, C.J. and Blizzard, R.M., *Metabolism*, **18,** 234, 1969.
[30] Blizzard, R.M., Johanson, A., Guyda, H., Baghdassarian, A., Raiti, S. and Migeon, C.J. In *Selected Topics in Adolescence*. Eds. F.P. Feld and W. Hung, New York: Appleton-Century-Croft Co. (in press).
[31] Penny, R., Guyda, H.J., Baghdassarian, A., Johanson, A.J. and Blizzard, R.M., *J. clin. Invest.*, **49**, 1847, 1970.
[32] Yen, S.S.C., Vicic, W.J. and Kearchner, D.V., *J. clin. Endocr. Metab.*, **29,** 382, 1969.
[33] Wieland, R.G., Yen, S.S.C. and Pohlman, C., *Am. J. med. Sci.* **259**, 358, 1970.
[34] Yen, S.S.C. and Vicic, W.J., *Am. J. Obstet. Gyn.*, **106,** 134, 1970.
[35] Burr, I.M,. Sizonenko, P.C., Kaplan, S.L. and Grumbach, M.M., *Ped. Res.*, **4,** 25, 1970.
[36] Sizonenko, P.C., Burr, I.M., Kaplan, S.L. and Grumbach, M.M., *Ped. Res.*, **4,** 36, 1970.
[37] Kulin, H.E., Kaplan, S.L. and Grumbach, M.M. In *Program of the 51st Meeting of The Endocrine Society*, p. 87. New York, 1969.
[38] Kulin, H.E., Grumbach, M.M. and Kaplan, S.A., *Science, N.Y.*, **166,** 1012, 1969.
[39] Greenblatt, R.B., *Fert. Steril.*, **12,** 402, 1961.
[40] Roy, S., Greenblatt, R.B., Mahesh, V.B. and Jungck, E.C., *Fert. Steril.*, **14,**575, 1963.
[41] Jacobson, A., Marshall, J.R., Ross, G.T. and Cargille, C.M., *Am. J. Obstet. Gyn.*, **102,** 284, 1968.
[42] Odell, W.D. and Parlow, A.F. In *Program of the 49th Meeting of the Endocrine Society*, p. 61. Bal Harbour, Florida, 1967.
[43] Franchimont, P., EURATOM Report EUR–2950 (d, f, e), p. 303, 1966.
[44] Faiman, C. and Ryan, R.J., *J. clin. Endocr. Metab.*, **27,** 1711, 1967.
[45] Midgley, A.R. Jr. and Jaffe, R.B., *J. clin. Endocr. Metab.*, **28,** 1699, 1968.
[46] Cargille, C.M., Ross, G.T. and Yoshimi, T., *J. clin. Endocr. Metab.*, **29,** 12, 1969.
[47] Ross, G.T., Cargille, C.M., Lipsett, M.B., Rayford, P.L., Marshall, J.R., Strott, C.A. and Rodbard, D., *Recent Prog. Hormone Res.* **26,** 1, 1970.
[48] Saxena, B.B., Demura, H., Gandy, H.M. and Peterson, R.E., *J. clin. Endocr. Metab.*, **28,** 519, 1968.
[49] Ross, G.T., Odell, W.D. and Rayford, P.L., *Science, N.Y.*, **155,** 1679, 1967.
[50] Schalch, D.S., Parlow, A.F., Boon, R.C. and Reichlin, S., *J. clin. Invest.*, **47,** 665, 1968.

[51] Burger, H.G., Brown, J.B., Catt, K.J., Hudson, B. and Stockigt, J.R. In *Proteins and Polypeptide Hormones*. Excerpta Medica Foundation, Part II, p. 412. Ed. M. Margoulies, New York, 1968.
[52] Midgley, A.R., and Jaffe, R.B., *J. clin. Endocr. Metab.*, **26,** 1375, 1966.
[53] Odell, W.D. and Swerdloff, R.S. In *Radioisotopes in Medicine: In Vitro Studies*, p. 165. Eds. R.L. Hayes, F.A. Goswitz, and B.E.P. Murphy, 1968.
[54] Tulchinsky, D. and Korenman, S.G., *J. clin. Endocr., Metab.*, **31,** 76, 1970.
[55] Abraham, G.E. and Klaiber, E.L., *Am. J. Obstet. Gynec.*, **108,** 528, 1970.
[56] Abraham, G.E. In *Program of the 51st Meeting of The Endocrine Society*, p. 115. New York, 1969.
[57] Korenman, S., Perrin, L. and Rao, B.R. In *Program of the 51st Meeting of The Endocrine Society*, p. 116. New York, 1969.
[58] Korenman, S.G., Rao, B.R. and Perrin, L.E., *J. clin. Endocr. Metab.* Submitted for Publication, 1970.
[59] Rünnebaum, B. and Zander, J., *Acta endocr. Copnh.*, **55,** 91, 1967.
[60] Neill, J.D., Johansson, E.D.B. and Knobil, E., *Endocrinology*, **84,** 45, 1969.
[61] Strott, C.A. Yoshimi, T., Ross, G.T. and Lipsett, M.D., *J. clin. Endocr. Metab.*, **29,** 1157, 1969.
[62] Crooke, A.C., Morell, M. and Butt, W.R. In *Gonadotropins 1968*, p. 147. Ed. E. Rosemberg, Los Altos, California: Geron-X, Inc., 1968.
[63] Coble, Y.D., Kohler, P.O., Cargille, C.M. and Ross, G.T., *J. clin. Invest.* **48,** 359, 1969.
[64] Yen, S.S.C., Llerena, O., Little, B. and Pearson, O.H., *J. clin. Endocr. Metab.*, **28,** 1763, 1968.
[65] Marshall, J.R., Jacobson, A. and Hammond, C.B., *J. clin. Endocr. Metab.*, **29,** 106, 1969.
[66] Short, R.V., *Recent Prog. Hormone Res.*, **20,** 303, 1964.
[67] Vande Wiele, R.L., Bogumil, J., Dyrenfurth, I., Ferin, M., Jewelewicz, R., Warren, M., Rizkallaht, T. and Mikhail, G., *Recent Prog. Hormone Res.*, **26**, 63, 1970.
[68] Kohler, P.O., Ross, G.T. and Odell, W.D., *J. clin. Invest.*, **47,** 38, 1968.
[69] Odell, W.D. and Swerdloff, R.S., *Proc. natn. Acad. Sci.*, **61,** 529, 1968.
[70] Swerdloff, R.S. and Odell, W.D., *J. clin. Endocr. Metab.*, **29,** 157, 1969.
[71] Everett, J.W., *Endocrinology*, **27,** 681, 1960.
[72] Everett, J.W., *Endocrinology*, **32,** 285, 1943.
[73] Greer, M.A., *Endocrinology*, **53,** 380, 1953.
[74] Nallar, R., Antunes-Rodrigues, J. and McCann, S.M., *Endocrinology*, **79,** 907, 1966.
[75] Redmond, W.C. and Everett, J.W. In *Program of the 49th Meeting of The Endocrine Society*, p. 58. Oklahoma City, 1967.
[76] Pfeiffer, C.A., *Proc. Soc. exp. Biol. Med.*, **75,** 455, 1950.
[77] McCormack, C.E. and Meyer, R.K., *Gen. comp. Endocr.*, **3,** 300, 1963.
[78] McCormack, C.E. and Meyer, R.K., *Fert. Steril.*, **16,** 384, 1965.
[79] Goldman, B.D., Kamberi, I.A., Shteri, P.K. and Porter, J.C., *Endocrinology.*, **85,** 1137, 1969.
[80] Kawakami, M. and Sawyer, C.H., *Endocrinology.*, **65,** 652, 1959.
[81] Caligaris, L., Astrada, J.J. and Taleisnik, S., *Acta endocr. Copnh.*, **59,** 177, 1968.
[82] Everett, J.W., *Endocrinology.*, **43,** 389, 1948.
[83] Brown-Grant, K., *J. Endocr.*, **43,** 529, 1969.

[84] Piper, E.L. and Foote, W.C., *J. Reprod. Fert.*, **16,** 253, 1968.
[85] Goding, J.R., Catt, K.J., Brown, J.M., Kaltenbach, C.C., Cumming, I.A. and Mole, B.J., *Endocrinology,* **85,** 133, 1969.
[86] Shirley, B., Wolinsky, J. and Schwartz, N.B., *Endocrinology.,* **82,** 959, 1968.
[87] Ferin, M., Tempone, A., Zimmering, P.E. and Vande Wiele, R.L., *Endocrinology,* **85,** 1070, 1969.
[88] Palka, Y.S., Ramírez, V.D. and Sawyer, C.H., *Endocrinology,* **78,** 487, 1966.
[89] Ramírez, V.D. In *Proceedings of the Third International Congress of Endocrinology.* Excerpta Medica International Series, No. 184, Progress in Endocrinology, p. 532, Mexico, D.F., 1968.
[90] Cargille, C.M., Ross, G.T. and Bardin, C.W., *Lancet,* **2,** 1298, 1968.
[91] Swerdloff, R.S. and Odell, W.D. In *Gonadotropins 1968,* p. 154. Ed. E. Rosemberg, Los Altos, California: Geron-X, Inc., 1968.
[92] Franchimont, P. In *Proteins and Polypeptide Hormones.* Excerpta Medica Foundation, Part I, p. 99. Ed. M. Margoulies, New York, 1968.
[93] Peterson, N.T., Midgley, A.R. and Jaffee, R.B., *J. clin. Endocr. Metab.,* **28,** 1473, 1968.
[94] Faiman, C. and Ryan, R.J., *Nature, Lond.,* **215,** 857, 1967.
[95] Swerdloff, R.S. and Odell, W.D., *Lancet,* **2,** 683, 1968.
[96] Lipsett, M.B., Wilson, H., Kirschner, M.A., Korenman, S.G., Fishman, L.M., Sarfaty, G.A. and Bardin, C.W., *Recent Prog. Hormone Res.,* **22,** 245, 1966.
[97] Ramírez, V.D. and McCann, S.M., *Endocrinology,* **76,** 412, 1965.
[98] Woods, M.C. and Simpson, M.E., *Endocrinology,* **69,** 91, 1961.
[99] Fortin, R., Swerdloff, R.S. and Odell, W.D., Unpublished Observations.
[100] Oakberg, E.F. In *Progress in Endocrinology.* Excerpta Medica Foundation, p. 1070. Eds. C. Gual and F.J.G. Ebling, Amsterdam, 1969.
[101] Paulsen, C.A. In *Textbook of Endocrinology,* p. 411. Ed. R.H. Williams. Philadelphia: W.B. Saunders Co., 1968.
[102] Paulsen, C.A., *Nuclear Sci. Abstracts,* **21,** 54, 1967.
[103] Paulsen, C.A. In *Gonadotropins 1968,* p. 163. Ed. E. Rosemberg. Los Altos, California: Geron-X, Inc., 1968.
[104] Walsh, P., Swerdloff, R.S. and Odell, W.D., *Surgical Forum,* **21,** 530, 1970.
[105] Longcope, C., Kato, T. and Horton, R., *J. clin. Invest.,* **48,** 2191, 1969.
[106] Lacy, D., *Endeavour,* **26,** 101, 1967.
[107] Martin, F.I.R., *J. Endocr.,* **38,** 431, 1967.
[108] Lostroh, A.J., *Endocrinology,* **85,** 438, 1969.
[109] Walsh, E.L., Cuyler, W.K. and McCullagh, D.R., *Am. J. Physiol.,* **107,** 508, 1934.

*Discussion of paper by Professor Odell*

*Johansson* Much of the controversy about the possible rise in plasma concentrations of 17α-hydroxyprogesterone, before the peak levels of plasma LH occur about midcycle, arose because of the manner of plotting the results; the scale used on the ordinates for this compound was often grossly expanded compared with that for plasma progesterone. In 16 menstrual cycles that we have examined and in 9 cycles described by Lipsett and his colleagues, the rise in plasma 17α-hydroxyprogesterone did not seem to be really significant.

*Odell* I agree with your statements concerning the plotting, but must point out that very small changes in the levels of circulating hormones may still be physiologically important. For example, the rise in FSH presumably initiating follicular growth is very small and was missed in some early studies of serum FSH. Cold exposure in adult humans leads to small (but presumably significant) increases in serum TSH, but nonetheless TSH concentrations remain 'within normal limits' (Raud and Odell, *Br. J. Hosp. Med.*, August 1969).

As regards the nature of the steroid signal involved in the midcycle peak of LH and FSH, it appears that oestradiol increases the level of LH, *but not that of FSH.* However, the midcycle gonadotrophin peak consists of both LH and FSH. Progesterone also is active in stimulating LH release in oestrogen treated castrate women; in addition it appears to lower the threshold for stimulation in certain parts of the central nervous system where the oestrogens are active. Thus, the function of progesterone might be to lower the threshold for the oestrogen induced LH surge and to stimulate the FSH surge.

*Naftolin* I would like to ask whether anybody had ever administered 17α-hydroxyprogesterone to see what effects this might have on gonadotrophin levels.

*Johansson* We have not done this.

*Odell* We have tested the ability of several progestogens to induce an LH–FSH peak in the rat using the oestrogen-suppressed, castrate female as a model. In this model 17α-hydroxyprogesterone did not produce an LH–FSH surge, whereas progesterone did. We do not know of course whether these data apply to the human.

*Hunter* May I raise the problem of the specificity of the methods of assay for gonadotrophins, especially at the low concentrations often encountered? I would like to quote two studies in the American literature, in one of which it proved impossible to distinguish between normal and hypophysectomized male subjects. In another, identical samples were assayed for gonadotrophins using different preparations of antisera.

Marked systematic differences arose in the results obtained, and with neither antiserum was it possible to distinguish between normal and hypophysectomized male subjects.

*Odell* Total hypophysectomy appears to be difficult in man. We have yet to find a patient after hypophysectomy in whom it was impossible to detect gonadotrophin either by immunoassay of serum or bioassay of urine concentrates, if sufficient samples were studied. In our studies the concentrations of gonadotrophin in hypophysectomized or hypopituitary patients clearly overlapped those found in normal men, but the mean concentrations in the former groups were significantly lower. Similar concerns were once raised for children, yet all would now agree that gonadotrophins are present in the urine and serum of prepubertal children. Very small increments in the secretion of gonadotrophins appear to be responsible for the changes at puberty in humans. As for the different antisera to which you referred, differences in the assay results obtained undoubtedly occur, but the same *pattern* of excretion is found, and there is quite close resemblance for menstrual cycle data between the results described by different laboratories.

*Loraine* I would like to comment on the relationship between endocrine function and the changes occurring before and at puberty. We have results from a serial study on girls starting at the age of 10 years and extending over four years. In 1966, using the mouse uterus test, gonadotrophic activity was detectable in the majority, but by no means all, of the urine specimens obtained from the 10-year-old girls. At the age of 11, there was activity in all the specimens assayed by this method. In 1968 and 1969 when the girls were aged 12 and 13 years, specific assays were used for the estimation of FSH and LH and both hormones were readily detected. An interesting point was that the pattern of excretion, particularly for LH, was atypical when compared with that found in older subjects during reproductive life. In particular the peak of gonadotrophin excretion that is so characteristic of the mature women was not readily discernible in these children. It would appear that reproductive life cannot be regarded as a homogeneous situation, and that at the extremes (puberty and the approach of the menopause) there are major aberrations in gonadotrophin excretion, as measured by bioassay. One interesting point about women approaching the menopause is that they sometimes excrete very large amounts of LH in the absence of menopausal symptoms. FSH levels may also rise at this time, but not to the same extent.

# The Chemistry of the Gonadotrophins

WILFRID ROGER BUTT

Department of Clinical Endocrinology
Birmingham and Midland Hospital for Women, Birmingham

¶ HUMAN pituitary glands are a rich source of both follicle stimulating hormone (FSH) and of luteinizing hormone (LH) and preparations of high potency can be obtained by fairly simple methods. The supply of glands, however, is limited and FSH for clinical applications must usually be prepared from the urine of postmenopausal women. Considerable advances have recently been made in the purification of human menopausal gonadotrophin (HMG) but the labour involved is considerable. As a substitute for pituitary LH, human chorionic gonadotrophin (HCG) is commonly employed in clinical and biological experiments since this is readily available in preparations of high potency.

Some of the present methods used for the preparation of pituitary and urinary FSH and LH and of HCG are summarized here. The chemical properties of the best available preparations are compared and some work in progress on their structure is described.

*Methods of preparation.* These have now become well established: considerable use is made of salting-out procedures, ion-exchange celluloses, gel-filtration and the techniques of electrophoresis and electrofocusing.

*Pituitary FSH.* The stability of the most highly purified preparations has presented some problems. There seems little doubt that material of up to 2,000 i.u. FSH per mg may be obtained which is stable in solution at −20°C and withstands freeze-drying. Preparations of much higher potencies have been described but none appears to have been obtained in the form of a stable dry powder. Roos [1] described a preparation containing 14,400 i.u. FSH per mg in solution. The protein concentration was assessed from the ultraviolet absorption at 280 nm assuming that the absorbance ($A_{1}^{1\%}$ cm) was 10. The final steps in the purification were chromatography on hydroxyl apatite and electrophoresis on polyacrylamide gel.

Peckham and Parlow [2] used ion-exchange chromatography, gel filtration on Sephadex G-100 and density gradient electrophoresis to obtain another preparation of high activity. The protein concentration was measured by the colorimetric Lowry procedure with albumin as a standard : the specific activity was calculated to be 304 units NIH–FSH–SI per mg, i.e., approximately 7,600 i.u. FSH per mg. The contamination with LH was very slight, being equivalent to 0·007 units NIH–LH–SI per mg. This preparation gave a single band in disc electrophoresis at pH 2·3.

We have repeatedly obtained preparations of comparable potency in good yield by using the method of Butt, Crooke and Cunningham [3] followed by fractionation on DEAE-cellulose in 0·15M ammonium acetate buffer and gel filtration on Biogel P-150 [4]. The protein concentration was measured by ultraviolet absorption at 280 nm assuming, as Roos, that $A_{1}^{1\%}$ cm = 10. The average potency of 11 preparations obtained by this method was 12,020 i.u. FSH per mg with a range of 6,600–18,200 i.u. The wide range is probably due to slight variations in sampling the fractions eluted from the DEAE column in addition to the error of the bioassay. The average yield per gland has been 45 i.u. FSH. The material has retained biological and immunological activities for seven months in solution a −15°C. It also appears to be stable to precipitation from ethanol and washing with ether, to freeze-drying and to rotary evaporation. One batch, however, lost potency rapidly when it was precipitated from ethanol and thoroughly dried by repeated washing with ethanol. The potency levelled off at 2,500 i.u. per mg and then remained at this figure for six months.

*Pituitary LH.* Highly purified preparations of pituitary LH have been available for several years. They may be obtained as dry powders by precipitation from ethanol or by freeze-drying with potencies ranging from 3·0 to 5·5 units NIH–LH–SI per mg, i.e., about 4,500–8,250 i.u. LH per mg [5–10]. The yield of purified LH per pituitary gland is of the order of 400 i.u. [7]. Peckham and Parlow [11] showed that a preparation containing about 5 units NIH–LH–SI per mg was heterogeneous by disc electrophoresis at pH 9·5, containing three fractions of potencies, 4·56, 6·42 and 5·10 units per mg. No evidence could be found that this heterogeneity was the result of the action of proteolytic enzymes in the pituitary extract.

Roos [1] has described a preparation of higher potency which he obtained by ammonium sulphate fractionation, chromatography on DEAE-cellulose, Sephadex G-100 and SE-Sephadex C-50, and finally, preparative polyacrylamide gel electrophoresis at pH 8·8. The potency by bioassay was 14,000 i.u. LH per mg, protein concentration being measured by ultraviolet absorption.

*Urinary FSH and LH.* FSH and LH in HMG have been purified by methods similar to those used for pituitary gonadotrophins. Donini et al. [12] employed chromatography on DEAE-cellulose, Sephadex G-100 and preparative electrophoresis on polyacrylamide gel to obtain material containing 1,255 i.u. FSH per mg with 3·2 i.u. LH per mg. It was homogeneous by ultracentrifugation and disc electrophoresis but immunoelectrophoretic studies showed that there were two protein components with the same electrophoretic mobility. Van Hell and Schuurs [13] have reported that FSH of similar potency was heterogeneous in electrofocusing experiments.

A major separation of urinary LH from FSH has been obtained by chromatography on DEAE-cellulose and the LH fraction has been purified on Sephadex G-100 [14]. The product contained 740 i.u. LH per mg but it also contained 10 i.u. FSH per mg. It has been reported that a similar preparation lost about 70 per cent of its biological activity but not its immunological activity, over a period of five months [15]. The preparation appeared to contain components with a range of electrophoretic mobilities.

*HCG.* Several preparations of HCG assaying between 12,000 and 18,000 i.u. per mg have been described [16–21]. There is a good deal of evidence, however, that even highly potent preparations may be heterogeneous. Hameshige et al. [22] found at least three distinct components with high activity after ion-exchange chromatography while Bell et al. [20] showed heterogeneity in charge of a product that was homogeneous in the ultracentrifuge and in amino-acid composition. Van Hell et al. [23] obtained a preparation homogeneous in the ultracentrifuge but heterogeneous by electrophoresis and also showed [24] by isoelectric focusing that biological activity was distributed in several fractions, all related immunochemically. It appears that the different charges on these HCG fractions is accounted for by their differing contents of N-acetyl neuraminic acid (NANA). It is not clear whether these differences are due to enzymic degradation or to artifacts produced during extraction.

*Biological activity and homogeneity.* The differing potencies reported for preparations of gonadotrophins do not always indicate the degree of chemical heterogeneity. Certain components are essential for the full biological activity of some gonadotrophins and not others. Thus terminal NANA groups are essential for the biological activities of FSH and HCG but not for LH : if a preparation of FSH or HCG contains less than the full complement of NANA groups it is less potent but may appear homogeneous. A loss of 0·3 per cent NANA in HCG has been reported to cause a drop in biological activity from 18,800 to 11,800 i.u. per mg [13].

*Analyses.* Complete amino-acid and carbohydrate analyses are now available for the pituitary and urinary gonadotrophins [15, 25]. The amino-acid compositions of HCG and pituitary LH appear to be quite similar but for slightly less serine and proline in LH than in HCG. Differences between FSH and LH are more marked and FSH contains considerably less proline, arginine and cysteine than LH. The best urinary preparations on which analyses are available are so much less potent than their pituitary counterparts that a comparison of their analyses is probably not meaningful at this stage.

There is a significant difference in the NANA contents of HCG and LH. Purified HCG contains about 9 per cent NANA and LH less than half this amount. This group is essential for the biological activity of HCG but not for LH [26], an interesting finding in view of the similar activities of these two hormones.

*Physico-chemical properties.* Some of the physico-chemical properties reported for the gonadotrophins are summarized in Table 1. The limitations

TABLE 1. Some physico-chemical properties of human gonadotrophins

| | Pituitary | | Urinary | |
|---|---|---|---|---|
| | FSH | LH | FSH | LH |
| $S_{20,w}$ (x$10^{-13}$) cm $sec^{-1}$/$dyne^{-1}$ | 2·96 [1]<br>2·80 [4]<br>2·04 [27] | 2·71 [26]<br>2·28, 1·57 [28] | 1·94 [12]<br>2·21 [1] | 2·89 [21]<br>2·7 [31]<br>2·76 [17] |
| $D_{20,w}$ (x$10^{-7}$) $cm^{-2}$ $sec^{-1}$ | – | 7·55 [29] | 5·98 [12] | 8·2 [31] |
| Frictional ratio | 1·68 [1] | 1·45 [29] | 1·75 [1] | 1·28 [31] |
| $\bar{v}$ $gm^{-1}$ $cm^3$ | 0·69 [1] | – | 0·69 [1] | 0·727 [21]<br>0·727 [31]<br>0·742 [17] |
| Stokes' radius mμ | 3·2 [28]<br>3·46 [32] | 2·84 [29]<br>3·02, 2·26 [28] | – | – |
| Isoelectric point (pI) | 4·25 [27] | 5·4 [26] | – | 2·95 [31] |
| Molecular wt. from sedimentation data | 41,000 [1]<br>35,000 [4]<br>31,000 [27] | 26,000 [26]<br>27,960, 14,400 [28] | 31,600 [12]<br>26,700 –29,400 [1] | 30,000 [31]<br>35,900 [17]<br>46,000 [20]<br>47,000 [21]<br>62,000 [23] |
| Molecular wt. from gel filtration | 64,000, 32,000 16,000 [30] | 26,100 [29] | 61,660 [12] | 59,000 [21]<br>35,500, 103,000 [17] |

inherent in the calculation of molecular weights from the Ve/Vo ratios calculated from gel filtration data are well known: as seen in the table some of these estimates are very different from the results of sedimentation studies.

There is good evidence that some gonadotrophins may dissociate into sub-units. Our own group reported that a preparation of pituitary FSH reversibly dissociated and behaved as a monomer of molecular weight approximately 16,000, a dimer, 32,000 and a tetramer, 64,000, during gel filtration in different salt concentrations [30]. There is also some evidence of dissociation in guanidine [33] and urea [32]. Work on the sub-unit structure of LH is further advanced. First observations were on ovine LH which dissociates readily with change of pH. Human LH is more difficult to dissociate but the demonstration and separation of sub-units has now been achieved. Papkoff and Li [26] separated the sub-units of ovine and bovine LH by means of countercurrent distribution in as few as nine transfers in the system 40 per cent $(NH_4)_2SO_4$ – 0·2 per cent dichloroacetic acid-*n*-propanol-ethanol (60:60:27:33). This system, slightly modified, has been used to separate the sub-units of human LH [29]. The dissociation may also be observed at pH 1·3 or below [34] and in both systems the sub-units appear to be about half the molecular weight of the native hormone and the dissociation is reversible. The sub-units are only slightly active biologically but retain considerable immunological activity. Reassociation occurs when the sub-units are incubated together for 16 hours at 40° and the biological activity of the mixture is over four times that expected, assuming no recombination of sub-units.

Structural studies on the sub-units are progressing and a considerable proportion of the amino-acid sequence of the ovine and bovine LH sub-units has been reported [35]. The units have been classified into CI and CII, CI having a low and CII a high partition coefficient in the counter-current distribution system. Nearly equal amounts of the two sub-units were obtained. CI contained much more lysine, aspartic acid, threonine, glutamic acid, tyrosine and phenylalanine than CII. CII, on the other hand, contained more arginine, proline and leucine. Carbohydrates are present in both fractions, but there is considerably more hexose and hexosamine in CI.

Preliminary studies have been made on the human fractions [29]. CI contains considerably less lysine and methionine, but more serine and glutamic acid than the corresponding bovine CI unit. It has also been shown that it is possible to form a hybrid molecule consisting of human CI and bovine C2 which possesses high biological and immunological activities [29].

There are indications that a sub-unit structure exists also for HCG. After reduction with Cleland's reagent (dithio threitol) and alkylation with iodoacetamide the molecular weight is approximately halved to 27,000 [36, 37]. Bahl [36] has performed sequential amino-acid studies on his product and found from the C-terminus a possible sequence -Val-Ala-Val-Tyr-Ser or -Val-Val-Ala-Tyr-Ser. He considered that the C-terminal sequence, as far as it has gone, is identical in the two chains. The sub-units have been separated by chromatography on DEAE-Sephadex A-50 [36] or by disc electrophoresis [37]. They are non-identical as judged by peptide mapping and by their amino-acid and carbohydrate composition. The individual sub-units show low biological activity but may be reconstituted with recovery of most of the initial activity.

*Carbohydrate structure.* Considerable progress has been made in the identification of the carbohydrate structure of HCG. Bahl [38] employed a series of purified enzymes to remove successive carbohydrate residues specifically. N-acetyl neuraminic acid occurs as terminal non-reducing units : after removal of these residues by mild acid hydrolysis the product was reduced with mercaptoethanol and carboxamidomethylated by iodoacetamide. After digestion with trypsin two chromatographically homogeneous glycopeptides were obtained. The monosaccharide sequence was then determined by stepwise cleavage of the sugars from the non-reducing ends with specific glycosidases. As a result it was tentatively suggested that the sequence was NANA-(Fucose)-Galactose-Glucosamine-Mannose with NANA or fucose being at the non-reducing ends of the chains. The carbohydrate units are composed of several of these chains linked to the polypeptide by an N-acetyl glucosamine-asparagine linkage. All the galactosamine residues appear to be linked through serine.

All the NANA in pituitary FSH occurs at terminal non-reducing ends of chains and the nature of some of the glycosidic linkages has been postulated as a result of periodate oxidation and borohydride reduction studies [39, 40]. The NANA groups appear to be linked at the 2-position while the fucose units are linked in the 1- and 2-positions or occur as terminal non-reducing units. About 80 per cent of the mannose units are 1- and 2- or 1- and 6- substituted while the remainder are linked 1- and 3- or occur at branch points. Studies with galactose oxidase suggest that the nine galactose residues in FSH for a molecular weight of 34,000 are next to terminal NANA residues. Four of these units appear to be linked in the 1- and 3-positions or are involved in branch points, while the remainder are linked 1- and 2- or 1- and 6-. More than 80 per cent of the hexosamines are 1- and 6- substituted or occur as end groups. Recent methylation studies have given results which are in accordance with these conclusions.

## REFERENCES


[1] Roos, P., *Human Follicle-stimulating Hormone*. Uppsala: Almqvist & Wiksell, 1967.

[2] Peckham, W.D. and Parlow, A.F., *Endocrinology*, **84**, 953, 1969.

[3] Butt, W.R., Crooke, A.C. and Cunningham, F.J., *Biochem. J.*, **81**, 596, 1961.

[4] Barker, S.A., Gray, C.J., Kennedy, J.F. and Butt, W.R., *J. Endocr.*, **45**, 275, 1969.

[5] Reichert, L.E. Jr. and Parlow, A.F., *Endocrinology*, **75**, 815, 1964.

[6] Parlow, A.F., *Endocrinology*, **76**, 27, 1965.

[7] Hartree, A.S., *Biochem. J.*, **100**, 754, 1966.

[8] Ryan, R.J., *J. clin. Endocr. Metab.*, **28**, 886, 1968.

[9] Shome, B., Parlow, A.F., Ramírez, V.D., Elrick, H. and Pierce, J.G., *Arch. Biochem. Biophys.*, **126**, 444, 1968.

[10] Bates, R.W., Garrison, M.M., Cooper, J.A. and Condliffe, P.G., *Endocrinology*, **83**, 721, 1968.

[11] Peckham, W.D. and Parlow, A.F., *Endocrinology*, **85**, 618, 1969.

[12] Donini, P., Puzzouli, D., D'Alessio, I., Bergesi, G. and Donini, S., In *Gonadotrophins and Ovarian Development*, p. 39. Eds. W.R. Butt, A.C. Crooke and M. Ryle. Edinburgh: E. & S. Livingstone, 1970.

[13] Van Hell, H. and Schuurs, A.H.W.M. Ibid.

[14] Stevens, V.C., Anderson, D.G. and Powell, J.E. Ibid.

[15] Anderson, D.G., Donini, P. and Stevens, V.C. Ibid.

[16] Wilde, C.E. and Bagshawe, K.D. In *Gonadotrophins*. Ciba Foundation Study Group No. 22, p. 46. Eds. G.E.W. Wolstenholme and J. Knight, London: Churchill, 1965.

[17] Tojo, S., *Human Chorionic Gonadotrophin* (Thesis). Kobe University, Japan, 1968.

[18] Van Hell, H., Goverde, B.C., Schuurs, A.H.W.M., de Jager, E., Matthijsen, R. and Homan, J.D.H., *Nature*, **212**, 261, 1966.

[19] Donini, P., Puzzuoli, D., D'Alessio, I., Bergesi, G. and Donini, S. In *Gonadotrophins 1968*, p. 37. Ed. E. Rosemberg. Los Altos, California: Geron-X, Inc., 1968.

[20] Bell, J.J., Canfield, R.E. and Sciarra, J.A., *Endocrinology*, **84**, 298, 1969.

[21] Bahl, O.P., *J. biol. Chem.*, **244**, 567, 1969.

[22] Hameshige, S., Astor, M.A., Arquilla, E.R. and Van Thiel, D.M. *J. clin. Endocr. Metab.*, **27**, 1690, 1967.

[23] Van Hell, H., Matthijsen, R. and Homan, J.D.H., *Acta endocr., Copnh.*, **59**, 89, 1968.

[24] Van Hell, H. and Schuurs, A.H.W.M. In *Gonadotrophins and Ovarian Development*, p. 70. Eds. W.R. Butt, A.C. Crooke and M. Ryle. Edinburgh: E. & S. Livingstone, 1970.

[25] Butt, W.R. In *Immunoassay of Gonadotrophins, Stockholm*. p. 13, Ed. E. Diczfalusy, Copenhagen: Bogtrykkeriet, 1969.

[26] Papkoff, H. and Li, C.H. In *Gonadotrophins and Ovarian Development*, p. 138. Eds. W.R. Butt, A.C. Crooke and M. Ryle. Edinburgh: E. & S. Livingstone, 1970.

[27] Saxena, B.B. and Rathnam, P. In *Gonadotrophins 1968*, p. 3. Ed. E. Rosemberg. Los Altos, California: Geron-X, Inc., 1968.

[28] Ryan, R.J., *Biochemistry*, **8**, 495, 1969.

[29] Reichert, L.E. Jr., Ward, D.N., Niswender, G.D. and Midgley, A.R. Jr. In *Gonadotrophins and Ovarian Development*, p. 149. Eds. W.R. Butt, A.C. Crooke and M. Ryle. Edinburgh: E. & S. Livingstone, 1970.

[30] Gray, C.J., *Nature*, **216**, 112, 1967.

[31] Got, R., *Eur. Rev. Endocr. Suppl.*, **1**, 191, 1965.

[32] Reichert, L.E. Jr. and Midgley, A.R. Jr. In *Gonadotropins 1968*, p. 25. Ed. E. Rosemberg. Los Altos, California: Geron-X, Inc., 1968.

[33] Ryan, R.J. Ibid, p. 50.

[34] Braikevitch, M. and Hartree, A.S. In *Gonadotrophins and Ovarian Development*, p. 131. Eds. W.R. Butt, A.C. Crooke and M. Ryle. Edinburgh: E. & S. Livingstone, 1970.

[35] Samy, T.S.A., Papkoff, H. and Li, C.H., *Arch. Biochem. Biophys.*, **132**, 315, 1969.

[36] Bahl, O.P. In *Gonadotrophins and Ovarian Development*, p.155. Eds. W.R. Butt, A.C. Crooke and M. Ryle. Edinburgh: E. & S. Livingstone, 1970.

[37] Canfield, R.E., Agosto, G.M. and Bell, J.J. Ibid.

[38] Bahl, O.P., *J. biol. Chem.*, **244**, 575, 1969.

[39] Kennedy, J.F. and Butt, W.R., *Biochem. J.*, **115**, 225, 1969.

[40] Chaplin, M., Gray, C.J. and Kennedy, J.F. In *Gonadotrophins and Ovarian Development*, p. 98. Eds. W.R. Butt, A.C. Crooke and M. Ryle. Edinburgh: E. & S. Livingstone, 1970.

*Discussion of paper by Dr Butt*

*Hobson* Is it possible to differentiate between pituitary LH and the LH activity of HCG by incubating HCG with neuraminidase, since in this way HCG activity might be destroyed and LH activity retained? I am of course referring to biological assays.
*Butt* Although I have not done such an experiment myself, I believe that this is theoretically possible. There is evidence published to show that LH is resistant to the action of neuraminidase, whereas HCG is certainly not resistant.
*Naftolin* Does HCG lose FSH activity under these conditions?
*Butt* The experiment has not been done, but I think that HCG would lose its FSH activity.
*Naftolin* Is it possible that sub-fractions of HCG in a treated mixture might give a higher immunological or biological potency than the original molecule?
*Butt* This has been suggested before, and I believe there is some evidence that the sub-fractions of LH recombine with some increase in potency, but not as much as twofold.
*Odell* Pierce has recently published evidence in the *J. biol. Chem.*, **244**, 6468, 1969 (also Pierce et al., *Recent Prog. Hormone Res.*, in press 1971) which indicates that one of the two polypeptide chains of FSH is very similar to one of the chains of LH. The immunological activity of both FSH and LH appears to reside predominantly in one of the polypeptide chains. However, I do not believe that in any instance, *increased* immunological potency occurs if the molecule is dissociated. Biological activity however is destroyed by dissociation.

# Mechanism of Action of the Gonadotrophins

KRISTEN B. EIK-NES

Division of Biochemistry and Physiology of Reproduction
and Department of Physiology
University of Southern California Medical School
Los Angeles, California

¶ IN 1952 West and his co-workers [1] isolated and identified the androgens testosterone and $\Delta^4$-androstenedione in spermatic venous blood of the dog and in 1957 we demonstrated [2] that the rate of secretion of these androgens into the spermatic venous blood increased following intravenous administration of human chorionic gonadotrophin (HCG). Later on it was shown that administration of interstitial cell stimulating hormone (ICSH) [3], pregnant mare serum gonadotrophin [4], or follicle stimulating hormone [FSH] contaminated with ICSH [3], to normal anaesthetized dogs, would increase the secretion of testosterone into the spermatic vein. Already in 1951 [5] some data were presented on the ability of gonadotrophins to promote conversion of radioactive acetate to radioactive testosterone when added to testicular tissue *in vitro*. This observation was repeated in our laboratory in 1962 [6] and conclusive proof delivered that such tissue indeed formed testosterone and that this formation was responsive to the addition of gonadotrophin *in vitro* [4–7]. Thus, published work supports the view that production and secretion of testosterone by the male gonad are augmented following administration of gonadotrophins. That the gonadotrophins accelerate production of progesterone in the ovary has also been amply illustrated [for review see Reference 8.]

Systems *in vitro* will only tell what an organ *can do*, and not necessarily what it is doing. We feel that in addition to production of steroids, secretion of steroids into the venous blood of steroid-producing organs must be explored in order to gain information about hormonal capacity of endocrine systems [9]. Thus, in this discussion on trophic stimulation of steroidogenesis in the male gonad we should like to present data from two testicular preparations *in vivo* in the dog [10]. All measurements of testosterone were made as published by our laboratory [11].

*Secretion of testosterone by the left and by the right testis of the same normal dog* (Animal Preparation II [10]). As can be seen in Figure 1, the left and right testis of the same dog secrete similar amounts of testosterone when infused at a constant rate with the animal's own arterial blood via the spermatic artery. Moreover, in this animal preparation the rates of secretion of testosterone tend to fall with the duration of the experiment (Table 1). Since the animal's own blood is infused via the spermatic artery it could well be that the concentration of gonadotrophins in the blood decreases as a function of anaesthesia [12]. Since testes infused through the spermatic artery with Krebs-Ringer bicarbonate buffer (pH 7·4) also reduce the secretion of testosterone with the duration of the experiment (Table 2), it is probable that the tissue concentration of the gonadotrophins declines with time of infusion, or also that the experimental manipulations involved in Animal Preparation II [10] are associated with impairment of the synthetic capacity of testicular cells producing and

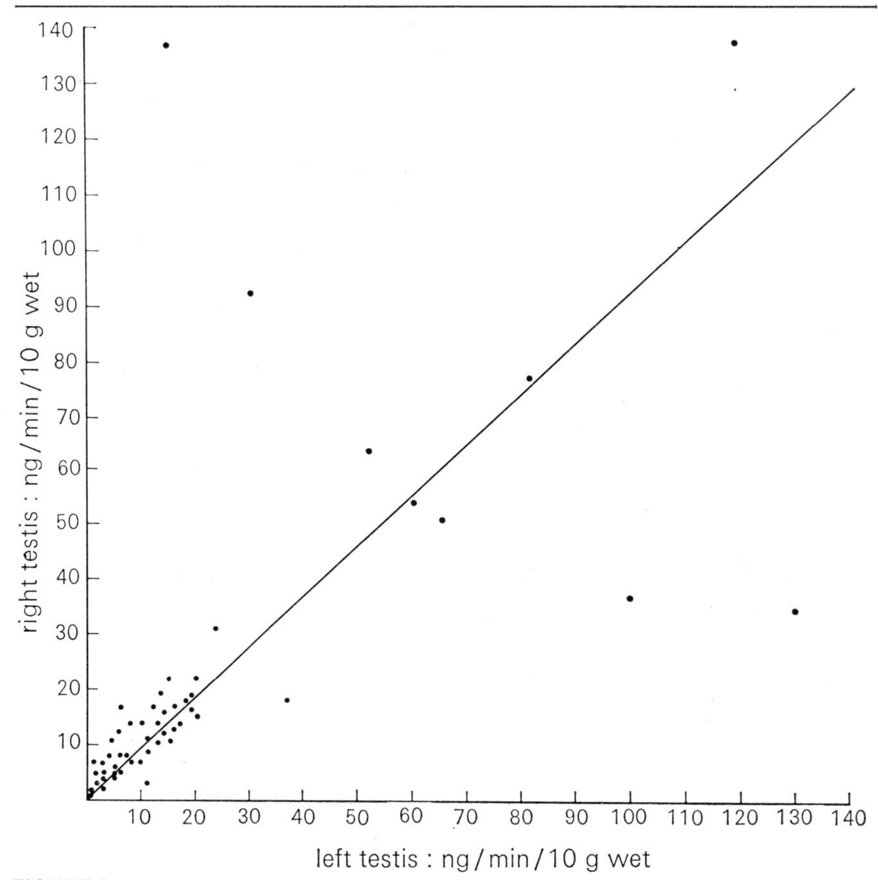


FIGURE 1

Correlation of testosterone secretion between the left and the right testis of the same, normal dog. Animal Preparation II [10] was used in these experiments and each testis was infused with 3·87 ml / min of the animal's own, oxygenated blood via the spermatic artery

secreting testosterone. It has been observed that barbiturates will increase the binding of calcium to phospholipids [13]. Whether binding of calcium to the membrane of the interstitial cell is responsible for the decline in testosterone secretion in animals anaesthetized with sodium pentobarbital is, however, not known.

Rates of secretion of testosterone by testes infused with Krebs-Ringer bicarbonate buffer are lower than by testes infused with the animal's own arterial blood (compare Figures 1 and 2.) It is possible that lack of gonadotrophins in the buffer is in part responsible for this difference in testosterone secretion.

*Effect of HCG administration on rates of testosterone secretion and production.* When HGC is administered at a constant rate via the spermatic artery of the dog, a spontaneous increase in the secretion of testosterone can be

TABLE 1. Rates of testicular secretion of testosterone (μg/min) in 12 different anaesthetized dogs infused with a mixture of 3·87 ml oxygenated, arterial blood and 0·38 ml 0·9% sodium chloride/min via the spermatic artery (Animal Preparation II [10])

| Time sample (min) | | | | | |
|---|---|---|---|---|---|
| 0–15 | 15–30 | 30–45 | 45–60 | 60–75 | 75–90 |
| ·257 | ·185 | ·205 | ·180 | ·150 | ·151 |
| ·173 | ·167 | ·138 | ·128 | ·136 | ·110 |
| ·146 | ·114 | ·109 | ·119 | ·116 | ·122 |
| ·131 | ·110 | ·101 | ·100 | ·089 | ·098 |
| ·110 | ·089 | ·085 | ·086 | ·077 | ·063 |
| ·103 | ·093 | ·084 | ·082 | ·090 | ·096 |
| ·068 | ·060 | ·050 | ·044 | ·044 | ·041 |
| ·045 | ·040 | ·040 | ·041 | ·033 | ·038 |
| ·042 | ·037 | ·032 | ·038 | ·032 | ·032 |
| ·040 | ·035 | ·031 | ·029 | ·030 | ·029 |
| ·038 | ·030 | ·028 | ·027 | ·025 | ·030 |
| ·022 | ·019 | ·018 | ·014 | ·015 | ·012 |

TABLE 2. Rates of testicular secretion of testosterone (μg/min) in 6 different anaesthetized dogs infused with 4 ml oxygenated Krebs-Ringer bicarbonate buffer/min via the spermatic artery (Animal Preparation II [10])

| Time sample (min) | | | | | |
|---|---|---|---|---|---|
| 0–15 | 15–30 | 30–45 | 45–60 | 60–75 | 75–90 |
| ·041 | ·031 | ·029 | ·022 | ·019 | ·023 |
| ·038 | ·029 | ·024 | ·020 | ·019 | ·017 |
| ·031 | ·023 | ·019 | ·020 | ·019 | ·017 |
| ·026 | ·023 | ·015 | ·010 | ·009 | ·008 |
| ·017 | ·012 | ·008 | ·006 | ·005 | ·003 |
| ·016 | ·013 | ·009 | ·006 | ·006 | ·002 |

measured (Figure 3). This early augmentation in hormone secretion (1–3 min after HCG) could be due to increased secretion of preformed testosterone in the testicular tissue, but synthesis *de novo* of this steroid hormone will occur within 5 min after HCG through the spermatic artery [7]. The rates of secretion of testosterone are elevated during continuous administration of HCG via the spermatic artery either by testes infused with the animal's own blood (Table 3) or with Krebs-Ringer bicarbonate buffer (Table 4), though the rise in testosterone secretion by testes infused with buffer is slow, particularly during the first 15 min of stimulation. Moreover, short exposure of the testis to HCG via the spermatic artery (1 min only) is associated with elevated rates of testosterone secretion (Figure 4). Thus, this trophin has fast and prolonged action on testicular cells producing and secreting testosterone.

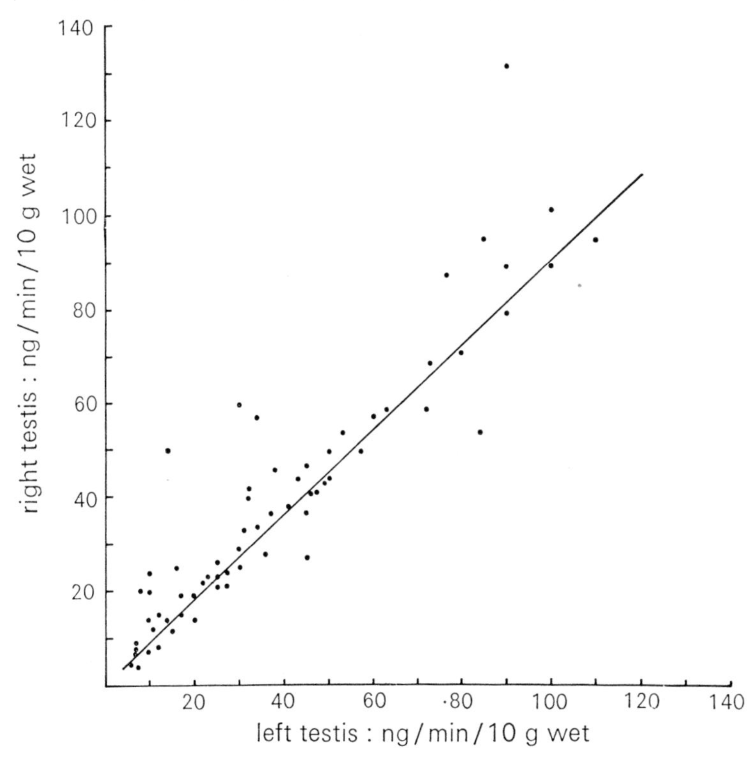


FIGURE 2
Correlation of testosterone secretion between the left and the right testis of the same, normal dog. Animal Preparation II [10] was used in these experiments and each testis was infused with 4 ml/min of oxygenated Krebs-Ringer bicarbonate buffer via the spermatic artery

TABLE 3. Rates of testicular secretion of testosterone (μg/min) in 9 different anaesthetized dogs infused with 3·87 ml oxygenated arterial blood and 0·38 ml 0·09% sodium chloride solution/min via the spermatic artery. During time period 15–90 min different doses of HCG were added at a constant rate to the infusion mixture (Animal Preparation II [10])

| | Time period (min) | | | | | |
|---|---|---|---|---|---|---|
| Dose of HCG infused (i.u/min) | 0–15 | 15–30 | 30–45 | 45–60 | 60–75 | 75–90 |
| 13 | ·026 | ·031 | ·049 | ·294 | ·424 | ·530 |
| 13 | ·036 | ·081 | ·343 | ·438 | ·668 | ·690 |
| 13 | ·051 | ·073 | ·210 | ·317 | ·498 | ·534 |
| 17 | ·020 | ·060 | ·210 | ·342 | ·561 | ·640 |
| 17 | ·041 | ·039 | ·310 | ·420 | ·522 | ·650 |
| 17 | ·088 | ·151 | ·310 | ·469 | ·580 | ·634 |
| 26 | ·026 | ·066 | ·279 | ·433 | ·529 | ·682 |
| 26 | ·116 | ·176 | ·610 | ·660 | ·731 | ·740 |
| 26 | ·010 | ·031 | ·161 | ·210 | ·311 | ·427 |

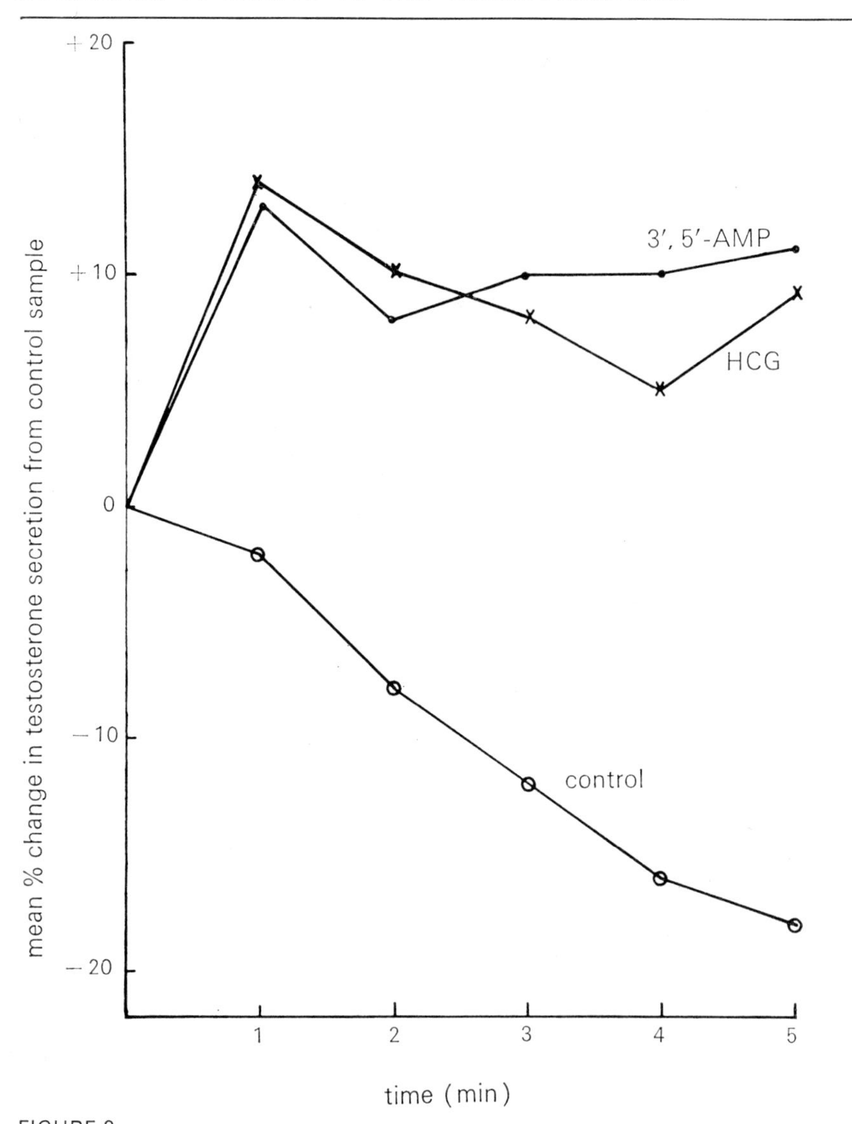


FIGURE 3
Mean % change in secretion of testosterone in control dogs (10 animals); dogs infused with HCG (13 animals) or with cyclic–3′,5′-AMP (6 animals) via the spermatic artery. Animal Preparation I [10] was used in these experiments. During time 1–5 min from 3·5–30 μg cyclic-3′,5′-AMP/g testis wet weight, or from 0·012–2·3 i.u. HCG/g were added per min to the blood in the spermatic artery at a constant rate. These substances were dissolved in 0·9% sodium chloride solution. In the control animals the equivalent amount of 0·9% sodium chloride solution was added/min to the blood in the spermatic artery

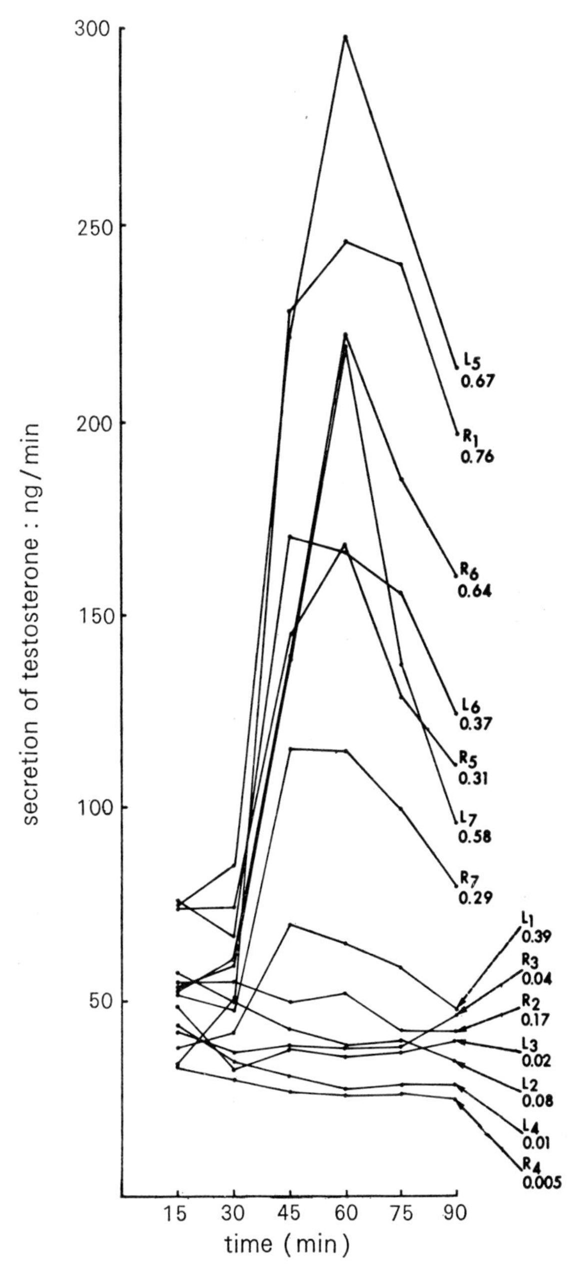


FIGURE 4

Secretion of testosterone by the left (L) and by the right (R) testis of the same dog. Animal Preparation II [10] was used in these experiments. During time 15–16 min HCG was added to the blood in the spermatic artery at a constant rate. The doses of HCG used (i.u./g testis wet weight) are given in the figure

TABLE 4. Rates of testicular secretion of testosterone (μg/min) in 20 different anaesthetized dogs infused with 4 ml oxygenated Krebs-Ringer bicarbonate buffer/min via the spermatic artery. From time 15–90 min the different compounds indicated in the table were added at a constant rate to the buffer (Animal Preparation II [10])

| Compound infused from 15–90 min | Time sample (min) 0–15 | 15–30 | 30–45 | 45–60 | 60–75 | 75–90 |
|---|---|---|---|---|---|---|
| *Isoproterenol* | | | | | | |
| 2·6 μg/min | ·077 | ·060 | ·084 | ·103 | ·089 | ·080 |
| 2·6 μg/min | ·045 | ·046 | ·056 | ·049 | ·042 | ·042 |
| 2·6 μg/min | ·023 | ·022 | ·030 | ·042 | ·043 | ·039 |
| 2·6 μg/min | ·021 | ·031 | ·035 | ·059 | ·050 | ·057 |
| 2·6 μg/min | ·022 | ·021 | ·040 | ·055 | ·042 | ·024 |
| 2·6 μg/min | ·021 | ·031 | ·035 | ·059 | ·050 | ·057 |
| 2·6 μg/min | ·019 | ·018 | ·023 | ·030 | ·038 | ·039 |
| 2·6 μg/min | ·018 | ·020 | ·029 | ·042 | ·051 | ·043 |
| 2·6 μg/min | ·006 | ·005 | ·008 | ·018 | ·022 | ·026 |
| 2·6 μg/min | ·005 | ·002 | ·008 | ·012 | ·013 | ·011 |
| 2·6 μg/min | ·010 | ·026 | ·032 | ·037 | ·051 | ·067 |
| *HCG* | | | | | | |
| 22 i.u./min | ·060 | ·061 | ·077 | ·195 | ·253 | ·294 |
| 22 i.u./min | ·044 | ·036 | ·044 | ·055 | ·054 | ·039 |
| 22 i.u./min | ·034 | ·045 | ·063 | ·066 | ·083 | ·109 |
| 22 i.u./min | ·006 | ·005 | ·013 | ·024 | ·014 | ·013 |
| 22 i.u./min | ·002 | ·002 | ·009 | ·028 | ·052 | ·064 |
| 22 i.u./min | ·032 | ·049 | ·063 | ·072 | ·081 | ·110 |
| 22 i.u./min | ·016 | ·022 | ·034 | ·051 | ·062 | ·073 |
| 22 i.u./min | ·017 | ·015 | ·031 | ·044 | ·052 | ·061 |
| 22 i.u./min | ·013 | ·012 | ·019 | ·023 | ·031 | ·029 |

*Site of action of the gonadotrophins.* For some time it has been known that the concentration of cholesterol in steroid-producing organs is altered following trophic stimulation [14]. Experiments on the metabolic fate of exogenous cholesterol in such organs are difficult to interpret since the endogenous pool of cholesterol is large and cholesterol is almost insoluble in aqueous media. In adequately designed experiments, however, ICSH will promote synthesis *de novo* of progesterone in the corpus luteum both from endogenous and exogenous cholesterol [15]. ICSH will moreover increase the formation of testosterone-$^3$H from cholesterol-$^3$H, but not from $\Delta^5$-pregnenolone-$^3$H in slices of rabbit testis [16]. Thus, the most probable locus for trophic action in the ovary and in the testis is between cholesterol and $\Delta^5$-pregnenolone. One should, however, note that cholesterol can be metabolized to dehydroepiandrosterone (DHEA) in the gonads via a pathway which does not involve either $\Delta^5$-pregnenolone or 17α-hydroxypregnenolone [17]. Whether this pathway is stimulated by gonadotrophins is not known, but testicular tissue will produce and secrete rather substantial amounts of DHEA following trophic stimulation [18].

The pathway cholesterol $\rightarrow\Delta^5$-pregnenolone involves 20α-hydroxycholesterol and 20α,22R-dihydroxycholesterol as intermediates, but only during the last year have data been forthcoming to show that these intermediates are produced when steroid-forming tissues are synthesizing $\Delta^5$-pregnenolone from cholesterol [19]. The production of 20α-hydroxycholesterol was disappointingly low in these experiments [19]. When 20α-hydroxycholesterol-$^3$H is incubated with steroid-producing tissues, no increment can be measured in $^3$H-containing hormonal end products when the proper trophins are added to the incubation media [20]. Such data could indicate that the trophins either acted before the formation of 20α-hydroxycholesterol or also that in the pathway cholesterol $\rightarrow\Delta^5$-pregnenolone unknown intermediates are formed. One notes with interest that Chen and Lin [21] have isolated tetralin hydroperoxide as an intermediate in the hydroxylation of tetralin *in vitro*. Information on ovarian steroidogenesis could indicate that ICSH may act at more than one site in sterol conversion to steroid hormones in this organ [22]. More information on cholesterol metabolism in the gonadal tissue is therefore needed, since such information appears important in understanding the site of action of gonadotrophic hormones.

*Mechanism of action of gonadotrophins.* In order to form one mole of testosterone from acetate at least 35 moles of TPNH are required. If the gonadotrophins act between cholesterol and $\Delta^5$-pregnenolone (or DHEA),* hydroxylation reactions which require TPNH are involved [23]. Sidechain cleavage of cholesterol has been obtained by endocrine tissue fractions in a system containing added flavoprotein, nonheme iron and cytochrome P-450 [24] (see 11β OH formation). Sidechain cleavage of cholesterol is inhibited by hyperbaric oxygen and succinate protects against this inhibition [25]. Hall has therefore postulated [26] that the sidechain cleavage system for cholesterol in the steroid-producing organs has its 'own pool of reduced $TPN^+$ generated via reversed electron transport,' i.e., reduction of $DPN^+$ through reversed electron transport and transhydrogenation of $TPN^+$ by DPNH via a transhydrogenase or a coupled enzymic system employing $DPN^+$ and $TPN^+$. The nature of the needed transhydrogenation reaction (s) of this system is not known, but this interesting theory is worth further exploration.

Another mechanistic scheme for trophic action on steroid production is that of Haynes and Berthet [27], implicating increased formation of cyclic-3′,5′-AMP and activation of phosphorylase in endocrine tissues.

* Since this paper was written considerable doubt has been expressed as to the existence of direct conversion of cholesterol to DHEA.

Glucose-1-phosphate released from glycogen would then enter the pentose phosphate pathway (as glucose-6-phosphate) and yield TPNH via oxidation. In spite of the many and rather serious objections which can be levelled against this scheme (for review see References 8 and 26), the original theory of Haynes and Berthet has promoted numerous interesting investigations and the experimental support for this theory of trophic action is much greater than allowed for by many investigators. Gonadotrophins will increase the activity of adenyl cyclase in the ovary [28] and in the testis [29, 30], and cyclic-3′,5′-AMP administration will result in increased production of ovarian steroids [31] and increased production [32] and secretion [33] of testicular steroids (Figure 3). With regard to the latter parameter, this effect of cyclic-3′,5′-AMP is very specific [34] and the early testosterone secretion pattern following gonadotrophin administration via the spermatic artery cannot be distinguished from that following cyclic-3′,5′-AMP administration via the spermatic artery. Increased cyclic-3′,5′-AMP concentration in testis tissue following trophic stimulation is not due to inactivation of the enzyme phosphodiesterase but occurs via augmented synthesis of cyclic-3′,5′-AMP from ATP [29, 35].

Conversion of cholesterol to $\Delta^5$-pregnenolone (or DHEA) takes place in gonadal mitochondria. Such organelles do contain adenyl cyclase activity which can be stimulated with gonadotrophins [30]. It has been reported that cyclic-3′,5′-AMP stimulates corticosteroidogenesis by acting on mitochondrial enzymes [36]. We have failed to demonstrate [30] that gonadotrophins or cyclic-3′,5′-AMP will augment the formation of $\Delta^5$-pregnenolone from either endogenous or exogenous cholesterol when added to mitochondria of the dog testis. Production of $\Delta^5$-pregnenolone from cholesterol by mitochondria of the canine testis is increased when they are exposed to $Ca^{2+}$ [35]. Thus, the initial action of gonadotrophins on steroid-producing cells in the testis could be outside the mitochondria and associated with changes in $Ca^{2+}$ distribution within membrane structures of the cells of Leydig. This view is supported by the findings of Bär and Hechter [37] who observed that addition of a $Ca^{2+}$ complexing agent to adrenocortical mitochondria inactivated ACTH-sensitive adenyl cyclase. It is not known if $Ca^{2+}$ is required for binding of the trophins to selective membrane receptors in the adrenal gland, the testis or the ovary. Moreover, the fact that trophic-sensitive adenyl cyclase in the adrenal gland [38] and in the testis [30] is found in various membrane systems following high-speed centrifugation does not preclude the possibility that in the intact cell this enzymic activity is concentrated on the plasma membrane.

Since cyclic-3′,5′-AMP could be the 'second messenger' for many hormones [39], the question of how these hormones bind to specific target cells and promote increased production of cyclic-3′,5′-AMP must be answered, i.e., why will ACTH promote increased steroidogenesis in the adrenal gland only and not in the testis and the ovary? Specific trophic stimulation of each of these three steroid-producing organs will result in activation of adenyl cyclase and steroidogenesis. If such binding sites exist, some must be similar in certain cells of the testis and the ovary, since the same trophin (ICSH) causes activation of adenyl cyclase in both. Lipolytic hormones have been found to act as hormone-specific receptors and to affect a single adenyl cyclase in fat cells [40]. Similar experiments are needed for the steroid-producing organs. Moreover, the problem of adenyl cyclase activation by the catecholamines in the ovary and the testis needs clarification. We have reported that administration of catecholamines via the spermatic artery of the dog is associated with increased production and secretion of testosterone [10] (Table 4). This effect of the catecholamines can in part be blocked with β-cell inhibitors and enhanced slightly with an α-cell inhibitor. Recently it has been observed that the catecholamines will increase adenyl cyclase activity in the testis [29, 35]. Data from experiments *in vitro* clearly show that gonadotrophic activation of testicular adenyl cyclase occurs via different receptors from those involved for the catecholamines [29, 35]. Slices of testes will not increase production of testosterone when exposed to isoproterenol. It is well established that slices of testes will augment testosterone production in the presence of gonadotrophins or cyclic-3′,5′-AMP [7]. Finally, administration of a α-cell inhibitor via the spermatic artery of the dog will not markedly prevent testosterone secretion following stimulation with HCG [41]. Thus, testicular tissue appears to contain at least two different receptor sites for adenyl cyclase activation. Of interest is the observation that slices of corpus luteum will not augment adenyl cyclase activity following exposure to catecholamines [28].

The effect of gonadotrophins or of cyclic-3′,5′-AMP on free TPNH in steroid-producing cells needs further exploration. The negative data of Marsh [42] working with the ovary are inconclusive since both free and bound nucleotides were measured. If it can be proved beyond reasonable doubt that the gonadotrophins or cyclic-3′,5′-AMP do not increase the concentration of *free* TNPH in gonadal cells producing the steroid hormones, the direct effect of these trophins on rate-limiting enzymes involved in steroidogenesis must be investigated. When testicular or ovarian tissue is exposed to high concentrations of metabolic inhibitors, known to decrease production *de novo* of proteins, synthesis [6, 43] and secretion [41] of steroid end products following administration of appropriate trophins are lower than in normal tissues. It is unfortunate that no data have been published on the effect of such inhibitors on purified gonadal enzymes directing rate-limiting steps in steroid formation. The observed effects [6, 41,

43] could also well be due to cell intoxication. It would be of interest to apply the techniques of Farese [44] to the gonadal tissue. In a critical study on the adrenal gland the conclusion was reached that ACTH 'may stimulate at the translational level the synthesis of certain proteins which are important in the steroidogenic process'. Cyclic-3',5'-AMP could still be the 'second messenger' for such an effect of a trophin since cyclic-3', 5'-AMP can induce enzyme synthesis in mammalian [45] as well as in non-mammalian cells [46].

It could be that the gonadotrophins or their 'second messenger', cyclic-3',5'-AMP, promote augmented production of steroids by increasing cell permeability [47, 48]. It has thus far not been possible to measure an increase in cell permeability of testis slices producing testosterone under the influence of gonadotrophins [49]. One should, however, recognize that the Leydig cells comprise about 10 per cent of the total testicular cell population. Thus, a marked change in permeability of the cells of Leydig would be so diluted by tubular elements that specific permeability changes of the steroid hormone producing cells would be difficult to measure. When compounds like dimethylsulphoxide [33], histamine [41] or insulin [35] are infused via the spermatic artery of the dog, a gonadotrophin-like response pattern in the secretion rates of testosterone is not seen.

Variations of arterial blood flow in the ovary [50] and in the testis [51] are known to alter steroid secretion. It is, however, difficult to prove that the output of spermatic venous blood is significantly increased following administration of HCG to anaesthetized dogs [2]. Still, an increase in the microcirculation of the cells of Leydig could occur with gonadotrophins and it is indeed possible that augmented testosterone secretion following administration of isoproterenol through the spermatic artery (compare Tables 2 and 4) is due to such an effect [10, also see discussion on page 85]. We have recently observed that when a purified preparation of relaxin (preparation no. 48 E 2103 A) is administered via the spermatic artery of the dog, blood circulation in the plexus pampiniformis appears to be increased. Whether this hormone increases flow of blood in the microcirculation of the Leydig cell is not known, but relaxin has little ability to increase the secretion of testosterone in the dog (compare Tables 2 and 5). Finally, it should be realized that slices of testes and of ovaries will increase hormone production following addition of gonadotrophins [6, 22]. This tissue preparation lacks arterial irrigation. Data on steroid production *in vivo* and *in vitro* following administration of gonadotrophins would aid in our comprehension of the relationship between blood flow and steroidogenesis in the gonad. It is worth noting parenthetically that both the mitochondria and the nuclear membrane fraction of the canine testis contain isoproterenol-sensitive adenyl cyclase [35].

TABLE 5. Rates of testicular secretion of testosterone ( μg / min ) in 12 different anaesthetized dogs infused with a mixture of 3·87 ml oxygenated arterial blood and 0·38 ml 0·9% sodium chloride / min via the spermatic artery. During time period 15–90 min different doses of relaxin were added at a constant rate to the infusion mixture (Animal Preparation II [10])

| Dose of relaxin* infused ( μg / min ) | Time period (min) 0–15 | 15–30 | 30–45 | 45–60 | 60–75 | 75–90 |
|---|---|---|---|---|---|---|
| 66·5 | ·058 | ·050 | ·051 | ·044 | ·049 | ·051 |
| 6·5 | ·057 | ·063 | ·060 | ·064 | ·064 | ·062 |
| 3·3 | ·020 | ·017 | ·017 | ·016 | ·016 | ·016 |
| 1·7 | ·040 | ·029 | ·031 | ·036 | ·036 | ·038 |
| 0·8 | ·076 | ·057 | ·060 | ·052 | ·060 | ·066 |
| 0·4 | ·056 | ·050 | ·045 | ·038 | ·044 | ·042 |
| 0·2 | ·035 | ·034 | ·041 | ·045 | ·040 | ·041 |
| 0·2 | ·063 | ·054 | ·047 | ·039 | ·044 | ·036 |
| 0·1 | ·040 | ·040 | ·041 | ·062 | ·051 | ·047 |
| 0·1 | ·079 | ·102 | ·059 | ·048 | ·047 | ·045 |
| 0·05 | ·103 | ·084 | ·092 | ·093 | ·105 | ·096 |
| 0·025 | ·205 | ·170 | ·216 | ·194 | ·201 | ·200 |

*A gift from R. Kroc, Warner-Lambert Research Institute, New Jersey, USA.
It should be noted that relaxin has been isolated from the rooster testis [52]

$\Delta^5$-Pregnenolone appears to inhibit its own formation from cholesterol in adrenal mitochondria, probably via inhibition of 20α-hydroxylation of cholesterol [53]. Removal of $\Delta^5$-pregnenolone from the mitochondria could therefore control steroid production. When $\Delta^5$-pregnenolone and testosterone are measured in spermatic venous blood of the dog, the relative increase in secretion of $\Delta^5$-pregnenolone following administration of HCG via the spermatic artery is greater than that of testosterone during the first hour after HCG stimulation [54]. The absolute rates of secretion of these steroids by the canine testis are, however, vastly different [33]. Nothing is known about whether or not this is a functioning control mechanism. Do trophins or cyclic-3′,5′-AMP promote transfer of $\Delta^5$-pregnenolone out of the mitochondria of steroid-producing cells, thus releasing inhibition of 20α-hydroxylation of cholesterol? With current knowledge of 20α-hydroxylation of this sterol it seems futile even to propose a working theory for this possible regulatory mechanism. It should be noted, however, that when data on ACTH-induced secretion of adrenal hormones are subjected to system analysis [55] release of 20α-hydroxylation inhibition by $\Delta^5$-pregnenolone removal is a highly probable answer. In the ultimate analysis of this proposal for trophic action, the fact that two pathways may lead to formation of $\Delta^5$-steroids from cholesterol in steroid-producing organs [17] must not be overlooked or underestimated.

Reduction of the $C_{20}$ keto group of progesterone increases in the testis [56] and the ovary [57] following administration of gonadotrophins.

Through this reduction the gestagenic effects of progesterone are almost lost and 17α,20α-dihydroxyprogesterone is no longer a substrate for the $C_{17-20}$ lyase system in the testis [58]. It is possible that the gonadotrophins control excess production of progesterone and testosterone in the gonads by this mechanism and the reaction may be of biological significance for maintaining proper balance between the two major functions of the male gonad : production of normal spermatozoa and production of testosterone. When progesterone is infused via the spermatic artery of the dog, the testis exhibits meiotic chromosome alterations [59]. Such alterations are not seen when oestrogens or HCG are infused via the spermatic artery in our animal preparation *in vivo* [59]. It would be of interest to study whether concomitant infusion of progesterone and gonadotrophins through the spermatic artery would abolish the meiotic chromosome alterations induced by progesterone infusion.

In 1968 we reported that infusion of prostaglandin $E_1$ via the spermatic artery of the dog was associated with increased secretion of testosterone in spermatic venous blood during the first 15 min of prostaglandin $E_1$ administration [34]. When ovarian [60, 61] or adrenal [62] tissues are incubated with prostaglandin, increased production of steroid end products can be measured. The prostaglandins are present in gonadal tissues [63], but their role in local control of steroidogenesis in these tissues is currently unknown, as are also their effects on gonadal formation of cyclic-3′,5′-AMP [63]. Moreover, data are needed on the formation of the prostaglandins in the ovary and the testis and on their mode of transport from other sites of production to the hormone-producing cells of the male and female gonad. It could be that these compounds promote regulation of steroidogenesis independent of the pituitary gonadotrophins and thus provide a 'short-loop' feedback system depending on a prostate-testis interaction in the male gonad and on a uterus-ovary interaction in the female gonad.

In summary, the detailed mechanism of gonadotrophic action in the ovary and the testis is unknown, and currently only potentials, possibilities and patterns in this complex field of experimental work can be discussed. The very complexity of this problem immediately suggests caution in making general deductions from a few experiments in one animal species. Data from future work will decide if we will succeed in coming to an understanding of trophic action on steroidogenesis. There is hope that the different mechanisms of action of gonadotrophins discussed can in due time be shaped into a coherent mechanism of action of gonadotrophins.

ACKNOWLEDGMENT

Investigations from the author's laboratory were supported in part by research grant (HD-04195-02) from the US Public Health Service, Bethesda, Maryland, USA.

REFERENCES

[1] West, C.D., Hollander, V.P., Kritchevsky, T.H. and Dobriner, K., *J. clin. Endocr. Metab.*, **12**, 915, 1952.
[2] Brinck-Johnsen, T. and Eik-Nes, K.B., *Endocrinology*, **61**, 676, 1957.
[3] Eik-Nes, K.B., *Endocrinology*, **71**, 101, 1962.
[4] Eik-Nes, K.B. and Hall, P.F., *J. Reprod. Fert.*, **9**, 233, 1965.
[5] Brady, R.O., *J. biol. Chem.*, **193**, 145, 1951.
[6] Hall, P.F. and Eik-Nes, K.B., *Biochem. Biophys. Acta*, **63**, 411, 1962.
[7] Connell, G.M. and Eik-Nes, K.B. In *The Gonads*. Ed. K.W. McKerns, p. 491. New York: Appleton, 1969.
[8] Eik-Nes, K.B., *Physiol. Rev.*, **44**, 609, 1964.
[9] Eik-Nes, K.B. and Hall, P.F., *Vitam. Hormones*, **23**, 153, 1965.
[10] Eik-Nes, K.B., *Am. J. Physiol.*, **217**, 1764, 1969.
[11] Brownie, A.C., van der Molen, H.J., Nishizawa, E.E. and Eik-Nes, K.B., *J. clin. Endocr. Metab.*, **24**, 1091, 1964.
[12] Everett, J.W. and Sawyer, C.H., *Endocrinology*, **47**, 198, 1950.
[13] Blaustein, M.P. and Goldman, D.E., *Science*, **153**, 429, 1966.
[14] Stone, D. and Hechter, O., *Arch. Biochem. Biophys.*, **51**, 457, 1954.
[15] Hall, P.F. and Koritz, S.B., *Biochemistry, N.Y.*, **4**, 1037, 1965.
[16] Hall, P.F., *Endocrinology*, **78**, 690, 1966.
[17] Jungmann, R.A., *Biochem. Biophys. Acta*, **164**, 110, 1968.
[18] Hall, P.F. and Eik-Nes, K.B., *Endocrinology*, **74**, 35, 1964.
[19] Burstein, S. and Gut, M., *Steroids*, **14**, 270, 1969.
[20] Hall, P.F. and Young, D.G., *Endocrinology*, **82**, 559, 1968.
[21] Chen, C. and Lin, C.C., *Biochem. Biophys. Acta*, **170**, 366, 1968.
[22] Savard, K., Marsh, J.M. and Rice, B.F., *Recent Prog. Hormone Res.*, **21**, 285, 1965.
[23] Samuels, L.T. and Eik-Nes, K.B. In *Metabolic Pathways*. Ed. D.M. Greenberg, p. 168. New York: Academic Press, 1968.
[24] Simpson, E.R. and Boyd, G.S., *Biochem. Biophys. Res. Commn*, **28**, 945, 1967.
[25] Hall, P.F., *Biochemistry, N.Y.*, **6**, 2794, 1967.
[26] Hall, P.F. In *The Androgens of the Testis*. Ed. K.B. Eik-Nes, p. 91, New York: Dekker, 1970.
[27] Haynes, R.C. and Berthet, L., *J. biol. Chem.*, **225**, 115, 1957.
[28] Marsh, J.M., Butcher, R.W., Savard, K. and Sutherland, E.W., *J. biol. Chem.*, **241**, 5436, 1966.
[29] Murad, I., Strauch, B.S. and Vaughan, M., *Biochim. Biophys. Acta*, **177**, 591, 1969.
[30] Pulsinelli, W.A. and Eik-Nes, K.B., Fed. Proc. abstract no. 3828, 1970.
[31] Mason, N.R., Marsh, J.M. and Savard, K., *J. biol. Chem.*, **237**, 1801, 1962.
[32] Sandler, R. and Hall, P.F., *Endocrinology*, **79**, 647, 1966.
[33] Eik-Nes, K.B., *Ciba Foundation Colloq. Endocr.*, **16**, 120, 1967.
[34] Eik-Nes, K.B., *Gen. comp. Endocr. Suppl.*, **2**, 87, 1969.

[35] Pulsinelli, W.A. and Eik-Nes, K.B., unpublished, May 1970.
[36] Roberts, S., McCune, R.W., Creange, J.E. and Young, P.L., *Science*, **158,** 372, 1967.
[37] Bär, H.-P. and Hechter, O., *Biochem. Biophys. Res. Commn*, **35,** 681, 1969.
[38] Hechter, O., Bär, H.-P., Matsuba, M. and Soifer, D., *Life Sci.*, **8,** 935, 1969.
[39] Sutherland, E.W., Robinson, G.A. and Butcher, R.W., *Circulation*, **37,** 279, 1969.
[40] Birnbaumer, L. and Rodbell, M., *J. biol. Chem.*, **244,** 3477, 1969.
[41] Eik-Nes, K.B., *J. Reprod. Fert. Suppl.*, **2,** 125, 1967.
[42] Marsh, J.M., *Adv. exp. Med. Biol.*, **2,** 213, 1968.
[43] Marsh, J.M. and Savard, K., *J. Reprod. Fert. Suppl.*, **1,** 113, 1966.
[44] Farese, R.V., *Endocrinology*, **85,** 1209, 1969.
[45] Jost, J.-P., Hsie, A., Hughes, S.D. and Ryan, L., *J. biol. Chem.*, **245,** 351, 1970.
[46] DeCrombrugahe, B., Perlman, R.L., Vampus, H.E. and Paston, J., *J. biol. Chem.*, **244,** 5828, 1969.
[47] Ahren, K. and Kostyo, J.L., *Endocrinology*, **73,** 81, 1963.
[48] Orloff, J. and Handler, J.S., *J. clin. Invest.*, **41,** 702, 1962.
[49] Hall, P.F. and Eik-Nes, K.B., *Proc. Soc. exp. Biol. Med.*, **110,** 148, 1962.
[50] Romanoff, E.B., Deshpande, N. and Pincus, G., *Endocrinology*, **70,** 532, 1962.
[51] Eik-Nes, K.B., *Can. J. Physiol. Pharmac.*, **42,** 671, 1964.
[52] Kroc, R.L., Personal communication, June 1969.
[53] Koritz, S.B. and Hall, P.F., *Biochemistry, N.Y.*, **3,** 1298, 1964.
[54] Tcholakian, R.K. and Eik-Nes, K.B., unpublished, May 1970.
[55] Urquhart, J., *The Physiologist*, **13,** 7, 1970.
[56] Fevold, H.R. and Eik-Nes, K.B., *Gen. comp. Endocr.*, **2,** 506, 1962.
[57] Kidwell, W.R., Balogh, K. and Wiest, W.F., *Endocrinology*, **79,** 352, 1966.
[58] Inano, H., Nakano, H., Shikita, M. and Tamaoki, B.-I., *Biochim. Biophys. Acta*, **137,** 540, 1967.
[59] Williams, D.L., Runyon, J.W. and Hagen, A.A., *Nature, Lond.*, **220,** 1145, 1968.
[60] Bedwani, J.R. and Horton, E.W., *Life Sci.*, **7,** 389, 1968.
[61] Speroff, L. and Ramwell, P.W., *J. clin. Endocr. Metab.*, **30,** 345, 1970.
[62] Flack, J.D., Jessup, R. and Ramwell, P.W., *Science*, **163,** 691, 1969.
[63] Bergström, S., *Science*, **157,** 382, 1967.

*Discussion of paper by Professor Eik-Nes*

*Mills* I was interested in the study you described with prostaglandin; I presume this belonged to the E series, but the dose of 11 μg that you mentioned seems to be of mammoth proportions.
*Eik-Nes* The prostaglandin used was initially in a dose of 11 μg/min, but lower doses (down to 100 ng/min) have now been shown to give similar results.
*Leymarie* Do HCG and prostaglandins have additive effects?
*Eik-Nes* Yes, but like catecholamines they appear to act at different receptor sites.
*Odell* Do prolactin and HCG have additive effects?
*Eik-Nes* Prolactin has no gonadotrophic effect on the dog testis, but in the female rat increments in progesterone output can be demonstrated both *in vivo* and *in vitro* : the doses used however are relatively high, and there is considerable controversy about the mechanism of action.
*Odell* As I am sure you are aware, it has been reported that prolactin will stimulate androgen production when given simultaneously with ACTH to the castrated rat (Tullner and Hertz). Are there any data to suggest that prolactin has an effect on the testis of the rat?
*Eik-Nes* I am not aware of any such experiment.

## SESSION II. GENERAL DISCUSSION

*Macnaughton* Could I ask Odell whether very small doses of ethinyl oestradiol, say 0·01 mg daily, would stimulate FSH secretion?
*Odell* To my knowledge no oestrogen will stimulate FSH secretion in castrate or menopausal women if administered alone. However, a synthetic oestrogen (Mestranol) in a dose of 100 μg per day can stimulate LH but not FSH secretion in *normal* women (ovaries intact and secreting a variety of steroids). The recent evidence concerning the effects of ethinyl oestradiol is rather conflicting. At a recent workshop meeting Dr Yen reported that he had given intravenous infusions of oestradiol to women, using stepwise increments, and had had difficulty in showing any increase in LH secretion at all. The time of day at which the steroid was given seemed to be important.
*Fotherby* Following the last question, I think it has been shown that small doses of oestradiol (between 1 and 10 μg/day) will stimulate ovulation in women, but FSH and LH assays have not been carried out in these experiments.
*Odell* This effect has also been shown in rats. But it is worthy of emphasis that these of necessity were in intact subjects in a steroid milieu different

from the castrate or postmenopausal women. Again in studies in our laboratory (Swerdloff, Jacobs and Odell, *Prog. Endocrine Soc.*, p. 59, 1970), it has been shown that oestrogen alone will stimulate LH but not FSH in castrated female rats. We have given 'Premarin' intravenously to men, and over a period of one hour found neither a rise nor a fall in LH.

*Baird* I have two comments on Professor Odell's paper. Although the concentration of both oestrone and oestradiol in peripheral plasma shows a biphasic pattern throughout the menstrual cycle, the magnitude of the increase in concentration is different for the two steroids, i.e., oestrone concentration increases 3–4-fold while that of oestradiol tenfold (Baird and Guevara, *J. clin. Endocr. Metab.*, **29**, 149, 1969). Whereas the peak concentration of oestradiol occurs 24–36 hours before the peak of LH in plasma, that of 17α-OH progesterone occurs synchronously with the LH peak. Do we assume that both oestradiol and 17α-OH progesterone originate from the same cells in the follicle?

*Odell* I don't think we can answer that.

*Baird* There is some evidence from the analysis of the concentration of these steroids in ovarian venous plasma, that 17α-OH progesterone may not arise exclusively from the follicle. In at least one subject the concentration of 17α-OH progesterone was higher in the plasma collected from the contralateral ovary than in the plasma from the ovary containing the preovulatory follicle (Lloyd, Lobotsky, Weisz, Baird, McCracken, Pupkin, Zanartu and Puga, *J. clin. Endocr. Metab.*, **32**, 155, 1971).

*Odell* The dimensions of the changes in hormone secretion which we are discussing are becoming progressively smaller, and present us with a considerable methodological problem, because very small changes could be of physiological importance. For example, if the TSH levels are measured serially in soldiers exposed to arctic conditions, these remain within the normal range. However if each man is used as his own control, then the average rise in TSH concentration is about 60 per cent. This presumably is sufficient to stimulate the thyroid gland to do all the things usually associated with exposure to cold. Dr Cargille, Dr Ross and I have some data showing the results of a collaborative study on changes in plasma FSH during the menstrual cycle which helps to emphasize the point I made earlier in reply to Dr Hunter. These data show a *similarity* in the pattern of change in FSH levels, even though the magnitude of change observed differs considerably when different techniques are used to assay the same samples of blood.

Turning to the question of changes in the concentration of progesterone in peripheral blood, let me use the data published by Johansson and his colleagues to demonstrate how the peak of plasma LH concentration may follow the beginning of the rise in progesterone. If you will refer to their

Figure 3 (Neill et al., *J. clin. Endocr. Metab.*, **27**, 1171, 1968) you will observe that according to the 'statistics' of these assays, it was about three days before the day of LH peak ovulation that the plasma progesterone concentrations were distinguishable from zero. The changes therefore are small, but they could be very important in a physiological sense. These data after all refer to peripheral and not to ovarian vein blood, and therefore represent the concentrations affecting the central nervous system.

*Naftolin* It might be valuable to reconsider some results obtained in the rat by Vande Wiele's group. They administered antibodies to oestrogen and to progesterone and were able to stop ovulation with the former but not with the latter. It seemed clear that oestradiol was the more important steroid as far as the 'signal' was concerned, but progesterone might have profound effects on the central nervous system threshold for various stimuli. Also, in some animal models, ovulation can be brought about by progesterone and by other progestogens.

*Van der Molen* Without anticipating unduly what I have to say tomorrow, we have studied several cycles in which the progesterone level in plasma rose by 0·15 to 0·20 μg/100 ml at midcycle, but LH assays were not done. However, it is well known that LH and other gonadotrophins stimulate the production of progesterone by the luteinized follicle. It might therefore be necessary to differentiate between follicular progesterone and luteal phase progesterone.

*Odell* That is an excellent point. Studies by Neill, Johansson and Knobil (*Endocrinology*, **85**, 75, 1969) have shown that in the monkey progesterone levels begin to rise two *days* before ovulation and this might be considered 'follicular phase progesterone'. Ovulation itself probably occurs about 20 hours after the LH peak.

*Cooke* We also have been doing serial estimations of plasma progesterone throughout the menstrual cycle, and have found what appears to be a second peak in the luteal phase. I noticed something similar in the last slide showing Johansson's data. May I ask if this is a general finding?

*Johansson* This might occur in a particular patient, but if the results of some 34 cycles are averaged, there appeared to be a smooth plateau of plasma progesterone. I cannot be certain about the significance of this at present.

*Fotherby* Concerning the changes in 17α-hydroxyprogesterone levels at midcycle, if one measures the excretion of pregnanetriol (the major urinary metabolite of 17α-hydroxyprogesterone) and the urinary oestrogens, there is a marked increase in the excretion of pregnanetriol on the day of the oestrogen peak. If you then compare the values on the day preceding and the day following the midcycle peak of oestrogen excretion, the amount of pregnanetriol excreted is doubled over this period. This suggests that large amounts of 17α-hydroxyprogesterone are being produced at the time of ovulation.

*Mills* With regard to the question of the peak of LH levels and the time of ovulation, the work of Edwards and Steptoe may be important. They have been attempting to collect ova from women for extracorporeal fertilization. They have found by laparoscopy that ovulation occurred about 36 hours after the administration of HCG. This was much later than expected.

*Odell* This apparent delay may have been due to the intramuscular administration of HCG with delayed absorption.

*Gemzell* If a single ovulation is induced, it usually occurs about 20 hours after the administration of HCG.

*Oakey* May I ask the panel for their views on the possible role of the gonadotrophins in the control of the aromatization of C19 steroids. We have studied the acute effects of gonadotrophins on follicular tissue dissected out from bovine ovaries. A single follicle was divided in two and each portion was incubated with labelled testosterone. Samples were assayed for labelled oestrogens at 20-minute intervals. After one hour a gonadotrophic preparation was added to one portion and the incubations continued. Samples were then assayed at intervals of 20 minutes for labelled oestradiol and oestrone. Addition of gonadotrophic preparations with FSH and LH activity did not appear to alter the rate of oestrogen synthesis in this system. Sometimes the conversion is depressed, perhaps due to a reduction of the specific activity of the substrate.

*Eik-Nes* Gonadotrophins do not appear to influence aromatization. Data to show whether follicular maturation, once initiated, proceeds autonomously, are going to be difficult to gather.

# Assessment of Gonadal Function. Formation and Secretion of Gonadal Steroids

H. J. VAN DER MOLEN *and* H. W. A. DE BRUYN

Department of Biochemistry
Medical Faculty at Rotterdam
The Netherlands

## INTRODUCTION

¶ SOME basic problems concerning the relationship between gonadal function and gonadal steroid production may be reflected in the following questions : 'Does gonadal steroid production reflect or affect gonadal function (i.e. ovulation or spermatogenesis)?' and 'Which extra-gonadal functions may be affected or reflected by gonadal steroid production?' Some specific questions related to the pattern of steroids produced by the ovary and testis are depicted in Tables 1 and 2. Within the framework of these questions examples of factors which may be involved in the secretion of gonadal steroids (see Table 3) will be discussed.

TABLE 1. Some questions related to the pattern of steroid production by the ovary

1. What are the patterns of steroids produced by the various cell types (granulosa, theca) of the follicle, the interstitium and the corpus luteum?
2. What is the relationship between steroid production and the process of ovulation?
3. Is the (qualitative and quantitative) production of steroids in the ovary reflected in the pattern of steroid concentrations in ovarian vein plasma, in peripheral plasma, in urine?
4. What is the relationship between the results of 1–3 and the pattern of pituitary factors that regulate ovarian function?

TABLE 2. Some questions related to the pattern of steroid production by the testis

1. What are the patterns of steroids produced by the various cell types (Leydig cells, seminiferous tubules, Sertoli cells) of the testis?
2. Do steroids freely exchange between the different cell types in the testis?
3. What is the direct effect of steroids produced in the testis on spermatogenesis?
4. Is the (qualitative and quantitative) production of steroids in the different cell types of the testis reflected in steroid concentrations in testicular venous plasma, in peripheral plasma and in urine?
5. What is the relationship between steroid secretion by the testis (levels in blood and urine) and spermatogenesis?

TABLE 3. Some factors involved in the secretion of gonadal steroids

Presence of specific cell types
*Ovary:* follicle, interstitium, corpus luteum
*Testis:* Leydig cells, seminiferous tubules, Sertoli cells

Qualitative and quantitative biosynthesis of steroids in different cell types

Gonadotrophic stimulation of tissue development and/or steroid biosynthesis

Vascularization of specific gonadal cell types

Permeability of cellular and subcellular membranes of specific cell types to steroids

Rate of blood flow

## BIOSYNTHESIS AND SECRETION OF GONADAL STEROIDS

Gonadal cell types whether from the ovary or testis differ quantitatively rather than qualitatively in their pattern of steroid secretion. Although the basic pattern for steroid biosynthesis may be qualitatively similar in all tissue cells, the quantitative amounts of the various steroids produced in different compartments may be very different. In this regard knowledge of common factors for biochemical control such as the presence of the required substrates and co-factors, regulation of enzyme activities by enzyme induction, product or substrate inhibition, may be of paramount importance.

### *Biosynthesis of steroids in the human ovary*

Information about the capacity for steroid biosynthesis of the various cell types in the *human* ovary has almost exclusively been derived from incubation studies *in vitro*. Several investigators [1–4] have presented evidence that in incubations *in vitro* with whole ovarian tissue Δ5-pregnenolone may be the preferred precursor for oestrogen biosynthesis when compared to progesterone, regardless of the state of the ovarian cycle. Investigations with isolated ovarian cell types have, however, revealed more details about specialized biosynthetic capacities of the different cell types (Fig. 1).

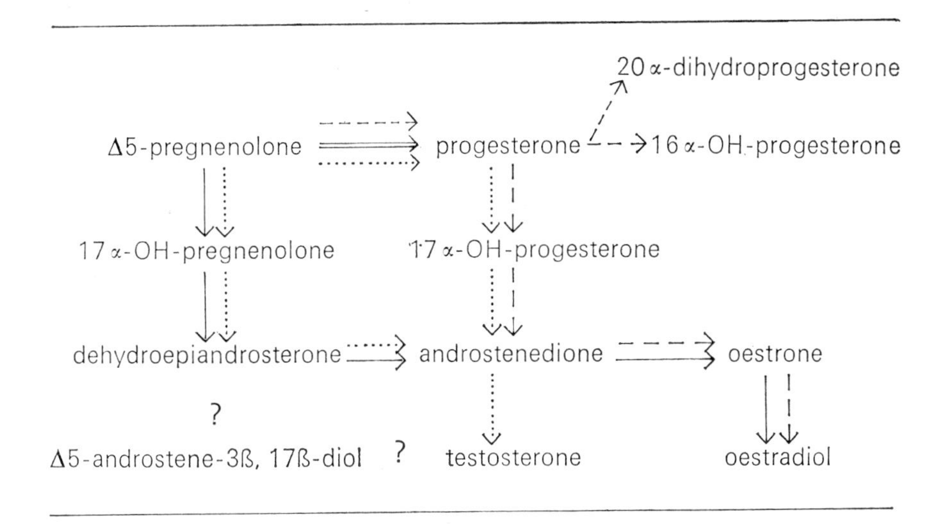


FIGURE 1
Pathways for *in vitro* biosynthesis of steroids in different cell types of the normal human ovary

*Follicle.* Ryan and Petro [5] have incubated granulosa cells and theca cells from normal human ovarian follicles. Their results have led to the conclusion that in the granulosa cell little conversion occurs through the '$\Delta 5,3\beta$-hydroxy pathway'. Also there is little $17\alpha$-hydroxylase and 17, 20-desmolase activity in these cells and progesterone is the main metabolite of pregnenolone. In contrast the theca cells convert radioactive substrates to oestrogens through both the $\Delta 5,3\beta$-hydroxy and $\Delta 4,3$-keto pathways, but it was suggested that oestrogen formation in the theca cells occurred preferentially from pregnenolone through dehydroepiandrosterone and androstenedione. These observations may explain, to some extent, why during the follicular phase of the menstrual cycle granulosa cells may secrete progesterone, whereas the theca cells may be responsible for the secretion of larger amounts of oestrogens in addition to small amounts of progesterone.

*Corpus luteum.* The most prominent steroid formed by corpus luteum cells *in vitro* is progesterone, though small amounts of the oestrogens and other $\Delta 4,3$-keto steroids are also produced. Minute amounts of the $\Delta 5,3\beta$-hydroxy steroids and testosterone are synthesized in the corpus luteum. Based on studies *in vitro* with radioactive precursors [1, 6–10] it has been concluded that biosynthesis of oestrogens in the human corpus luteum occurs largely through the $\Delta 4,3$-keto pathway. If the $\Delta 4,3$-keto pathway is the preferred route for biosynthesis in the normal corpus luteum *in vivo*, the steroid biosynthetic pattern of the normal corpus luteum resembles qualitatively that of the follicular granulosa cells.

*Interstitium.* Savard and co-workers have studied the biosynthetic capacity of interstitial cells from normal human ovaries *in vitro* [1, 10, 11]. They demonstrated that also in this cellular compartment both the $\Delta 5,3\beta$-hydroxy pathway and the $\Delta 4,3$-keto pathway operate. The principal steroids formed under their conditions *in vitro* were androstenedione, dehydroepiandrosterone and testosterone. This observation has led to the view that the interstitial tissue may represent the 'androgenic compartment' of the ovary.

### *Secretion of ovarian steroids in normal women*

Patterns of steroids in plasma and urine reflecting ovarian steroid production in normal women have recently been reviewed [12, 13].

*Androgens.* When Lobotsky, Wyss, Segre and Lloyd [14] plotted individual estimates for concentrations of testosterone in peripheral blood for several women against the cycle day, it was observed that the highest concentration of plasma testosterone was found around the day of the thermal nadir. We have not observed significant variations in plasma testosterone concentrations throughout the cycle (Fig. 2; Table 4). Even if the peri-

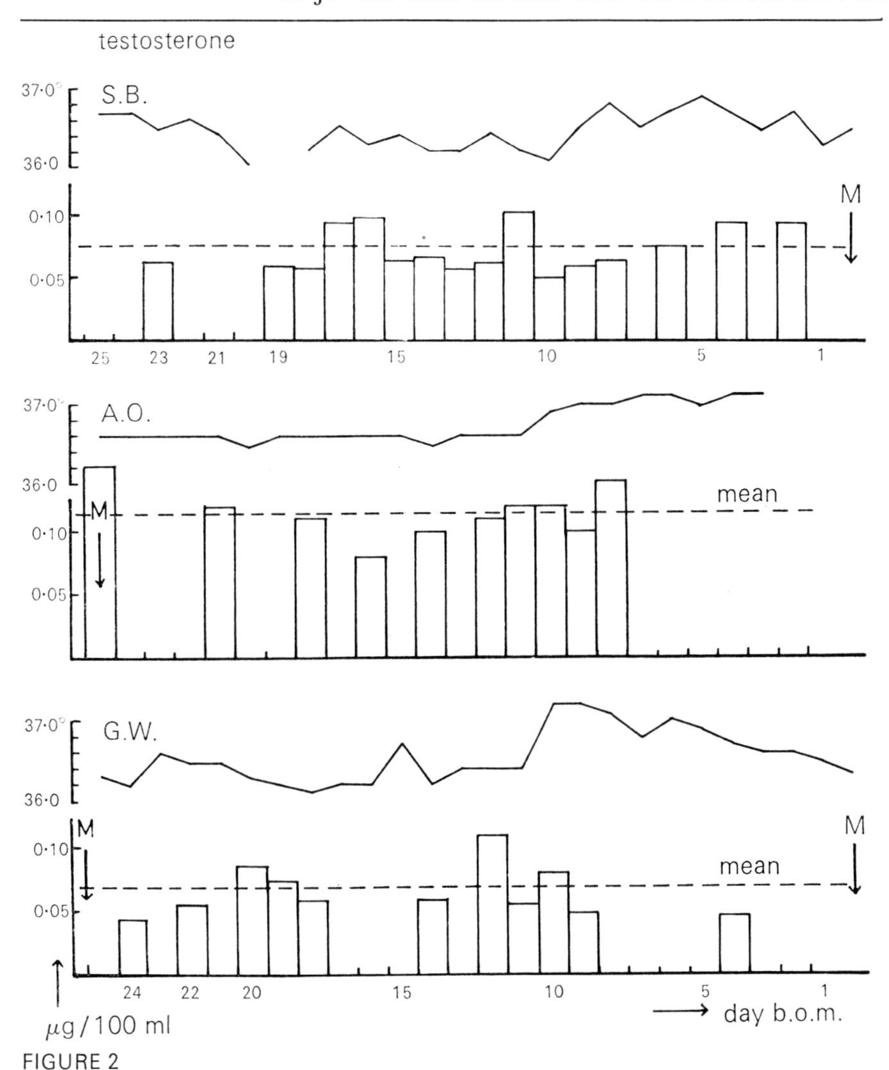


FIGURE 2
Basal body temperature and plasma testosterone concentrations in normal women at different stages of their menstrual cycle. M = day of onset of menstruation; b.o.m. = day before onset of menstruation

pheral plasma levels of testosterone or androstenedione did not show a distinct variation throughout the menstrual cycle in our studies, some other arguments may indicate that the production and secretion of androgens by the ovary fluctuate (Table 5). In addition to the surge of LH around the time of ovulation and the stimulation of androgen biosynthesis *in vitro* in interstitial cells and corpus luteum tissue, Mikhail [15] has shown that the secretion of androstenedione and testosterone is increased when a ripe follicle or corpus luteum is present in the ovary. Furthermore several groups of investigators [16–20] have shown that the excretion of testosterone

TABLE 4. Testosterone ($\mu g$/100 ml) in peripheral plasma

| Subject | Throughout the cycle N | mean | s.d. | During the day N | mean | s.d. |
|---|---|---|---|---|---|---|
| S.B. | 17 | 0·075 | 0·017 | | | |
| A.O. | 10 | 0·116 | 0·022 | | | |
| G.W. | 13 | 0·068 | 0·022 | | | |
| v.H. | | | | 7 | 0·060 | 0·016 |
| Ne | | | | 6 | 0·058 | 0·024 |
| Sch | | | | 8 | <0·030 | |
| | Standards | | | | | |
| | 10 | 0·052 | 0·014 | | | |
| | 10 | 0·104 | 0·021 | | | |

TABLE 5. Observations in support of a cyclic ovarian 'androgen' secretion throughout the normal menstrual cycle

1. Plasma LH is increased around the time of ovulation
2. LH stimulates *in vitro* biosynthesis of androstenedione and testosterone in interstitial tissue and corpus luteum tissue
3. Secretion of androstenedione and testosterone into ovarian venous blood is increased when a ripe follicle or a corpus luteum is present in the ovary
4. Concentrations of testosterone in peripheral plasma of normal women may be higher around and after the time of ovulation
5. The urinary excretion of testosterone glucosiduronate (and androstenedione?) is increased around the time of ovulation and during the luteal phase of the normal menstrual cycle
6. The urinary excretion of androsterone and etiocholanolone shows a positive correlation with the urinary excretion of oestrogens throughout the normal menstrual cycle

(glucuronide) in urine of normal women shows peaks at around the time of expected ovulation and during the luteal phase of the cycle (Fig. 3). Results of Ismail, Davidson and Loraine [21] suggest, that the excretion of androstenedione in urine may show a similar fluctuating pattern.

Androstenedione and testosterone are metabolized to 17-ketosteroids. Under normal physiological conditions the contribution of these steroids to the urinary 17-ketosteroid excretion in women is rather small. Most of the urinary 17-ketosteroids are derived from adrenocortical steroids. For a long time no variation of the excretion of total or of individual 17-ketosteroids in urine throughout the menstrual cycle could be detected [22]. Recently, however, with a refined gas-chromatographic method for accurate measurement of steroids in urine Adlercreutz, Luukkainen and Svanborg (1967) found a significant correlation between the excretion of the three oestrogens and of androsterone and etiocholanolone in urine of normal women throughout the menstrual cycle [23]. This finding tends to support the view that these steroids are somehow derived from the same precursor. From biosynthetic studies with ovarian tissues *in vitro* it may well

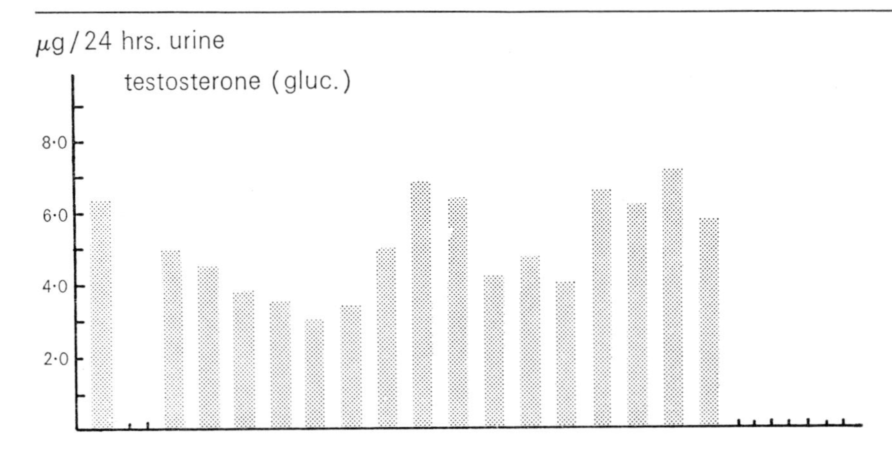


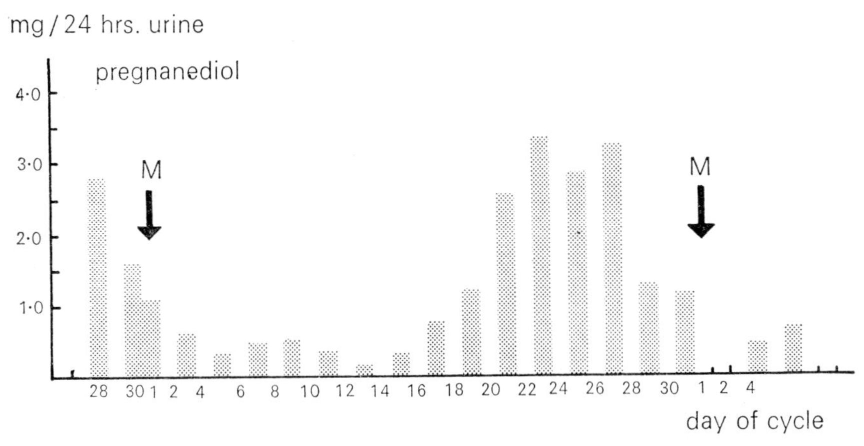


FIGURE 3
Concentrations of testosterone (glucosiduronate) and pregnanediol in urine of a normal woman at different days of the menstrual cycle

be that ovarian androstenedione can serve as this precursor. Also Adlercreutz and his co-workers [23] observed a correlation between the excretion of dehydroepiandrosterone and pregnanediol in the urine during the menstrual cycle. This finding might provide evidence for the postulate that dehydroepiandrosterone and progesterone are derived from the same precursor, such as ovarian pregnenolone. Such observations from urine do not, of course, imply that the concentrations of testosterone and androstenedione in peripheral plasma should necessarily fluctuate throughout the menstrual cycle.

These findings might indicate, however, that either the presently available techniques for measurement of androstenedione and testosterone in peripheral plasma are hardly sufficiently precise to detect possible fluctuations; or, less likely, it could be postulated that some other factor might affect the metabolism of androgens that would result in the fluctuating excretion patterns in urine.

Worthy of notice are the observations concerning the occurrence of epitestosterone (the 17α-hydroxyl epimer of testosterone) in urine of women. In urine of normal women testosterone and epitestosterone may be present in almost equal quantities and may show the same excretion pattern [17]. In pathological situations, however, such as in Stein-Leventhal patients or in virilized women the excretion of epitestosterone appears increased when the excretion of testosterone is either normal or slightly elevated [24]. Although there is some information that epitestosterone may be formed from androstenedione or testosterone [25, 26] it is not definitely established if the ovary plays any role whatsoever with regard to the urinary excretion pattern of epitestosterone.

In 1944 Gaarenstroom, De Jongh and Paesi [27] described how an interplay between ovarian 'androgen' and follicle stimulating hormone in the rat would facilitate the formation of follicular cavities and subsequently lead to the formation of ripe Graaffian follicles. In fact they presented experimental evidence that ovulation, as the climax of cavity formation, could be induced in immature rats following administration of testosterone only [28]. The biochemical information concerning ovarian steroid biosynthesis and levels of testosterone and androstenedione in blood and urine of the female, as discussed above, has made it highly likely that the interstitium of the normal human ovary does produce and may secrete androgens in a cyclic fashion. Such observations may furnish the basis for future work on the role of fluctuating ovarian androgen production for the promotion of cyclic ovulation processes in the normal human ovary.

*Progesterone.* The pattern that arises from daily estimations of peripheral plasma progesterone levels throughout the menstrual cycle can be considered to reflect the changes in ovarian function discussed in the introduction of this paper. During the first half of the cycle progesterone levels are low and may be considered to reflect predominantly progesterone production of the theca cells. During the luteal phase on the days immediately after ovulation the levels of progesterone in blood plasma are higher than at the time when regression of the corpus luteum is believed to occur. The excretion of pregnanediol in urine correlates well with the level of progesterone in peripheral plasma [29, 30].

Rünnebaum and Zander (unpublished observations, personal communication) have not been able to detect significant variation of progesterone concentrations throughout the day in peripheral plasma of normal women in the luteal phase of the cycle. Recently there has been some discussion concerning a preovulatory rise of progesterone concentrations in peripheral plasma of normal women. Woolever [31] estimated daily progesterone levels throughout several menstrual cycles. His results suggest a slight increase in the concentrations of the hormone at about the time of ovulation before onset of the major rise in progesterone levels during the second half of the cycle. In a study, specifically undertaken to investigate if a preovulatory rise in peripheral plasma progesterone levels occurred, Rünnebaum and Zander [32] collected plasma pools of women at nine days and four days before presumed ovulation. In the plasma pool collected four days before ovulation the plasma level of progesterone (0·28 μg/100 ml) tended to be higher than the level nine days before ovulation (0·08 μg/100 ml). In a collaborative study with Rünnebaum and Zander we have studied the daily progesterone levels in peripheral plasma in relation to the basal body temperature. This study was conducted in several normal women with regular cycles. It appears that in at least part of these cycles a small, but significant increase in plasma progesterone takes place before the dip in the temperature curve is observed (Fig. 4). Similar results have been obtained by Johansson [43]. The weakest link in studies of this nature is the exact timing of ovulation. The parameters normally used for timing of ovulation are related one way or another to the increased progesterone production. Notably the increase in basal body temperature is a direct sign

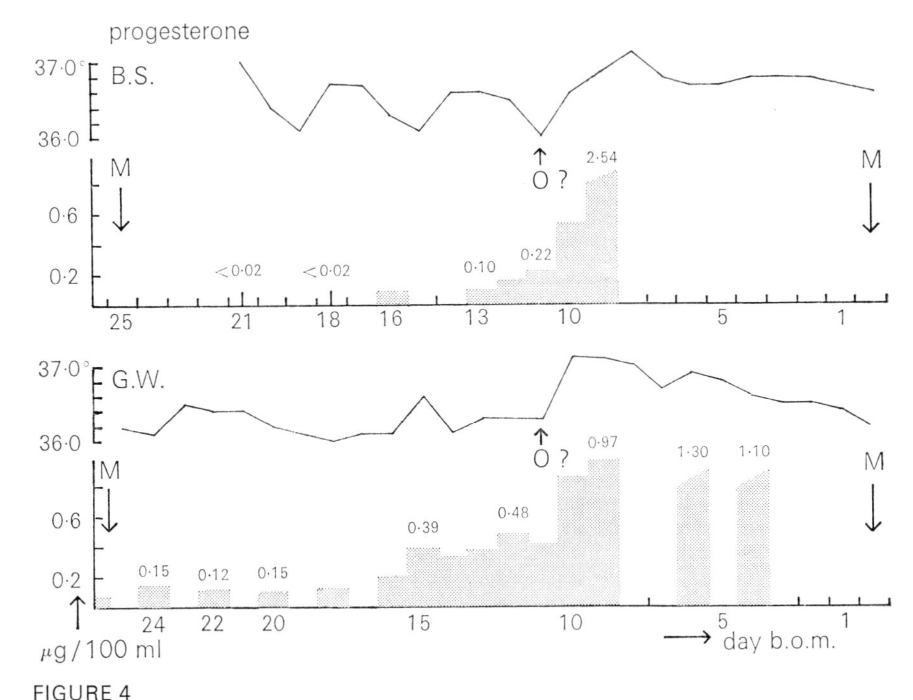


FIGURE 4

Basal body temperature and plasma progesterone concentrations in normal women at different stages of their menstrual cycle. 0 ? = presumed day of ovulation; M = day of onset of menstruation; day b.o.m. = day before onset of menstruation.

of progesterone secretion and not necessarily a significant sign of ovulation. The small rise in plasma progesterone may occur as long as three to four days before the shift in the temperature curve, and may result from an increased follicular progesterone production. Zander and co-workers [33] measured an increase in progesterone concentrations in the fluid of the pre-ovulatory Graaffian follicle towards the time of ovulation. Mikhail's findings [15] clearly demonstrate that the ovary containing a ripe follicle can secrete significant amounts of progesterone into its venous blood. Granulosa cells of the follicle are not close to blood vessels and their secretory products are not expected to enter the blood stream in a rapid fashion. Therefore it could be postulated that increased progesterone secretion into the blood by the follicle may either represent an increase in hormone secretion by the theca cells or an improvement of vascularization of the granulosa cells.

Although in a number of other animals like the horse, cow, sheep and pig, there is no evidence for a preovulatory rise in progesterone secretion, some animals (guinea-pig, rat, rhesus monkey) do show a preovulatory rise [34–37]. In rhesus monkeys the day of ovulation has been determined by visual inspection of the ovaries at laparotomy [33, 34]. The patterns of plasma progesterone concentrations in rhesus monkeys and human females are remarkably similar during the menstrual cycle. Four days prior to ovulation in the rhesus monkey the plasma progesterone concentration did not differ from that earlier in the follicular phase. An increase in the plasma progesterone concentration beginning on the third day before ovulation was observed [33, 34] and this increase was highly significant on the day before ovulation. On the day of ovulation the mean plasma concentration did not differ from that on the day before. The postovulatory rise in plasma progesterone concentration in the rhesus monkey reached a plateau three to four days after ovulation.

There has been discussion about the relationship between gonadotrophins and a preovulatory rise in progesterone. The development of competitive protein binding methods for progesterone estimation and the development of radioimmunochemical assays for gonadotrophins have permitted the simultaneous measurement of progesterone and both LH and FSH in relatively small plasma samples. Odell and Swerdloff [38] reported the interesting observation that administration of progesterone to postmenopausal women increased the LH and FSH concentrations in plasma. This induced LH–FSH peak lasted for 24–72 hours after initiation of the progesterone administration and was comparable to the midcycle peak of plasma levels of LH and FSH in menstruating women.

Simultaneous measurement of progesterone, LH and FSH in the same plasma sample [30, 39–42] has shown that a large increase in plasma progesterone concentration is only observed two to three days after the peak levels of gonadotrophins. Although a slight rise in plasma progesterone concentrations has occasionally been observed as early as five to six days before the LH peaks, it is not known whether the small preovulatory rise in circulating progesterone is either dependent upon LH activity or that it may trigger the midcycle peak of gonadotrophins.

Information from a study by Hart, Bakker and van der Molen [44] makes it unlikely that the follicular cells in the human ovary will always increase progesterone secretion after stimulation with gonadotrophins. Anovulatory amenorrhoeic women with clinical normal ovaries were treated with human menopausal gonadotrophins and human chorionic gonadotrophins for a period of twelve days. Several of these women did not show any clinical signs of ovulation after treatment, nor did the steroid concentrations in urine and blood give any indication of an increased steroid production by the ovary (Table 6). Another group of women, however, ovulated following gonadotrophic stimulation. In addition to the observed increase in plasma progesterone levels in this group the excretion of several steroids in urine (pregnanediol, pregnanetriol, total 17-hydroxycorticosteroids, total 17-ketosteroids) was also increased (Table 7). This again may be considered as evidence for the production of precursors for these urinary steroids in the (stimulated) corpus luteum.

In human females 17α-hydroxyprogesterone (and possibly oestrogens) in peripheral plasma parallels theca interna cell function during follicle maturation and during development of the corpus luteum [42]. Plasma levels of 17α-hydroxyprogesterone show a preovulatory peak at the time of the peak in gonadotrophin levels. After a fall during the time of ovulation a second peak in plasma 17α-hydroxyprogesterone is observed during the luteal phase of the cycle. Follicle maturation may therefore best be reflected in plasma 17α-hydroxyprogesterone (and oestrogens) rather than in progesterone and it may be asked if 17α-hydroxyprogesterone (and oestrogens) affect secretion of gonadotrophins.

*Biosynthesis and intercellular transfer of steroids in the testis*

Some current opinions about the formation of steroids in the testis and about the transport of steroids between different cell types of the testis may be related to the question if, and how, gonadal steroid production does affect gonadal function.

Christensen and Mason [45] showed in 1965 that both interstitial cells and seminiferous tubules from rat testis are capable of converting progesterone to testosterone *in vitro*. Hall and co-workers [46] observed that isolated interstitial cells would convert cholesterol to androstenedione and testosterone, but that under the same conditions the tubules from

TABLE 6. Plasma levels (µg/100 ml plasma) and urinary excretion (mg/24 h steroids during treatment (on days 1–12 with human gonadotrophins of 12 amenorrhoeic women who did not respo with ovulation or bleeding

| Day of treatment | Plasma concentration of: | | | |
|---|---|---|---|---|
| | Progesterone | | Testostero | |
| | mean | s.d.m. | mean | s.d |
| 0 | 0·08 | 0·02 | 0·10 | 0·( |
| 12 | 0·06 | 0·02 | 0·10 | 0·( |
| 20 | 0·05 | 0·01 | 0·11 | 0·( |
| 30 | 0·11 | 0·03 | 0·09 | 0·( |

TABLE 7. Plasma levels (µg/100 ml plasma) and urinary excretion (mg/24 h steroids during treatment (on days 1–12 with human gonadotrophins of 21 amenorrhoeic women who did respond w ovulation and vaginal bleeding

| Day of treatment | Plasma concentration of: | | | |
|---|---|---|---|---|
| | Progesterone | | Testostero | |
| | mean | s.d.m. | mean | s.d |
| 0 | 0·07 | 0·02 | 0·11 | 0·C |
| 12 | 2·57 | 0·20 | 0·14 | 0·C |
| 20 | 0·14 | 0·04 | 0·14 | 0·C |
| 30 | 0·08 | 0·02 | 0·15 | 0·C |

the same testis did not convert cholesterol to androgens. When the biosynthetic capacity of the total amount of interstitial cells from one whole testis was compared with the total amount of tubules from the same testis it was concluded [45, 46] that the capacity for conversion of progesterone to androgens by the interstitial tissue of a testis was 2–10 times higher than the capacity for conversion by the tubules. Even if both cell types *in vivo* would contain comparable amounts of (progesterone) substrate these investigations may indicate that the interstitial cells (of rat testis), although they represent only 2–5 per cent of the volume of the testis, are the major source of testicular androgens under physiological conditions.

It has been known for many years that androgens affect spermatogenesis [48]. It might be assumed that the amount of testosterone produced in the Leydig cells would be large enough to take care of this effect, but Lacy and co-workers [48, 51] have recently rejuvenated the idea that in the seminiferous tubules the Sertoli cells may be a source of steroid hormones that influence the development of germ cells. This idea was mainly based on the following observations:

| Urinary excretion of: | | | | | | | |
|---|---|---|---|---|---|---|---|
| nanediol | Pregnanetriol | | Total 17-OHCS | | Total 17-KS | | |
| s.d.m. | mean | s.d.m. | mean | s.d.m. | mean | s.d.m. | |
| 0·12 | 0·53 | 0·12 | 15·6 | 2·1 | 10·5 | 2·1 | |
| 0·12 | 0·87 | 0·31 | 16·6 | 1·5 | 11·8 | 2·0 | |
| 0·11 | 0·91 | 0·11 | 15·9 | 1·9 | 10·3 | 1·7 | |
| 0·15 | 0·76 | 0·15 | 17·1 | 1·6 | 11·6 | 1·9 | |

| Urinary excretion of: | | | | | | | |
|---|---|---|---|---|---|---|---|
| nanediol | Pregnanetriol | | Total 17-OHCS | | Total 17-KS | | |
| s.d.m. | mean | s.d.m. | mean | s.d.m. | mean | s.d.m. | |
| 0·20 | 0·62 | 0·08 | 15·0 | 1·1 | 12·1 | 0·9 | |
| 0·61 | 3·46 | 0·80 | 26·5 | 3·3 | 18·5 | 2·4 | |
| 0·29 | 1·21 | 0·22 | 18·3 | 1·9 | 14·3 | 1·5 | |
| 0·10 | 0·56 | 0·55 | 16·8 | 1·6 | 12·4 | 0·9 | |

(i) Lacy and co-workers [50] have observed that under the influence of FSH, but not LH, lipid droplets (supposedly containing cholesterol) in Sertoli cells disappear at the same time that spermatogenesis is stimulated. They suggest that this reflects biosynthesis of steroids in the Sertoli cells.

(ii) Seminiferous tubules of both normal rats and rats whose testes were subjected to heat treatment will convert pregnenolone and progesterone to testosterone. Lacy [49] considers this conversion in heat-treated animals to reflect the biosynthetic capacity of the Sertoli cells, because heat treatment destroys the germinal epithelium of seminiferous tubules, whilst leaving the Sertoli cells intact.

(iii) On the basis of the analysis of substances in testicular blood, lymph, and rete testis fluid, it has been considered difficult for substances such as testosterone to enter the seminiferous tubules. According to Lacy, seminiferous tubules are devoid of blood and lymphatic vessels, while being enclosed by a boundary tissue. Leydig cells, on the other hand, are localized closely to blood capillaries in the interstitial tissue. It is therefore necessary for substances passing from the arterial blood into seminiferous tubules to be transported through the interstitial fluid and the boundary tissue around the tubules. Rete testis fluid is generally considered to reflect the concentration of substances in seminiferous tubules (Fig. 5). Following administration of substances through the arterial blood and analyzing the rete testis fluid in rams, Setchell [52] concluded that substances which did not appear in the rete testis fluid could not pass a barrier, supposedly the boundary tissue around the tubules.

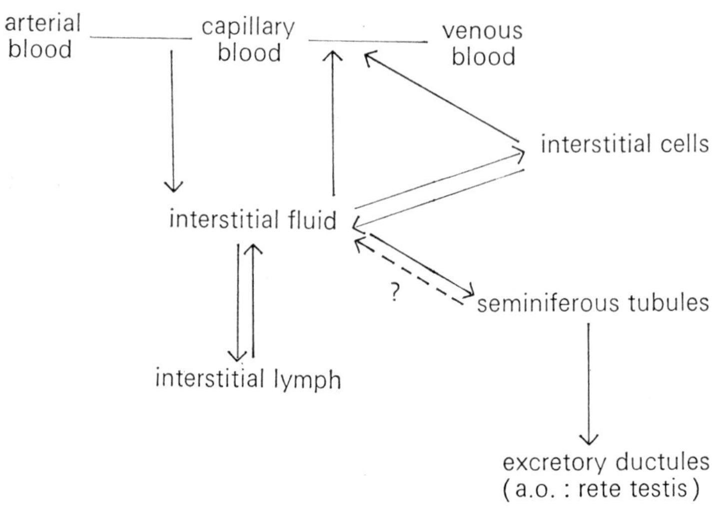


FIGURE 5
Some compartments involved in transport of substances through the testis

Lindner [53] found in testicular lymph of rams testosterone levels which were eight to ten times higher than arterial plasma levels, but somewhat lower than venous plasma levels. Moreover testosterone levels in lymph increased after administration of gonadotrophins. If therefore testosterone or other steroids which are produced in the Leydig cells do not enter the seminiferous tubules, it is highly likely that the transport from the lymph into the tubules is slow. Also, the observation that spermatogenesis in hypophysectomized animals can be maintained, or restored, only through the administration of relatively large doses of androgens [47] was interpreted [49] as reflecting the difficulty in substances reaching the seminiferous tubules.

On the basis of this information, Lacy and Pettitt [49] have re-emphasized that the Leydig cells produce the androgens which are secreted into the peripheral circulation, and that the androgens which might affect spermatogenesis are produced by the Sertoli cells in the seminiferous tubules.

This hypothesis concerning the function of Sertoli cells is mainly based on indirect evidence. There is little reason to argue the microscopic evidence that the lipids of the Sertoli cells represent material that normally disappears during the development of the germ cells. It has not been proved, either with *in vitro* or with *in vivo* experiments, that utilization of the lipid in the Sertoli cell results in increased steroid production in the tubules. Neither has it been shown with biochemical techniques that Sertoli cells can produce androgens such as testosterone. Furthermore it has not been decided if testosterone which is produced in the Leydig cells (or a precursor of testosterone) is not, or cannot be, transported to the tubules.

Recently, Fawcett et al. [54] have described the existence of an extensive lymphatic system in the interstitial tissue. The lymphatic vessels appear to connect the lamina propria of the seminiferous tubules on the one side, and clusters of interstitial cells on the other. It was suggested that these lymphatics may have an important function in the distribution of androgens within the testis [54].

In order to obtain more information about the sites of production and the distribution of steroids within the testis an attempt was made to analyze microgram amounts of morphologically defined structures from the testis (Gaasbeek, De Bruyn, Galjaard and Van der Molen, unpublished results).

Rabbit testis has been infused *in situ* with radioactive pregnenolone during periods varying from five minutes to one hour. After infusion the testis was immediately frozen with carbon dioxide or with isopentane in liquid nitrogen. Cryostat sections (8–20 $\mu$) were cut and subsequently freeze-dried (15 hrs at $-45°C$, $10^{-3}$ mm Hg). From the frozen dried sections the interstitium and seminiferous tubules were isolated under a dissecting microscope (120$\times$ magnification). The dry weight of the dissected samples was determined using quartz fibre balances according to Lowry (with a sensitivity of $10^{-9}$ grams $\pm$ 1 per cent). After weighing the tissue, the radioactivity of the different samples was determined by liquid scintillation counting.

The results (Table 8) show that after short periods of infusion the radioactivity per unit dry weight in the interstitium is higher than in the tubules. After longer periods of infusion the radioactivity per unit weight becomes equal in both cell compartments. Even if the isolated seminiferous tubules might have been contaminated with small amounts of interstitium this does not explain the amount of radioactivity in the tubules which in some experiments is comparable to that in the interstitium.

From these experiments we have tentatively concluded that radioactivity originating from pregnenolone which was infused into the spermatic artery was transported to the Leydig cells as well as to the seminiferous tubules. Furthermore the composition of the infusion medium appeared to influence the distribution of the radioactivity through the testis. Table 8 shows that when the infusion was carried out with Krebs-Ringer buffer instead of blood much less radioactivity could be demonstrated in the

TABLE 8. Distribution of radioactivity in seminiferous tubules and in interstitial tissue of rabbit testis perfused with $^{3}H$-pregnenolone via the spermatic artery *†

| Infusion medium | Duration of infusion (min) | dpm $^{3}H/\mu g$ tissue in: Interstitial tissue (A) | Seminiferous tubules (B) | A/B |
|---|---|---|---|---|
| Whole blood | 10 | 66 | 30 | 2·2 |
| Whole blood | 55 | 72 | 70 | 1·0 |
| Blood/KR 1/1 | 5 | 113 | 84 | 1·3 |
| Blood/KR 1/1 | 60 | 380 | 254 | 1·5 |
| Blood/KR 1/2 | 60 | 286 | 71 | 4·0 |
| KR-buffer | 30 | 286 | 11 | 26·0 |

*Gaasbeek, De Bruyn, Galjaard, van der Molen, unpublished results
†From 7 to 55 μg interstitial tissue and from 4·2 to 24 μg seminiferous tubules were isolated from frozen dried tissue sections

tubules even after sixty minutes infusion. These results could reflect an influence of proteins in the blood and the intercellular transport of steroids. In this respect it may be of importance to recall that Mancini et al. [55] have shown that after *in vivo* injection in rats $I^{131}$ labelled albumin could be localized around Sertoli cells in the seminiferous tubules.

We conclude, therefore, that some caution should be exercised in assuming that steroids produced in the interstitium cannot freely enter the seminiferous tubules. Although Lacy [49] favours the Sertoli cells as the source of androgens in the seminiferous tubules, the possibility cannot be excluded that steroids which are produced in the interstitium may also affect spermatogenesis.

## SPECIFIC RADIOACTIVITIES OF STEROIDS IN TESTIS TISSUE AND IN SPERMATIC VENOUS BLOOD DURING INFUSION OF RADIOACTIVE PRECURSORS INTO THE CANINE TESTIS

The level of steroids in gonadal tissue is generally small compared to the rate of production or the level in the venous blood. It is normally assumed that the rate of transport of for example testosterone from the interstitium to the venous blood is not a controlling factor in the secretion of testicular steroids [56]. Some information about the relationship between biosynthesis of steroids in the testis and the secretion into the venous blood may be derived from experiments in which radioactive steroids have been infused into the testis. Eik-Nes and co-workers have previously infused different radioactive steroids into the spermatic artery of the dog. They observed that in the infused dog testis the rate of testosterone biosynthesis from pregnenolone through 17α-hydroxypregnenolone and dehydroepiandrosterone is higher than the rate of formation through progesterone and 17α-hydroxyprogesterone [for a review see 57].

Experiments with radioactive precursors may give information about the possible pathways of biosynthesis, but do not give adequate information about the quantitative significance of a certain precursor or pathway. In order to obtain more information about the quantitative significance of compounds and processes that may regulate testosterone biosynthesis and secretion, we have in collaboration with Dr Eik-Nes estimated both incorporation of radioactivity and the mass amounts of steroid intermediates during infusion of the dog testis.

Labelled steroids were infused into the spermatic artery of the testis in anaesthetized dogs. Both the left and the right testis of the same animal were infused with the animal's own peripheral blood to which the radioactive steroid was added. One testis was used as a control, when gonadotrophins, cyclic AMP, or other substances were infused into the other testis.

During the infusion consecutive plasma samples were collected for thirty minutes. After the infusion the testes were removed and homogenized for further extraction and analysis. After purification of the steroids with paper- and thin-layer chromatography, the small amounts of steroids in the plasma and tissue samples were estimated with gas-chromatographic techniques.

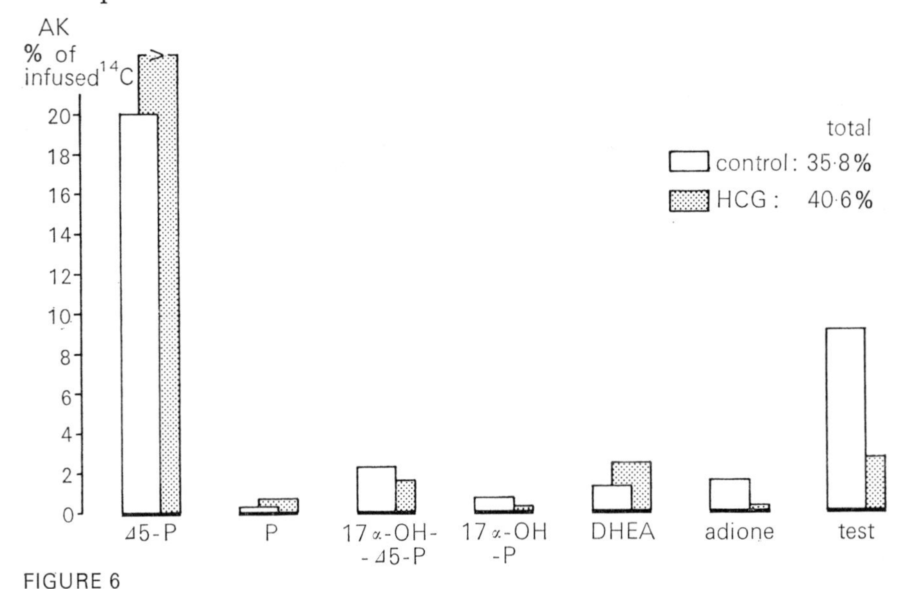


FIGURE 6

Radioactivity in spermatic venous blood of dogs after infusion of $^{14}$C pregnenolone into the spermatic venous artery. $^{14}$C pregnenolone was continuously infused at a constant rate and blood was collected for 90 minutes

The results in Figure 6 show that after infusion of radioactive pregnenolone, radioactivity is present in all the postulated steroid intermediates in the biosynthesis of testosterone, which are secreted into the spermatic venous blood. From the results in Figure 7 it is evident that only a small amount of infused radioactivity is stored in testicular tissue. The distribution pattern of the radioactive steroids in testis tissue greatly resembles that of the steroids in spermatic venous plasma.

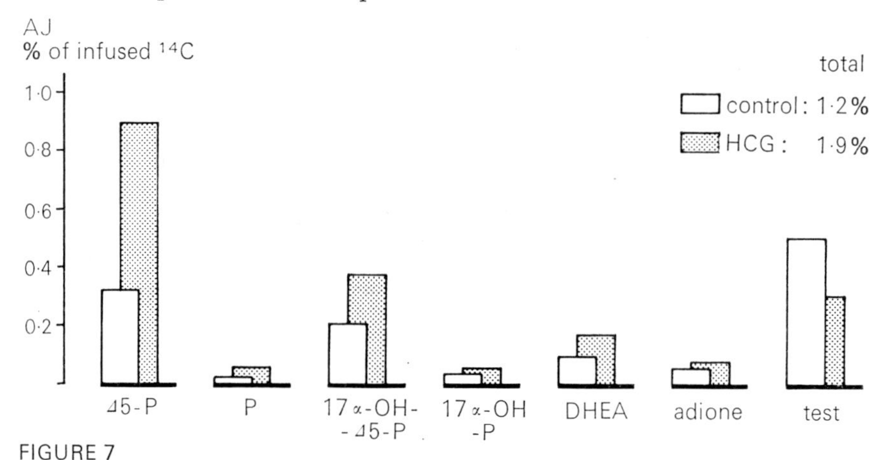


FIGURE 7
Radioactivity in testis tissue of dogs after infusion of $^{14}$C pregnenolone into spermatic venous artery. $^{14}$C pregnenolone was continuously infused at a constant rate and blood was collected for 90 minutes. The testis was removed immediately after collecting the blood samples

When either HCG or cyclic AMP was simultaneously infused during infusion of radioactive pregnenolone, the specific radioactivities of all intermediates between pregnenolone and testosterone decreased. This decrease confirms conclusions from observations by other workers, in that gonadotrophins do stimulate biosynthesis at some step (or steps) prior to pregnenolone formation. Resulting from the larger mass amount of pregnenolone, the specific activities of other steroids that can be synthesized from pregnenolone decrease. The stimulatory effect of gonadotrophins prior to pregnenolone formation does not exclude, however, effects of gonadotrophins on other processes after pregnenolone formation. Both HCG and cyclic AMP stimulate the secretion of all steroids that were analyzed (Figure 8). It is striking, however, that DHEA secretion is stimulated far more than the secretion of testosterone.

If DHEA is synthesized only through 17α-hydroxypregnenolone as an immediate precursor, and if only one 17α-hydroxypregnenolone pool is present in the tissue, the specific activities of the two steroids should be the same. If the ratio of the specific activities is not equal to one, the value of the ratio will give an impression about the fraction of DHEA that is derived from the 17α-hydroxypregnenolone pool. The results in Table 9 show that in control samples only 10–20 per cent of the DHEA is derived from 17α-hydroxypregnenolone. Under the influence of HCG even less, that is in the order of 5–10 per cent of DHEA, originates from 17α-hydroxypregneno-

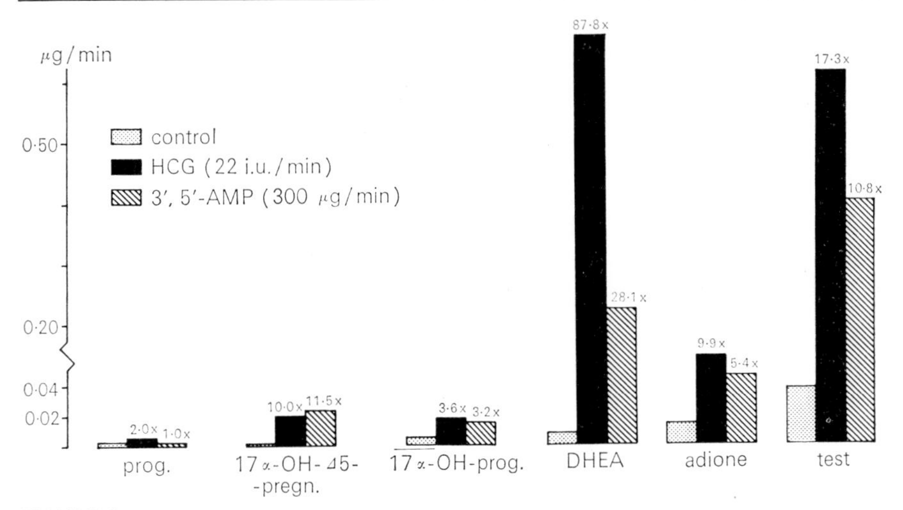


FIGURE 8
Steroids in spermatic venous plasma of dogs

TABLE 9. Ratios of specific activities of steroids isolated from spermatic venous blood during infusion of $^{14}C$- or $^{3}H$-pregnenolone into dog testes

| | Ratio of specific activities of DHEA/17α-OH-pregnenolone | |
|---|---|---|
| | $^{3}H$-Pregnenolone infusions | $^{14}C$-Pregnenolone infusions |
| Control* | 0·11 ± 0·03 | 0·26 |
| HCG † | 0·08 | 0·03 ± 0·007 |

*Only radioactive pregnenolone was infused
†In addition to the radioactive steroid also HCG was infused

lone. Therefore DHEA in spermatic venous blood under the influence of gonadotrophins most probably reflects production from a source other than pregnenolone. Tentative data indicate that it is unlikely that DHEA-sulphate is an important precursor of DHEA in the testis. Neither is the conversion of DHEA-sulphate to DHEA in the testis stimulated by HCG to such an extent that it can explain the observed discrepancy. It may well be that the direct conversion of cholesterol to dehydroepiandrosterone is of paramount importance. Jungmann [58] has clearly demonstrated that during *in vitro* incubations with an acetone powder of calf testis the direct conversion of cholesterol to dehydroepiandrosterone and methylheptanone may be faster than the conversion of cholesterol to pregnenolone and isocaproic acid. As another theoretical explanation for the discrepancy between the specific activities of 17α-hydroxypregnenolone and dehydroepiandrosterone the possibility may be considered that 17α-hydroxypregnenolone and dehydroepiandrosterone in spermatic venous blood reflect tissue pools, which are converted into each other with different rates. Therefore, it may be asked to what extent the specific radioactivities of steroids in the spermatic venous plasma reflect the specific radioactivities in the tissue. The results in Table 10 show that the specific activities of the steroids in the venous plasma are generally higher than the specific activities of steroids in the tissue of the testis removed directly after the infusion. $^{14}C$-pregnenolone infusions and $^{3}H$-pregnenolone infusions give similar results. Calculations of statistical significance levels make it unlikely that during these experiments the ratios of specific activities of the steroids in the plasma and tissue for 17α-hydroxyprogesterone, androstenedione and testosterone differed significantly from one. However, the ratios for progesterone and the Δ5,3β-hydroxy steroids differ significantly from one. Further support for the significance of this discrepancy may be obtained from the results in Table 11. The specific activities of the analyzed steroids in consecutive plasma samples remain almost constant. Therefore, it seems likely that at least the picture in spermatic venous plasma reflects a steady state situation.

TABLE 10. Comparison of specific activities of steroids in spermatic venous plasma and in testis tissue

| Infused: | $^{14}C$-Pregnenolone | | | $^{3}H$-Pregnenolone | | |
|---|---|---|---|---|---|---|
| | R | s.e.m. | n | R | s.e.m. | n |
| $\Delta^5$-Pregnenolone | 18·7 | 6·2 | 6 | 65·0 | 38·0 | 4 |
| Progesterone | 6·4 | 3·0 | 6 | 21·5 | 4·4 | 6 |
| 17α-OH-$\Delta^5$-Pregnenolone | 12·3 | – | 2 | 3·8 | – | 3 |
| 17α-OH-Progesterone | 1·1 | – | 2 | 1·8 | – | 1 |
| Dehydroepiandrosterone | 3·7 | – | 2 | 5·5 | 1·7 | 6 |
| Androstenedione | 1·7 | 0·3 | 6 | 3·3 | 1·2 | 7 |
| Testosterone | 1·7 | 0·2 | 6 | 2·3 | 0·5 | 6 |

$$R = \frac{\text{specific activity steroid in plasma (60–90 min)}}{\text{specific activity steroid in testis tissue}}$$

Theoretically, several explanations could be suggested for the discrepancy between the specific activities of steroids in plasma and in the tissues. The possibility may be considered that the testis tissue contains different pools of the same steroid and that the radioactive steroids in blood are not in equilibrium with the steroids in the tissue. This could result from the design of the experiment. Equilibrium between the endogenous tissue steroids and the infused radioactive steroids may be achieved slowly, so that within the ninety minutes of the experiment no equilibrium is obtained. In that case, it could be concluded that pregnenolone infused into the arterial blood is a rather poor precursor for several of the steroids that are secreted into the venous blood.

TABLE 11. Comparison of specific activities of steroids in consecutive spermatic venous plasma samples

| Infused: | $^{14}C$-Pregnenolone | | | $^{3}H$-Pregnenolone | | |
|---|---|---|---|---|---|---|
| | R | s.e.m. | n | R | s.e.m. | n |
| $\Delta^5$-Pregnenolone | 1·79 | 0·91 | 6 | 1·03 | – | 3 |
| Progesterone | 1·23 | 0·53 | 6 | 0·71 | 0·30 | 6 |
| 17α-OH-$\Delta^5$-Pregnenolone | 0·83 | – | 3 | 0·72 | – | 3 |
| 17α-OH-Progesterone | 0·76 | – | 2 | – | – | – |
| Dehydroepiandrosterone | 0·78 | – | 2 | 0·81 | 0·30 | 7 |
| Androstenedione | 1·12 | 0·47 | 6 | 0·79 | 0·29 | 8 |
| Testosterone | 0·80 | 0·05 | 6 | 1·22 | 0·20 | 8 |

$$R = \frac{\text{specific activity steroid in plasma (60–90 min)}}{\text{specific activity steroid in plasma (30–60 min)}}$$

As another explanation, however, it may be considered that different cell types or subcellular compartments might contain several pools of steroids which are not equally active in steroid biosynthesis, but which will add to the total tissue pool. If only part of the total tissue content of a steroid will be in equilibrium with infused radioactivity and if only this part of the steroid will add to the secretion into the venous blood, the specific activity of the blood steroid will be higher than the specific activity of the tissue steroid. These observations may support the idea that certain steroids in the testis may be present in different compartments. These different compartments are not equally derived from infused pregnenolone and do not equally add to the secretion of steroid into spermatic venous blood.

These two examples may have illustrated the usefulness of estimating specific radioactivities of steroids to study the fate of radioactive steroids infused into the testis. It is evident from these data that: (i) There may be a source other than pregnenolone which contributes to the formation of dehydroepiandrosterone secreted into the testicular venous blood. (ii) During steady state infusions of radioactive pregnenolone there is a discrepancy between the specific activities of steroids in venous blood and in testis tissue. This indicates that factors other than the rates of biosynthesis may be involved in the regulation of testicular secretion.

## INFLUENCE OF THE DISTRIBUTION AND CONCENTRATION OF STEROIDS IN SUBCELLULAR FRACTIONS ON STEROID BIOSYNTHESIS IN TESTIS OF NORMAL AND OF EFA-DEFICIENT RATS

The enzymes that are required for the conversion of cholesterol to pregnenolone are localized almost exclusively in mitochondria. The conversion of pregnenolone to testosterone is further catalyzed by enzymes in the cytoplasma [59, 60].

Apart from this subcellular localization of *enzymes*, there are also some indications that the pattern of subcellular distribution of steroid *substrates* and the concentrations of steroids in subcellular fractions may influence the biosynthesis of steroids.

Whereas most of this information is derived from *in vitro* experiments, it may be worthwhile to consider the physiological relevance of these results.

*Substrate and/or product inhibition*

During *in vitro* experiments the activities of enzymes for the metabolism of steroids may be inhibited by steroids which are products or substrates of these conversions [61–64].

If, however, all possibilities for product and/or substrate inhibition for steroid metabolism which have been demonstrated under *in vitro* conditions are really in operation under *in vivo* conditions, then it is highly unlikely that any steroid would be produced at all.

Koritz and Hall [65] have suggested that the stimulating effect of ACTH on biosynthesis of steroids in the adrenal might result from an effect on the permeability of the mitochondrial membrane and a decrease of product inhibition. If increased permeability of the mitochondria membrane for pregnenolone resulted in a lower pregnenolone concentration inside the mitochondria, this might decrease the inhibitory effect of pregnenolone on the conversion of cholesterol to pregnenolone. The conversion of cholesterol to pregnenolone and other steroids under the influence of ACTH might then increase as a result of this decreased inhibition. Very little is known about the subcellular concentrations and distribution of steroids in endocrine organs *in vivo*. Whether substrate and/or product inhibition should really be considered as factors which regulate the biosynthesis of steroids *in vivo*, rather than as artifacts of the concentrations of steroids under *in vitro* conditions, remains to be investigated.

*Subcellular distribution of steroids*

Samuels and co-workers [66, 67] have presented evidence that the solubility of steroids in subcellular fractions does influence the biosynthesis of steroids *in vitro*. After incubation of testis tissue with equimolar amounts of progesterone and 17α-hydroxyprogesterone they observed that more of the progesterone than of the 17α-hydroxyprogesterone was converted to androstenedione and testosterone. They showed that this observation could be explained because progesterone 'dissolves' better in the endoplasmatic reticulum which contains the enzymes necessary for the conversion of progesterone and 17α-hydroxyprogesterone to testosterone.

We could confirm that the solubility of progesterone in mitochondrial and microsomal fractions is better than the solubility of 17α-hydroxyprogesterone (Table 12). Also after *in vitro* incubations of testis tissue with

TABLE 12. Distribution of progesterone and 17α-hydroxyprogesterone in subcellular fractions of testis homogenates

| | Rat testis | | | Rabbit testis | | |
|---|---|---|---|---|---|---|
| | Prog | 17αOH-P | P/17αP | Prog | 17αOH-P | P/17αP |
| *Incubated** | 10 | 10 | 1·0 | 10 | 10 | 1·0 |
| *Isolated* (%) in: | | | | | | |
| Mitochondria | 24 | 7 | 3·4 | 28 | 7·6 | 3·7 |
| Microsomes | 4 | 2 | 2·0 | 4·0 | 2·4 | 1·7 |
| 105,000 g Sup. | 72 | 91 | 0·79 | 69 | 90 | 0·76 |

*in nM/100 mg tissue

equimolar amounts of progesterone and 17α-hydroxyprogesterone, more progesterone than 17α-hydroxyprogesterone is converted to testosterone (Table 13). But comparison of the ratios of progesterone and 17α-hydroxyprogesterone converted to testosterone during infusion studies shows that the testosterone isolated from either testis tissue or testicular venous effluent contains more of the 17α-hydroxyprogesterone label than of the progesterone label (Table 13). Whereas the uptake of the two steroids during infusion does not differ very much (Table 14), it remains doubtful whether the subcellular distribution of a steroid will play an important role in the regulation of steroid biosynthesis under physiological conditions.

TABLE 13. Ratios of incorporation of equimolar amounts of precursors into testosterone after incubation or infusion of rabbit testicular preparations

| Testosterone isolated after | | Precursors | | |
|---|---|---|---|---|
| | | P/17αP | 17αP/A | A/T |
| *Incubation* | | 1·31 | 0·055 | 1·23 |
| *Infusion* | | | | |
| Venous effluent | 0–30 min | 0·29 | 0·25 | 0·09 |
| | 30–60 min | 0·44 | 0·22 | 0·07 |
| | 60–90 min | 0·53 | 0·29 | 0·21 |
| | 90–120 min | 0·27 | 0·25 | 0·55 |
| Testis tissue | | 0·15 | 0·85 | 1·02 |

TABLE 14. Recovery of radioactivity after infusion of $^{14}C$-progesterone and $^{3}H$-17α-hydroxyprogesterone into rabbit testis

| | 14C-Prog | $^{3}H$-17α-OH-P | $^{14}C/^{3}H$ |
|---|---|---|---|
| Infused | 91 nmol | 90 nmol | |
| *Radioactivity* isolated from: | | | |
| Epididymal fat | 25·6% | 18·6% | 1·37 |
| Testis tissue | 9·7% | 5·2% | 1·91 |
| Venous effluent | 54·2% | 64·4% | 0·84 |
| Total | 89·9% | 88·6% | |

*Biosynthesis of steroids in testis of EFA-deficient rats*

Ahluwalia and co-workers [68–70] observed that testis tissue of rats which were fed a diet deficient in essential fatty acids ('EFA-deficient rats') showed an increased rate of conversion of cholesterol to androstenedione and testosterone. In their *in vitro* experiments, the conversion of progesterone to androstenedione and testosterone was not different in testis of normal and of EFA-deficient rats. They postulated that as a result of a changed lipid composition in EFA-deficient rats the permeability of mitochondrial membranes might be changed. As a result the mitochondrial production of pregnenolone from cholesterol might be increased which in turn would cause the increased production of androstenedione and testosterone from cholesterol.

The relationship between an increased production of androgens and the absence (or deficiency) of spermatogenesis in testes of EFA-deficient rats might be interesting from a physiological point of view. We have therefore tried to investigate the subcellular distribution of steroids which are intermediates in the conversion of cholesterol to testosterone in testis of normal rats and EFA-deficient rats.

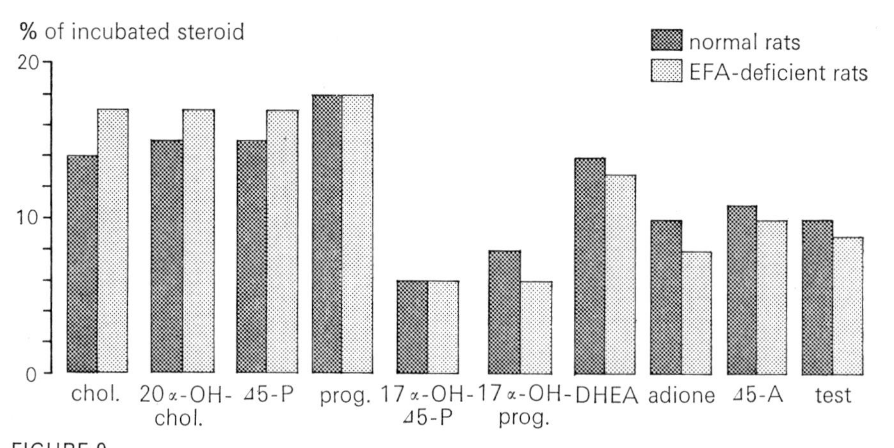


FIGURE 9

Uptake of steroids by mitochondrial fractions of testis homogenates of normal rats and of essential fatty acid deficient rats. 10 per cent w/v tissue homogenates were incubated with radioactive steroids (20 nM steroid/100 mg tissue/ml medium) in the presence of 1 mM oxidized glutathione. Under these conditions metabolism of steroids was inhibited

EFA-deficient rats were fed a diet containing coconut fat. Control animals received sunflower seed oil in their diets instead of the coconut fat. We have studied the distribution of steroids in different subcellular fractions after incubation of testis homogenates in the presence of excess oxidized glutathione, so that metabolism of steroids was inhibited. Our results (Figs. 9 and 10) indicate no difference in the uptake of steroids in mitochondrial and in microsomal fractions between testis of normal rats and of EFA-deficient rats. These data therefore do not support the hypothesis of Ahluwalia et al. [69], that testicular mitochondria in EFA-deficient rats differ from those in normal rats as far as the uptake of steroids is concerned. This does not of course exclude the possibility that mitochondria might somehow be involved in the altered steroid biosynthesis in testis of EFA-deficient rats. If the normal and EFA-deficient rats differ either in activity of the mitochondrial desmolase which converts cholesterol to pregnenolone or in the *rate* of release of pregnenolone from the mitochondria, this may still explain a difference in the rate of conversion of cholesterol. Also it may be worthwhile to consider other explanations, such as alternative pathways for the increased production of androstenedione and testosterone from cholesterol.

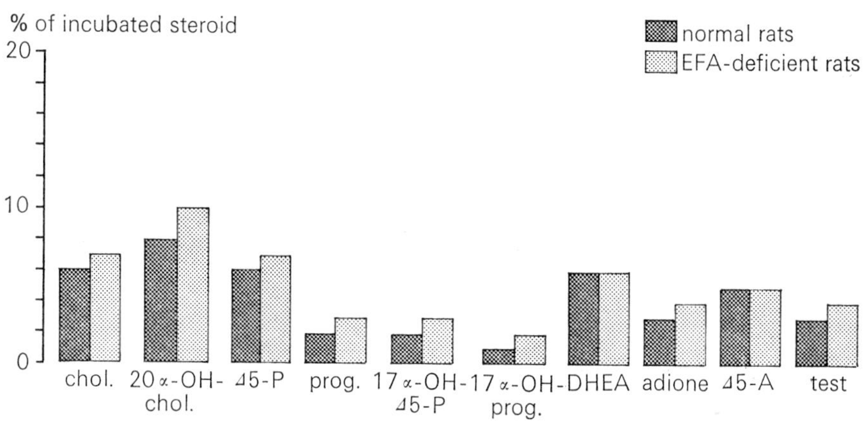


FIGURE 10

Uptake of steroids by microsomal fractions of testis homogenates of normal rats and of essential fatty acid deficient rats. For further explanation see Figure 9

From our *in vitro* incubation studies with minces of testis tissue from EFA-deficient rats (Table 15) it appears that tissue from EFA-deficient rats, as compared to normal rats, converts far more progesterone than cholesterol to androstenedione and testosterone.

Even if on a weight basis the capacity of testis tissue of EFA-deficient animals to produce androgens is increased this does not necessarily imply that in the whole animal the intact testis of EFA-deficient rats produces or secretes more testosterone into the blood than in a normal rat. The mean weights of testis of a series of normal and EFA-deficient rats were $1{\cdot}50 \pm 0{\cdot}10$ gm and $0{\cdot}33$ gm respectively. Levels of testosterone in peripheral plasma of EFA-deficient rats were generally lower than levels in peripheral plasma of normal rats (Table 16). Because the plasma samples from both the normal and deficient rats were collected under ether anaesthesia, it should be kept in mind that ether anaesthesia reduces testosterone levels in testis and in testicular venous blood to 20 to 30 per cent of levels in unanaesthetized animals [71, 72].

TABLE 15A. Conversion of equimolar amounts of $^{14}C$-cholesterol and $^{3}H$-progesterone to different steroids by minced testis tissue*

| Steroid isolated: | | Progesterone | | | 17α-OH-Progesterone | | |
|---|---|---|---|---|---|---|---|
| | | % converted from: | | | % converted from: | | |
| | NADPH | Chol | Prog | Chol/Prog | Chol | Prog | Chol/Prog |
| Normal rats | – | 0·08 | 12·3 | 0·0065 | 0·02 | 0·6 | 0·033 |
| | + | 0·14 | 16·5 | 0·0084 | 0·02 | 1·2 | 0·016 |
| EFA-deficient | – | 0·21 | 3·9 | 0·054 | 0·01 | 1·0 | 0·010 |
| rats | + | 0·16 | 2·3 | 0·070 | 0·01 | 1·4 | 0·007 |

*Incubation conditions: 20 nM steroid/100 mg tissue/ml incubation medium

TABLE 15B. Conversion of equimolar amounts of $^{14}C$-cholesterol and $^{3}H$-progesterone to different steroids by minced testis tissue*

| Steroid isolated: | | Androstenedione | | | Testosterone | | |
|---|---|---|---|---|---|---|---|
| | | % converted from: | | | % converted from: | | |
| | NADPH | Chol | Prog | Chol/Prog | Chol | Prog | Chol/Prog |
| Normal rats | – | 0·03 | 1·2 | 0·025 | 0·15 | 4·3 | 0·035 |
| | + | 0·02 | 0·9 | 0·022 | 0·22 | 3·0 | 0·073 |
| EFA-deficient | – | 0·07 | 3·8 | 0·018 | 0·25 | 20·4 | 0·012 |
| rats | + | 0·09 | 4·4 | 0·020 | 0·41 | 20·9 | 0·020 |

*Incubation conditions: 20 nM steroid/100 mg tissue/ml incubation medium

TABLE 16. Testosterone (μg/100 ml plasma) in peripheral plasma of ether anaesthetized normal and EFA-deficient male rats

| | Normal rats | EFA-deficient rats |
|---|---|---|
| | 0·05 | 0·06 |
| | 0·59 | 0·16 |
| | 0·08 | 0·06 |
| | 0·13 | 0·05 |
| | 0·13 | 0·04 |
| | 0·52 | 0·11 |
| | 0·12 | 0·10 |
| | | 0·34 |
| | | 0·50 |
| | | 0·04 |
| | | 0·05 |
| mean | 0·23 | 0·14 |
| s.d. | 0·21 | 0·14 |
| n | 7 | 11 |

REFERENCES

[1] Savard, K., Marsh, J.M. and Rice, B.F., *Recent Prog. Hormone Res.*, **21**, 285, 1965.
[2] Ryan, K.J. and Smith, O.W., *Recent Prog. Hormone Res.*, **21**, 367, 1965.
[3] Kumar, L. and Goldzieher, J.W., *Acta endocr., Copnh.*, **52**, 455, 1966.
[4] Axelrod, L.R. and Goldzieher, J.W., *Acta endocr., Copnh.*, **56**, 255, 1967.
[5] Ryan, K.J. and Petro, Z., *J. clin. Endocr. Metab.*, **26**, 46, 1966.
[6] Huang, W.Y. and Pearlman, W.H., *J. biol., Chem.*, **238**, 1308, 1963.
[7] Ryan, K.J., *Acta endocr., Copnh.*, **44**, 81, 1963.
[8] Hammerstein, J., Rice, B.F. and Savard, K., *J. clin. Endocr. Metab.*, **24**, 597, 1964.
[9] Rice, B.F., Hammerstein, J. and Savard, K., *J. clin. Endocr. Metab.*, **24**, 606, 1964.
[10] Rice, B.F., Hammerstein, J. and Savard, K., *Steroids*, **4**, 199, 1964.
[11] Rice, B.F. and Savard, K., *J. clin. Endocr. Metab.*, **26**, 593, 1966.
[12] Van der Molen, H.J. In *Progress in Endocrinology*, Proceedings of the Third International Congress of Endocrinology, Mexico, 1968. Exc. Medica Int. Congr. Series **184**, 894, 1969.
[13] Richardson, G.S. In *Ovarian Physiology*. London: J.A. Churchill Ltd., 1967.
[14] Lobotsky, J., Wyss, H. I., Segre, E.J. and Lloyd, C.W., *J. clin. Endocr. Metab.*, **24**, 1261, 1964.
[15] Mikhail, G., *Clin. Obstet. Gynec.*, **10**, 29, 1967.
[16] Hudson, B., Coghlan, J.P., Wintour, M. and Dulmanis, A. In Proceedings of the Second International Congress of Endocrinology, London, 1964. Exc. Medica Int. Congr. Series **83**, 1127, 1964.
[17] Apostolakis, M., Becker, H. and Voigt, K.D., *Steroids*, **7**, 146, 1966.
[18] Ismail, A.A.A., Harkness, R.A. and Loraine, J. In *Testosterone*, p. 211. Ed. J. Tamm. Stuttgart: Thieme Verlag, 1968.
[19] Horn, H., Statter, M. and Finkelstein, M., *Steroids*, **7**, 118, 1966.
[20] Van der Molen, H.J., unpublished observations.
[21] Ismail, A.A.A., Davidson, D.W., Faro, L.C.F. and Loraine, J.A. In *Testosterone*, p. 19. Ed. J. Tamm. Stuttgart: Thieme Verlag, 1968.
[22] Loraine, J.A. and Bell, E.T., *Hormone Assays and their Clinical Application*. Edinburgh/London: E. & S. Livingstone, 1966.
[23] Adlercreutz, H., Luukkainen, T. and Svanborg, A., *Ann. Med. exp. Fenn.*, **45**, 277, 1967.
[24] De Nicola, A.F., Dorfman, R.I. and Forchielli, E., *Steroids*, **7**, 351, 1966.
[25] Acevedo, A.F. and Corral-Gallardo, *J. clin. Endocr. Metab.*, **25**, 1675, 1965.
[26] Brooks, R.V. and Giuliani, G., *Steroids*, **4**, 101, 1964.
[27] Gaarenstroom, J.H., De Jongh, S.E. and Paesi, F.J.A. *Ned. Akad. Wetensch., Afd. Nat.*, **53**, 71, 1944.
[28] Gaarenstroom, J.H. and De Jongh, S.E. In *Monographs on the Progress of Research in Holland*, p. 97. New York/Amsterdam: Elsevier Publishing Company Inc., 1946.
[29] Van der Molen, H.J. and Groen, D., *J. clin. Endocr. Metab.*, **25**, 1625, 1965.
[30] Larsson-Cohn, U., Johansson, E.D.B., Wide, L. and Gemzell, C. *Acta endocr., Copnh.*, **63**, 216, 1970.
[31] Woolever, C.A., *Am. J. Obstet. Gynec.*, **85**, 981, 1963.
[32] Rünnebaum, B. and Zander, J., *Acta endocr., Copnh.*, **55**, 91, 1967.
[33] Zander, J., Forbes, T.R., von Münstermann, A.M. and Neher, R., *J. clin. Endocr. Metab.*, **18**, 337, 1958.
[34] Johansson, E.D.B., Neill, J.D. and Knobil, E., *Endocrinology*, **82**, 143, 1968.

[35] Kirton, K.T., Niswender, G.G., Midgley, A.R., Jaffe, R.B. and Forbes, A.D., *J. clin. Endocr. Metab.*, **30,** 105, 1970.
[36] Feder, H.H., Resko, J.A. and Goy, R.W., *J. Endocr.*, **40,** 505, 1968.
[37] Feder, H.H., Goy, R.W. and Resko, J.A., *J. Physiol.* (Lond.), **191,** 136, 1967.
[38] Odell, W.D. and Swerdloff, R.S. *Proc. natn. Acad. Sci.* (U.S.A.), **61,** 529, 1968.
[39] Neill, J.D., Johansson, E.D.B., Datto, J.K. and Knobil, E., *J. clin. Endocr. Metab.*, **27,** 1167, 1967.
[40] Saxena, B.B., Demura, H., Gandy, H.M. and Peterson, R.E., *J. clin. Endocr. Metab.*, **28,** 519, 1968.
[41] Yoshimi, T. and Lipsett, M.B., *Steroids*, **11,** 527, 1968.
[42] Strott, C.A., Yoshimi, V.T., Ross, G.T. and Lipsett, M.B., *J. clin. Endocr. Metab.*, **29,** 1157, 1969.
[43] Johansson, E.D.B., *Acta endocr., Copnh.*, **61,** 592, 1969.
[44] Hart, P.G., Bakker, J.H.J. and van der Molen, H.J., *Ned. T. Verlosk.*, **69,** 169, 1969.
[45] Christensen, A.K. and Mason, N.R., *Endocrinology*, **76,** 646, 1965.
[46] Hall, P.F., Irby, D.C. and De Kretser, D.M., *Endocrinology*, **84,** 488, 1969.
[47] Clermont, Y. and Harvey, S.C. In *Endocrinology of the Testis*. Ciba Foundation Coll. on Endocrinology, vol. 16, p. 173. London: J.A. Churchill Ltd., 1967.
[48] Lacy, D., Vinson, G.P., Collins, P., Bell, J., Fyson, P., Rudney, J. and Pettitt, A.J., In *Progress in Endocrinology*. Proceedings of the Third International Congress of Endocrinology, Mexico, 1968, Exc. Med. Int. Congress Series. **104,** 1019, 1969.
[49] Lacy, D. and Pettitt, A.J., *Br. med. Bull.*, **26,** 87, 1970.
[50] Collins, P. and Lacy, D., *Proc. R. Soc.* B., **172,** 17, 1969.
[51] Bell, J.B.G., Vinson, G.P., Hopkin, D.J. and Lacy, D., *Biochim. biophys. Acta.*, **164,** 412, 1968.
[52] Setchell, B.P., Voglmayr, J.K. and Waites, G.M.H., *J. Physiol.*, **200,** 73, 1969.
[53] Lindner, H., *J. Endocr.*, **25,** 483, 1963.
[54] Fawcett, D.W., Heidger, P.M. and Leak, L.V., *J. Reprod. Fert.*, **19,** 109, 1969.
[55] Mancini, R.E., Vilar, R.E., Alvarez, B. and Seiguer, A.C., *J. Histochem. Cytochem.*, **13,** 376, 1965.
[56] Eik-Nes, K.B., *Physiol. Rev.*, **44,** 609, 1964.
[57] Eik-Nes, K.B. In *The Androgens of the Testis*. Ed. K.B. Eik-Nes. New York: Marcel Dekker, Inc., 1970.
[58] Jungmann, R.A., *Steroids*, **12,** 205, 1968.
[59] Samuels, L.T. In *Metabolic Pathways*, vol. II. Ed. D.M. Greenberg, New York/London: Academic Press, 1968.
[60] Shikita, M. and Tamaoki, B., *Endocrinology*, **76,** 563, 1965.
[61] Neher, R. and Kahnt, F.W., *Experientia*, **21,** 310, 1965.
[62] Koritz, S.B., *Biochemistry*, **3,** 1098, 1964.
[63] Inano, H., Nakano, H,. Shikita, M. and Tamaoki, B., *Biochim. Biophys. Acta*, **137,** 540, 1967.
[64] Menon, K.M.J., Drowsdowsky, M., Dorfman, R.I. and Forchielli, E., *Steroids*, **Suppl. I,** 95, 1965.
[65] Koritz, S.B. and Hall, P.F., *Biochemistry*, **3,** 1298, 1964.
[66] Samuels, L.T., Matsumoto, K., Aoshima, Y. and Bedrak, E. In *Progress in Endocrinology*. Proceedings of the Third International Congress of Endocrinology, Mexico, 1968, Exc. Medica Int. Congress Series **184,** 845, 1969.
[67] Matsumoto, K. and Samuels, L.T., *Endocrinology*, **85,** 402, 1969.

[68] Ahluwalia, B., Shima, S. and Pincus, G., *J. Reprod. Fert.*, **17**, 263, 1968.
[69] Ahluwalia, B., Shima, S. and Pincus, G., *Fed. Proc.*, **27**, 814, 1968.
[70] Ahluwalia, B., *Fed. Proc.*, **28**, 558, 1969.
[71] Bardin, C.W. and Peterson, R.E., *Endocrinology*, **80**, 38, 1967.
[72] Fariss, B.L., Hurley, T.J., Hane, S. and Forsham, P.H., *Endocrinology*, **84**, 940, 1969.

## *Discussion of paper by Dr van der Molen*

*Baird* stated that he had been interested in trying to distinguish the effects of LH on steroid synthesis and release by the transplanted sheep ovary. Some of his evidence suggested that LH may cause a temporary increased release of preformed steroid in the ovary before effecting steroid synthesis. This conclusion was based on changes in the specific activity of the steroids for a few minutes after the infusion of LH and he wondered whether van der Molen had studied changes in radioactive conversion and specific activity in relation to the onset of LH or HCG infusions. In his experiments it had taken about 25 minutes to obtain steady state conditions but he was of the opinion that the effect of gonadotrophins on release of steroids was an extremely small part of its effect on steroid secretion.
*Van der Molen* stated that in his experiments all the blood collections were made for 30-minute periods and that they did not start collecting samples less than 30 minutes after the beginning of gonadotrophin administration. In these investigations it was difficult to achieve satisfactory conditions within 30 minutes. Comparing results from blood collected during the first 30 minutes with the second and third collections, he had always found a larger difference between specific activities of steroids in the first and second collections than between the second and the third and considered that steady state conditions were only obtained during the second and third collection periods.
*Eik-Nes* agreed with the remarks of Baird that in the very early part of gonadotrophin stimulation it was possible that there was a release of preformed gonadal steroids but he thought that synthesis *de novo* could be measured within 4 to 8 minutes after gonadotrophin stimulation. From this time onwards he thought that one was dealing only with the *de novo* formation of steroid end products. With regard to the problem of dihydrotestosterone and its secretion, he thought that the dog testis secreted extremely minute amounts of this compound. In recent experiments where he had been performing a double infusion, i.e., infusing the animal's own blood via the epididymal artery and via the spermatic artery of the same testis, they found rather high concentrations of dihydrotestosterone in the epididymal venous blood, whereas in spermatic vein blood the concentration was

extremely low. In many animals they were unable to prove that dihydrotestosterone was a secretory product of the testis. He had found that the adult prostate was secreting dihydrotestosterone and extragonadal tissue in the male dog may be contributing to the level of dihydrotestosterone in systemic blood much more than the gonad itself or even the epididymis.

*Van der Molen* reported that some studies indicate there is about 10 to 20 times as much dihydrotestosterone in the epididymis as compared to the testis. Although the prostate may be important in such conversions several other tissues, for example the hypothalamus of the two to three month old rat, could convert androstenedione or testosterone to dihydrotestosterone. The conversions by hypothalamic tissue *in vitro* were rather low, of the order of 4 to 5 per cent of the total amount of testosterone, but they had no information on the conversion by the hypothalamus *in vivo*.

*Naftolin* mentioned that he and his colleagues had used dihydrotestosterone to try to androgen-sterilize new-born rats and had been unsuccessful.

*Vermeulen* had measured dihydrotestosterone in human peripheral blood and found that the concentration was about 50 ng per 100 ml in male plasma with a metabolic clearance rate of about 500 litres per 24 hours giving an estimated production rate of about 250 μg per 24 hours. In the female the levels were about 25 ng per 100 ml plasma and the metabolic clearance rate was about 300 litres giving a production rate of about 75 μg per 24 hours. These amounts may not have been secreted by the gonads but may have arisen from the peripheral transformation of androstenedione or testosterone.

*Griffiths* quoted some of the work being done in Cardiff on the metabolism of androstenedione and testosterone by human breast tumours. When minced tissue was incubated with androstenedione, 5α-dihydrotestosterone was formed. The conversion of testosterone to 5α-dihydrotestosterone also occurred in nuclear preparations from breast tumours. After infusing androstenedione through tumours, 5α-dihydrotestosterone was found in the tumour tissue. These findings suggested that tumour cells can produce 5α-dihydrotestosterone and that some of the 5α-dihydrotestosterone in females may arise from normal breast tissue.

*Gemzell* referred to van der Molen's remarks that in women stimulated with HMG and HCG there was no effect on the plasma progesterone level and suggested this might be a dose effect because they had found that the effective dose of FSH may vary from 100 to 400 units a day before the follicles could be stimulated.

*Van der Molen* replied that he had observed three groups of women; the first consisted of 15 women who ovulated after the administration of HMG and HCG so that the dose administered was sufficiently large in these patients to stimulate ovulation; in a second group the women showed irregular bleeding after administration of the gonadotrophins; in the third group the women did not show any effect.

*Mills* commented in regard to the origin of dehydroepiandrosterone; he had incubated human foetal adrenals with $^3H$-pregnenolone in the presence of human pituitary fractions and had found no increased conversion of pregnenolone to dehydroepiandrosterone under these circumstances (*J. Endocr.*, **43**, xlvi, 1969). However he could show an increased formation of androstenedione which occurred whether the precursor was pregnenolone or progesterone, suggesting that there was a pituitary hormone, most probably LH, acting at a different part of the pathway which did not appear to stimulate the conversion of pregnenolone to dehydroepiandrosterone.

*Van der Molen* agreed that in his investigations there was an increased endogenous production of dehydroepiandrosterone that did not come from pregnenolone.

*Odell* quoted some recent work of Dr Lostroh using highly purified preparations of LH and FSH which indicated that whereas FSH plus testosterone treatment did not initiate spermatogenesis in the atrophic testis, FSH plus LH treatment would, suggesting that LH might be causing the secretion of some steroid other than testosterone.

# Assessment of Ovarian Function by Oestrogen and Pregnanediol Analysis

J.B.BROWN

Department of Obstetrics and Gynaecology
University of Melbourne

¶ THE present paper reviews the information obtained during the application of urinary oestrogen and pregnanediol assays to the assessment of ovarian function in gynaecological patients. It reviews the development of suitable assay procedures, first for the measurement of oestriol, oestrone and oestradiol and of pregnanediol in urine, and then, as the applications became more precisely defined, the further development of these procedures for specific purposes. A brief mention will be made of measurements of oestrogens and progesterone in blood.

## METHODS

*Methods for measuring oestrogens.* The method of Brown [1] or its modification described by Brown, Bulbrook and Greenwood [2] was used for the pioneer studies. This method measures the three 'classical' urinary oestrogens, oestriol, oestrone and oestradiol, and, as a result of its application, four main areas of usefulness were defined. Serial assays provided an assessment of ovarian oestrogen production and thus provided a test for the presence of normal or abnormal ovarian function. Likewise, in pregnancy, the assays provided a test of placental function. Thirdly, the method was applied, often beyond its limits of sensitivity, to the measurement of the very small amounts of oestrogens excreted by children, postmenopausal women and by patients with metastatic breast cancer following endocrine ablation. Fourthly, the method was applied to the study of oestrogen metabolism.

With the appreciation of these various applications, the required characteristics of methods designed specifically for each area of application could be more readily defined. The pioneer method depended on colorimetry using the Kober colour reaction. Development of the new methods depended on improvements in the Kober-Ittrich reaction which allowed the Kober-chromogenic oestrogens to be measured fluorimetrically with 10,000 times the sensitivity of the colour reaction and with an equivalent gain in specificity [3].

As will be shown in the results section, the application of the pioneer method to the study of dynamic ovarian function demonstrated that the cyclic patterns provided by each of the three urinary oestrogens were essentially the same, and that the best correlation with oestrogenic changes, as indicated by endometrial biopsies and subsequent menstrual bleeding, was obtained by summing the three urinary oestrogens [4]. In other words, the best assessment of oestrogen production was obtained from a figure for 'total' oestrogens and there was therefore little point in going to the trouble of separating them. This reasoning led to the development of a rapid method for 'total' urinary oestrogens based on a semi-automatic partition apparatus and on spectrophotofluorimetry [5]. Likewise, a related rapid procedure using spectrophotometry was developed for assessing placental oestrogen production during the third trimester of pregnancy. For applications requiring the highest sensitivity and specificity, a third method was developed based essentially on the '1957' method [2] but employing enzymic hydrolysis, internal radioactive standards, fractional elution from the alumina columns and spectrophotofluorimetry. This method has a working range for urine down to 0·04 μg per 24 hours urine or lower if required, and is applicable to plasma with a limit of sensitivity of 4 ng per 100 ml [6]. For investigating metabolism, the original method measuring only three urinary oestrogens is now clearly inadequate, and special methods are required for measuring the other urinary metabolites, particularly the major oestrogen, 2-hydroxyoestrone.

The emphasis in the present review is on the assessment of ovarian oestrogen production, and as the rapid method for 'total' urinary oestrogens [5] is now being used for this purpose, a restatement of some of its characteristics is warranted. The development and assessment of such a method presented certain difficulties in that the usual tests for specificity based on homogeneity are not applicable to mixtures and the two main oestrogens being measured, oestriol and oestrone, have different partition and fluorescence properties. The conditions for extraction and fluorescence development were selected so that oestriol and oestrone both contributed equivalently to the final result and no bias occurred in urines containing predominantly oestriol or those containing predominantly oestrone. To check specificity, the results obtained by summing oestriol, oestrone and oestradiol, measured by the pioneer method (x), were compared on the same urine specimens with those obtained for 'total' oestrogens measured by the rapid method (y). In 292 comparisons on urines containing between 0 and 100 μg per 24 hours of 'total' oestrogens, collected under all conditions likely to be encountered in practice, the relationship between the two sets of results was expressed by the regression line, $y = 1{\cdot}25\ (x-2)$ μg per 24 hours, and the correlation coefficient r was 0·924. The figure 2 in the equation was due to an overestimate of zero which occurred in the pioneer method but not in the rapid method. The rapid method usually gave a higher value than the pioneer method, because oestrogens other than oestriol, oestrone and oestradiol were being measured, but this was partly offset by lower recoveries, particularly of oestradiol. The ratio $y/x-2$ was $1{\cdot}25 \pm 0{\cdot}3$ (mean ± standard deviation) for the 292 comparisons. The fiducial range ($P = 0{\cdot}05$) for the ratio was therefore 0·65 to 1·85. The ratio tended to be constant for any one individual patient, so that the difference between the two methods did not cause random fluctuations in the patterns of excretion obtained. In practice, apart from allowing for the average factor of 1·25, this lack of exact correspondance between the two methods has not influenced the interpretation of the results obtained by the rapid procedure in terms of the earlier results, as is illustrated by the normal values shown in Table 1. This is perhaps not surprising because of the many assumptions and approximations involved in connecting endogenous urinary oestrogen output with production rates.

TABLE 1. Comparison of values obtained by the rapid method against the sum of oestriol, oestrone and oestradiol obtained by the pioneer method in normal subjects. Figures in parentheses are the number of individuals studied

| | Oestrogen excretion (μg/24 hr) | | |
|---|---|---|---|
| Subjects studied | Rapid method | | Pioneer method |
| Men (age range 22–47 yr) | Range | 8·4 – 23·0 | 7·2 – 19·6 |
| | Mean ± S.D. | 14·5 ± 3·9 (20) | 11·1 ± 3·1 (24) |
| Postmenopausal women | Range | 1·6 – 15·7 | 2·4 – 14·4 |
| (age range 52–86 yr) | Mean ± S.D. | 6·7 ± 3·5 (18) | 7·3 ± 3·1 (66) |
| Premenopausal women | | | |
| (age range 19–49 yr): | | | |
| Minimum value (post- | Range | 7–23 | 4–19 |
| menstrual) | Mean | 13·1 (13) | 11·2 (16) |
| Ovulatory peak | Range | 45–93 | 35–100 |
| | Mean | 63·3 (13) | 57·5 (16) |
| Luteal phase maximum | Range | 22–104 | 15–87 |
| | Mean | 46·2 (13) | 32·4 (16) |

The rapid method has the advantage of speed, with results on 12 urine specimens being available in 3½ to 4 hours, and with streamlining of laboratory practice, 36 to 48 analyses are regularly performed by one worker per day, compared with, at best, four analyses per day by the pioneer method. This provides the facility for mass clinical application and expendability of results which is essential when exploring the rarer conditions. The rapid method has proved to be exceptionally robust, which is an important characteristic when used for the study and management of patients. In five years of application, no interference has been encountered from administered drugs, including ethinyl oestradiol, mestranol, and the various progestogens and aperients which interfere in the pioneer method. The few gross errors that have been encountered have been from urines collected from patients with metastatic cancer of the breast and stored for long periods of time under doubtful conditions, an application for which the rapid method is obviously unsuitable.

*Methods for measuring urinary pregnanediol and plasma progesterone.* The method of Klopper et al. [7] was used for the pioneer studies. This has been replaced by a method using gas-liquid chromatography on Gas Chrom Q coated with 0·5 per cent neopentylglycol adipate polyester as described by Cox [8, 9] and assessed by Barrett and Brown [10]. By this method, 20 to 30 analyses per day are regularly performed by one worker. It has the advantage over Klopper's method that lower values are obtained during the follicular phase and a better differentiation can be made between follicular and luteal phase levels, which is the main information provided by the analyses.

Plasma progesterone was measured by a displacement procedure using chicken plasma as the binding protein and crude petroleum ether extracts of human plasma for the analyses [11, 12].

## RESULTS

*The normal ovulatory menstrual cycle.* The characteristic pattern of the ovulatory menstrual cycle is illustrated in Figure 1, which shows the daily urinary excretion of oestriol, oestrone and oestradiol, pregnanediol and gonadotrophins throughout a 33-day cycle of a 41-year-old patient with breast

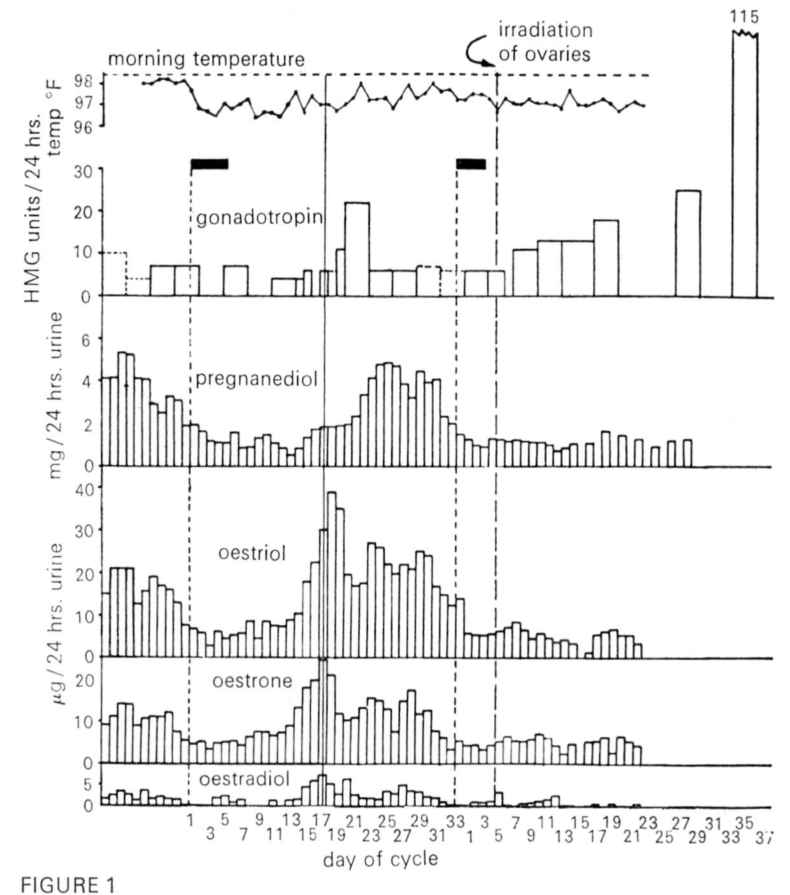


FIGURE 1
Mrs M. R. aged 41 years, para 2, with the history of regular menstrual cycles. Urinary oestriol, oestrone and oestradiol and pregnanediol and gonadotrophins were measured throughout a complete menstrual cycle and after ovarian ablation for metastatic breast cancer (from [13])

cancer and the history of regular menstrual cycles. She was also studied following ovarian irradiation on the fifth day of the next cycle [13]. The output of urinary oestrogens is lowest during the first week and then rises to a well-defined peak which, in this patient, occurred on day 17. The oestrogen excretion then falls and rises to a second maximum. This is usually lower than the first peak and in some women may be ill defined. During the last few days of the cycle, the oestrogen excretion falls and menstruation occurs. The midcycle peak has been observed in every ovulatory cycle studied including those fertile cycles induced with gonadotrophins. The evidence, including that derived from studies in the sheep [6], indicates that ovulation occurs 24 to 48 hours after the peak, at the time when the oestrogens have fallen and before they begin rising again. The peak has the following characteristics. The rise to the peak is gradual at first and then increases rapidly, and the fall after the peak is abrupt. The time interval between the peak and onset of menstruation is 12–16 days; a shorter time interval indicates a deficient luteal phase and an infertile cycle, and a longer time is usually associated with conception. The means and ranges of oestrogen values found during the normal menstrual cycle are given in Table 1.

Similarly, the pregnanediol values are low during the first weeks of the cycle and then begin to rise after the oestrogen peak to reach a well-defined maximum during the luteal phase. The ranges of pregnanediol values found during the ovulatory cycle are shown in Figure 2. The pregnanediol and oestrogen values provide complementary evidence that normal ovulatory function is occurring and both must show the patterns illustrated otherwise the cycle is infertile [14].

Urinary gonadotrophin levels were measured by the mouse uterus test; similar values were obtained by the hypophysectomized rat prostate test which is specific for luteinizing hormone (LH). In general, the midcycle peak of urinary LH occurs after the midcycle peak of urinary oestrogens as illustrated here [13]. More recent work using radioimmunoassay of LH has confirmed that the LH peak in plasma postdates the oestrogen peak in urine [15] and also in plasma [16, 17]. After ablation of the ovaries in this patient, 30 days elapsed before the urinary gonadotrophin levels reached the high values characteristic of postmenopausal or oophorectomized women, indicating that the feedback mechanism must operate comparatively slowly.

*Patients with absent ovarian activity.* Figure 3 illustrates the pattern and amounts of urinary oestrogens found in the absence of ovarian activity [4]. This patient, aged 29 years, had secondary amenorrhoea for 12 years Throughout the three weeks of study, the output of 'total' urinary oestrogens remained between 3·6 and 8·3 μg per 24 hours. At the end of the

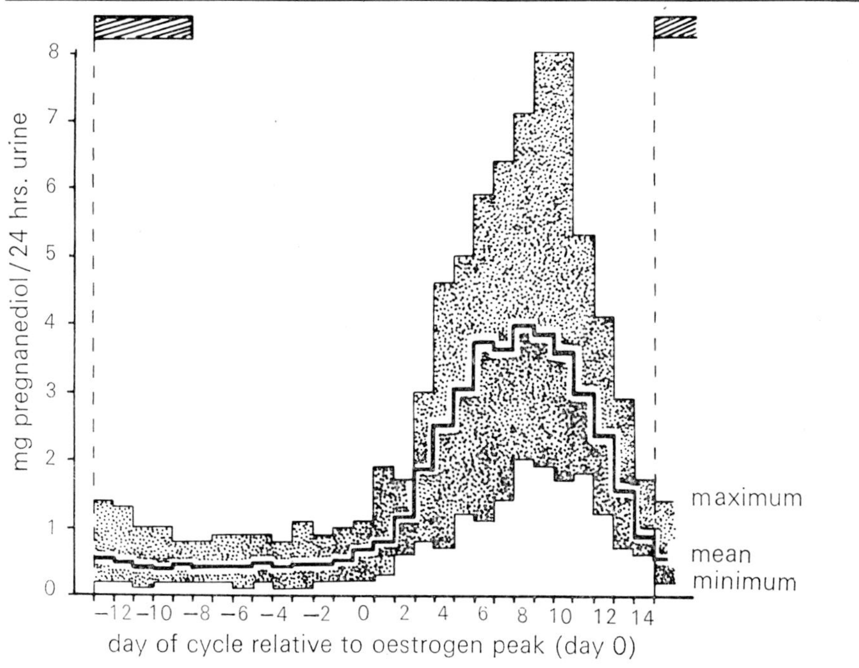


FIGURE 2

Pregnanediol values by gas-liquid chromatography throughout the menstrual cycles of 15 normal women aged 18–49, showing mean, maximum and minimum values

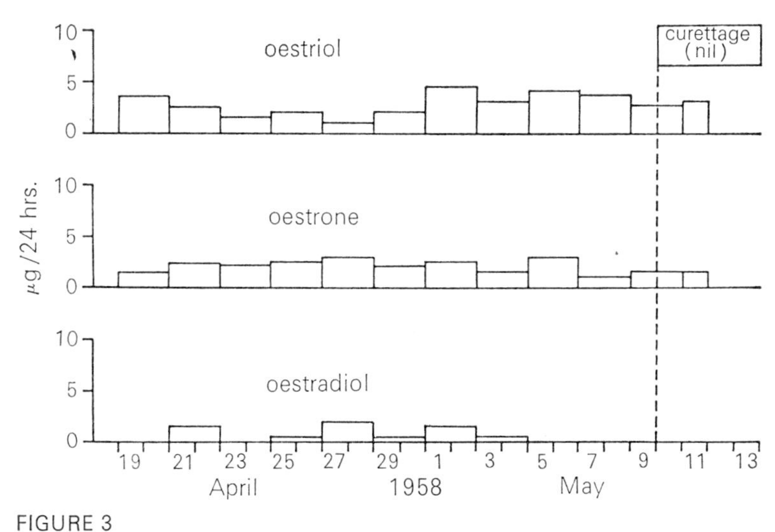


FIGURE 3

Oestriol, oestrone and oestradiol values in a patient aged 29 years (Mrs E. G.) with absent ovarian function (from [4])

study, no endometrium was obtained on curettage and no spontaneous menstruation occurred during the follow-up period of three years. These persistently low oestrogen values fall within the range for the normal postmenopausal woman (Table 1), and for oophorectomized women. These amounts are derived largely from the adrenals since they are considerably reduced by adrenalectomy [18]. MacDonald [19] has shown that the urinary oestrogens in postmenopausal women are derived entirely from the peripheral conversion of androstenedione to oestrone, the urinary metabolites of which are indistinguishable from those of ovarian oestradiol by the present assays. This accounts for the comparative lack of oestrogenic activity of this adrenal moiety, since it has been repeatedly shown that even a small addition of oestradiol from ovarian secretion can be detected by the proliferative changes it produces in the endometrium. There is a group of patients with primary amenorrhoea in whom the urinary oestrogen levels are below 1·5 μg per 24 hours, that is below the postmenopausal range and within the range found in children. Presumably in these the androgens for peripheral conversion are lacking or reduced.

The information required from oestrogen assays in this type of patient is whether the ovaries are functioning or not. Brown, Kellar and Matthew [20] considered that 'total' values by the pioneer method which were persistently below 10 μg per 24 hours indicated absence of ovarian activity since proliferative changes in the endometrium were rarely observed at such levels. There is obviously a zone of uncertainty and Beavis et al. [21] considered that values persistently below 15 μg per 24 hours by the rapid method indicated absence of ovarian activity. In a study of patients in this category, they found that the majority (94 per cent) had in fact values of less than 10 μg. They also found that the pregnanediol values as determined by gas-liquid chromatography were all less than 1·2 mg per 24 hours with the majority (97 per cent) less than 0·5 mg per 24 hours. It must however be emphasized that these statements refer to the interpretation of persistently low values recorded over a period of time because values as low as these may be encountered temporarily during the normal menstrual cycle (Table 1). Beavis et al [21] considered that values above 15 μg 'total' oestrogens indicated ovarian activity since these were often associated with cyclic changes, and Brown, Kellar and Matthew [20] generally found endometrial stimulation at these levels. The notable exception to this rule is the patient with amenorrhoea associated with polycystic ovarian disease and hirsutism in whom the 'total' urinary oestrogen excretion may be maintained in the range of 20 to 50 μg per 24 hours and yet no stimulation of the endometrium can be detected [4]. Presumably, as in the postmenopausal woman, these oestrogens are being derived from the peripheral conversion of the androgens causing the hirsutism. It would seem that oestrogens from this source need to be in high concentration to promote endometrial stimulation.

With the recent advances in hormone therapy, the treatment of amenorrhoea presents few problems unless the complaint is of infertility. Even so, therapy with clomiphene and gonadotrophins provides a high rate of success, the pregnancy rate in the Endocrine Clinic of the Royal Women's Hospital, Melbourne, being 73 per cent in such patients. A proportion respond simply to placebo or to low dose oestrogen, others require clomiphene, and the remainder require the more powerful stimulus of gonadotrophin therapy. Treatment in that order is warranted for all patients irrespective of their oestrogen output, although there is a tendency for patients with very low oestrogen values (less than 5 μg per 24 hours) to respond only to gonadotrophins [22].

In a patient who shows no spontaneous ovarian activity, it is sometimes desirable to know whether she has ovaries which are capable of being stimulated. This would apply in the case of the unmarried patient with primary amenorrhoea and normal or absent urinary gonadotrophins who, before contemplating marriage, wishes to know her chances of pregnancy later, or a woman with a suspected early menopause but with urinary gonadotrophins below the postmenopausal range. This information can usually be obtained by a gonadotrophin stimulation test in which exogenous gonadotrophin is given in increasing dosage until a rise in urinary oestrogens is elicited. The main problem here is to decide on the upper dose at which failure is accepted. We go up to a maximum dose of 1,000 i.u. of FSH per day whereas Crooke et al. go higher [23]. Those patients who fail to respond are then subjected to culdoscopy, laparoscopy or laparotomy for visualization and biopsy of the ovaries. In this way operative assessments are kept to a minimum.

*Dysfunctional uterine bleeding*. This term is used to denote some deviation from normal cyclical menstruation. It is a diagnosis which is reached only after exclusion of recognizable pelvic disease and may present, under the symptomatic guise of infertility, irregular bleeding or excessive menstrual loss. Such bleeding may occur from any degree of proliferative endometrium and also rarely from a secretory endometrium. The classical examples are (*a*) anovulatory menstruation from a proliferative endometrium, and (*b*) cystic glandular hyperplasia, when proliferation of the endometrium has progressed to an extreme degree [4]. The study has shown that, whereas the condition is often associated with anovulation, abnormal bleeding can occur with normal ovulatory activity and that local factors in the endometrium are also involved.

Two types of anovulatory cycles have been identified [4]. (*a*) Anovulatory cycles with constant raised levels of urinary oestrogens. Figure 4 shows

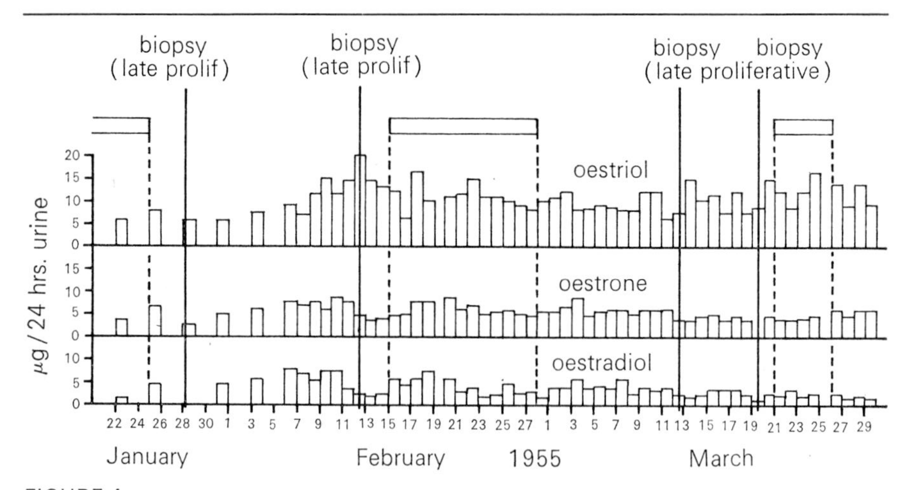


FIGURE 4
Oestriol, oestrone and oestradiol values during anovulatory bleeding of the break-through type with constantly raised oestrogen excretion (Miss J.K. aged 19 years) (from [4])

the oestrogen values in a patient, aged 19 years, with the history of irregular bleeding occurring at intervals of one to three months [4]. The two phases of bleeding shown were from a proliferative endometrium and therefore anovulatory in nature. Apart from the usual day-to-day variation, the urinary oestrogen levels showed no regular cyclical changes and remained more or less constant at approximately 18 μg per 24 hours. Bleeding occurred as a random breakthrough phenomenon. This pattern of constantly raised oestrogen excretion has also been recorded in women with a prolonged follicular phase in whom breakthrough bleeding commenced and then stopped as the oestrogen levels were rising to the preovulatory peak; it has also been recorded at higher levels in women exhibiting cystic glandular hyperplasia [4]. Such a pattern has been produced artificially during therapy with gonadotrophins by giving doses above the threshold requirement but insufficient to stimulate a follicle into full activity [14]. The pattern is also found in functioning ovarian tumours [4].

(*b*) Anovulatory cycles with fluctuating levels of urinary oestrogens. Figure 5 shows the oestrogen values in a patient, aged 13 years, with the history of 8 weeks' continuous bleeding [4]. The bleeding finally ceased on December 10th. Hormone assays were performed over a period of time which included two further episodes of bleeding, and according to the pregnanediol output and endometrial biopsy, both of these were anovulatory in nature. A single oestrogen peak reaching 90 to 125 μg 'total' oestrogens per 24 hours was observed between each phase of bleeding. A similar pattern in which the single oestrogen rise reached the same levels but was more prolonged and was associated with cystic glandular hyperplasia of the endometrium, was reported by Brown and Matthew [4]. It is

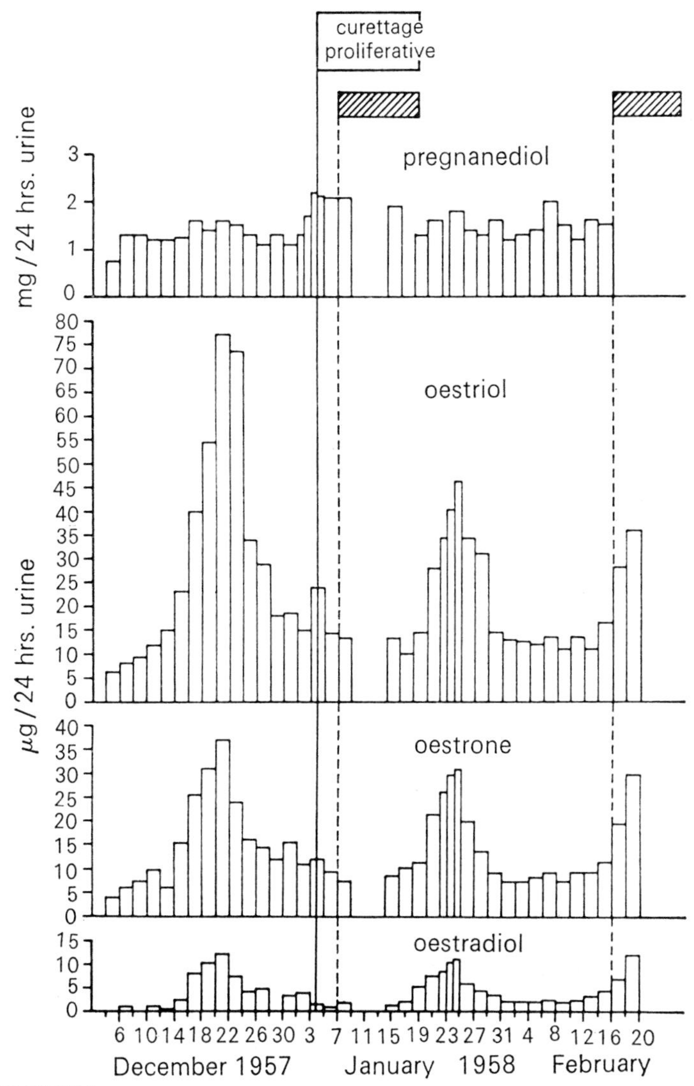


FIGURE 5
Oestriol, oestrone and oestradiol excretion during two anovulatory cycles with fluctuating oestrogen excretion (Miss I.M. aged 13 years) (from [4])

noteworthy that this has been the one condition in which oestrogen values above 100 μg per 24 hours have been encountered in non-pregnant subjects. Such a pattern of response is common during therapy with gonadotrophins in which follicular stimulation has been achieved but HCG has been withheld or has not been given in sufficient dose to induce ovulation. Such a failure of ovulation when HCG is given is usually accompanied by a synergistic effect between the two gonadotrophins leading to high levels of urinary oestrogens [14].

### MEASUREMENTS ON PLASMA COMPARED WITH URINE

Figure 6 demonstrates the values for urinary oestrone, 'total' oestrogens and pregnanediol and for plasma oestradiol, oestrone and oestrone sulphate obtained throughout the cycle of a subject, aged 21 years, with the history of regular menstruation. The analyses also included free oestriol, the sulphates of oestradiol and oestriol and the glucuronides of the three oestrogens but none of these gave valid results above 4 ng per 100 ml even though 10 ml of plasma was processed. Oestrone sulphate is quantitatively the most important plasma oestrogen, being present in approximately five times the concentration of oestradiol. The urinary metabolites showed essentially the same patterns as the plasma hormones, although the mid-cycle peaks of oestrogens in plasma were more diffuse than those in urine and the days of the peaks did not correspond exactly. The factors governing blood concentrations and their relationships with urine concentrations are obviously complex and are the subject of further investigation. There would seem to be no intrinsic advantages in monitoring ovarian hormone production by either blood or urinary analyses. Obviously, if blood is being collected for the measurement of gonadotrophins by radio-immunoassay, it is logical to use the same specimens for the measurement of the ovarian hormones. Vande Wiele et al. [16] have demonstrated the value of such measurements in the assessment of ovarian function during gonadotrophin therapy. However, when there is no special need to collect blood, collection of urine is easier for long-term studies, at least for the medical and laboratory staff, and specimens can be sent from a distance without the patient having to present at frequent intervals for venipuncture.

### GENERAL COMMENTS

When assessing hormone status in gynaecological patients by urinary oestrogen and pregnanediol analyses, a single estimation is seldom of value, and the longer the collections are made the more accurate the assessment. Normal and abnormal ovarian function can occur at different times in the same individual and the demonstration of an abnormality may be made by chance only after assessment over a considerable period of time. Even the simple procedure of collecting urine and the feeling by the patient that interest is being taken in her condition can rectify abnormal ovarian activity through the higher centres. For example, we have documented numerous cases in which infertile women with long-standing amenorrhoea have ovulated and conceived during their initial assessment by serial urinary oestrogen and pregnanediol analyses. Such chance findings are yielding valuable information on hormone function during conception and early pregnancy.

Interpretation of the results depends on the patterns of excretion and

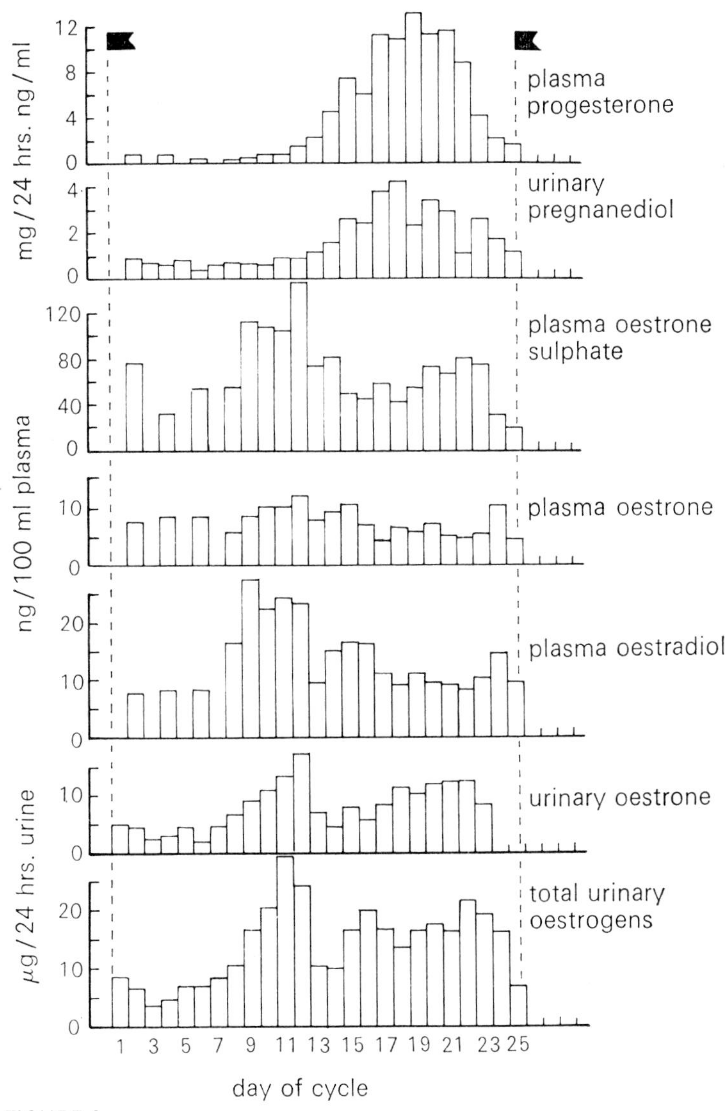


FIGURE 6
Plasma oestradiol, oestrone and oestrone sulphate measured by spectrophotofluorimetry compared with urinary oestrogens, and plasma progesterone measured by competitive protein binding compared with urinary pregnanediol throughout an ovulatory menstrual cycle (Miss P.F. aged 21 years)

on the amounts excreted. Oestrogen assays reflect overall ovarian activity whereas pregnanediol assays demonstrate whether ovulation has occurred and a functioning corpus luteum is present. There are two main spheres of application. The first is the identification of the events occurring around the time of ovulation. For this purpose, daily measurements of oestrogens are required, and only two or three measurements of pregnanediol are used to confirm that ovulation has occurred. This is used to identify the time of maximum fertility at the oestrogen peak [4], and of ovulation which occurs 24 to 48 hours after the peak. This information is of value, for example, in the infertile couple, in assessing the viable life of the sperm and ovum, in aiding women to identify their ovulation symptoms as a means of family planning, and in monitoring responses to clomiphene and gonadotrophin therapy. The other main application is to the overall assessment of ovarian activity in patients with some deviation from the normal menstrual pattern. Although serial analyses provide the most complete picture, they are seldom practicable for long-term studies because of the large numbers of assays required. For this purpose, we employ the procedure which we term 'tracking' in which a 24-hour urine collection is made once a week, usually from Sunday to Monday, for a period of six weeks or more until the pattern of ovarian activity has become clear. Oestrogens and pregnanediol are measured in each urine specimen and the pattern of the results and the amounts excreted provide a very reliable index of the presence or absence of ovarian activity, and of its type. Figure 7 is an example taken from the paper of Beavis et al. [21] in which the 'tracking' procedure was applied to the study of ovarian function after hysterectomy with conservation of the ovaries. The weekly results have been superimposed on a background of the ranges of values found during the menstrual cycles of 13 normally menstruating women aged 19 to 49 years. The patient shown was aged 52 years, 10 years after hysterectomy, and the results demonstrate the presence of the normal ovulatory pattern. The criteria used for interpreting such results have been defined [21]. The 'tracking' procedure has been applied to the study of more than 400 patients attending the Endocrine Clinic of the Royal Women's Hospital, Melbourne, and the results have yet to be published.

### ACKNOWLEDGEMENTS

Many collaborators have assisted in the development of the assay procedures described here and are listed in the publications quoted. The normal individuals studied have been mainly laboratory personnel and wives of colleagues, and, more recently, women of proven fertility attending the Catholic Family Planning Centre in Melbourne. Gynaecological patients have been derived mainly through the collaboration of Dr G.D. Matthew and Professors R.J. Kellar and J.A. Strong in Edinburgh and from the Endocrine Clinic of the Royal Women's Hospital and through Dr E.L. Beavis in Melbourne.

The earlier work was supported by the Medical Research Council of Great Britain, and the more recent work by the National Health and Medical Research Council of Australia.

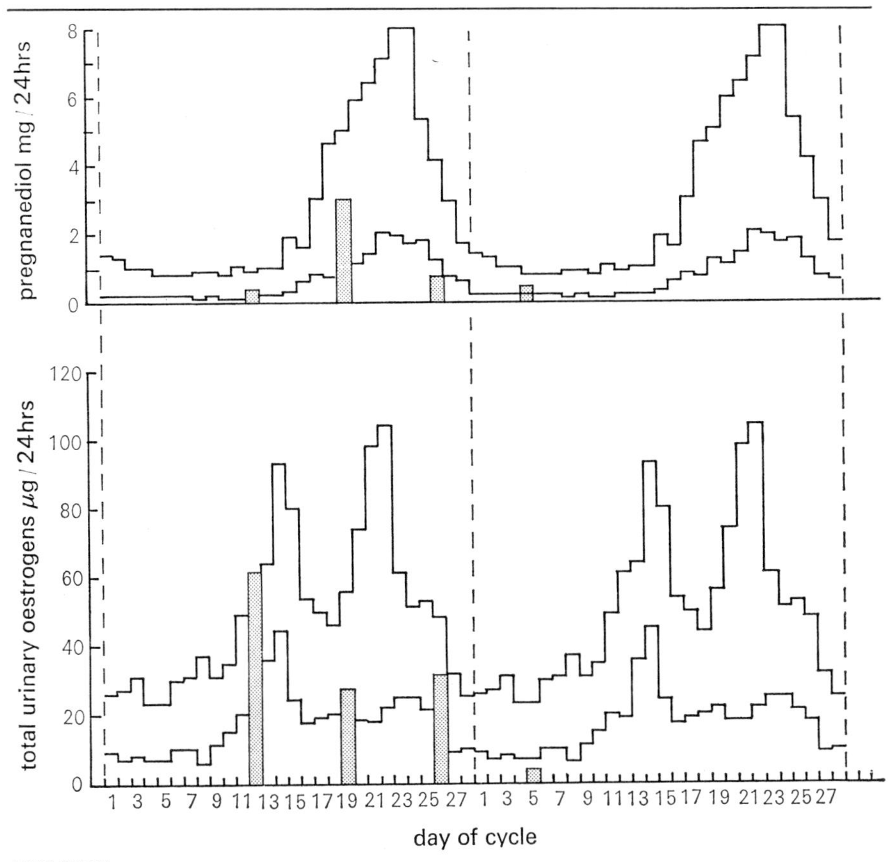


FIGURE 7

Weekly 'tracking' of 'total' urinary oestrogens and of pregnanediol applied to a patient aged 52 years, 10 years after hysterectomy showing an ovulatory pattern (from [21])

## REFERENCES


[1] Brown, J.B., *Biochem. J.*, **60,** 185, 1955.

[2] Brown, J.B., Bulbrook, R.D. and Greenwood, F.C., *J. Endocr.*, **16,** 49, 1957.

[3] Brown, J.B., Macnaughtan, C., Smith, M.A. and Smyth, B., *J. Endocr.*, **40,** 175, 1968.

[4] Brown, J.B. and Matthew, G.D., *Recent Prog. Hormone Res.*, **18,** 337, 1962.

[5] Brown, J.B., MacLeod, S.C., Macnaughtan, C., Smith, M.A. and Smyth, B., *J. Endocr.*, **42,** 5, 1968.

[6] Moore, N.W., Barrett, S., Brown, J.B., Schindler, I., Smith, M.A. and Smyth, B., *J. Endocr.*, **44,** 55, 1969.

[7] Klopper, A., Michie, E.A. and Brown, J.B., *J. Endocr.*, **12,** 209, 1955.

[8] Cox, R.I., *J. Chromatog.*, **12,** 242, 1963.

[9] Cox, R.I. In *Chromatographie en phase gazeuse des steroides hormonaux*, p. 309. Ed. Dunod (Paris). New York: Gordon and Breach.

[10] Barrett, S. and Brown, J.B., *J. Endocr.* **47,** 471, 1970.

[11] Johansson, E.D.B., *Acta endocr., Copnh.*, **61,** 592, 1969.

[12] Barrett, S., personal communication.
[13] Brown, J.B., Klopper, A. and Loraine, J.A., *J. Endocr.*, **17,** 401, 1958.
[14] Brown, J.B., Evans, J.H., Adey, F.D., Taft, H.P. and Townsend, L., *J. Obstet. Gynaec. Brit. Commonw.*, **76,** 289, 1969.
[15] Burger, H.G., Catt, K.J. and Brown, J.B., *J. clin. Endocr. Metab.*, **28,** 1508, 1968.
[16] Vande Wiele, R.L., Bogumil, J., Dyrenfurth, I., Ferin, M., Jewelewicz, R., Warren, M., Rizkallah, T. and Mikhail, G., *Recent Prog. Hormone Res.*, **26,** 63, 1970.
[17] Odell, W.D. This volume p. 48.
[18] Brown, J.B., Falconer, C.W.A., and Strong, J.A., *J. Endocr.*, **19,** 52, 1959.
[19] MacDonald, P.C. This volume p. 159.
[20] Brown, J.B., Kellar, R.J. and Matthew, G.D., *J. Obstet. Gynaec. Br. Emp.*, **66,** 177, 1959.
[21] Beavis, E.L.G., Brown, J.B. and Smith, M.A., *J. Obstet. Gynaec. Br. Commonw.*, **76,** 969, 1969.
[22] Townsend, S.L., Brown, J.B., Johnstone, J.W., Adey, F.D., Evans, J.H. and Taft, H.P., *J. Obstet. Gynaec. Br. Commonw.*, **73,** 529, 1966.
[23] Crooke, A.C. This volume p. 230.

*Discussion of paper by Dr Brown*

*Gemzell* remarked that he thought no one should be using gonadotrophin therapy without using oestrogen estimation in the control of such therapy and he had found that the measurement of total oestrogens described by Brown extremely satisfactory for this purpose.

The main topic of the discussion centred upon the question of the range of normal values that one obtained for the measurement of steroids in urine.

*Johansson* found a wide distribution in the level of total oestrogen excretion at the midcycle, the peak values varying from 11 to 120 μg per 24 hours; more figures were required to determine the true distribution in a normal population and the values might be age related.

*Brown* agreed that in the past the normal women studied had often been laboratory assistants who generally tended to be young women and therefore may not have been representative of the total population. However they were carrying out in Melbourne, in collaboration with the Catholic Family Planning Centre, a study of a large number of women of varying ages, and this should give a much better indication of the overall range of values found during the normal menstrual cycle.

*Klopper* thought that from his early studies of pregnanediol excretion during the menstrual cycle, young women had a lower level of pregnanediol excretion than mature women, and that values from multipara were even higher.

*Loraine* also remarked that factors such as age and parity might be of considerable importance. He noted that women in the age range 36 to 45 years had a lower oestrogen excretion than younger women; furthermore the excretion of urinary gonadotrophins might be higher in multiparous than in nulliparous women.

*Odell* asked about urinary excretion of pregnanetriol in the menstrual cycle and it was pointed out that Fotherby had shown a rise in urinary pregnanetriol excretion occurring at the time of the peak of oestrogen excretion.

*Macnaughton* added that in women who became pregnant as a result of gonadotrophin therapy, pregnanetriol excretion remained high for 8 to 10 weeks following ovulation and this might be a reflection of the activity of the corpus luteum of pregnancy.

# Androgen Production

R. A. HARKNESS

Department of Paediatric Biochemistry
Royal Hospital for Sick Children, Edinburgh

¶ TESTOSTERONE can be regarded as the most potent naturally occurring androgen. Androgen production is, therefore, concerned directly or indirectly with testosterone production which is linked to levels of the hormone in blood and in urine. These levels in normal and diseased states give some indication of the controlling mechanisms.

Evidence for the existence of variations in androgen production by the male has been reviewed. Although these changes are smaller than the changes in ovarian function, similar basic control mechanisms may exist. For example, oestrogens are more potent inhibitors of androgen production in the male than androgens. It has often been suggested that oestrogens represent at least part of the 'feedback' to the hypothalamus in both sexes. Gonadal control may be complicated by the production of oestrogens, not only by the gonads, but also by adrenal cortex and probably other tissues such as liver. On the basis of the available evidence, it is suggested that this biosynthesis may be through systems which can be 'induced' by drugs and steroids.

*Blood and urinary testosterone levels in human adults.* Blood levels have been obtained by a number of methods, many of them involving double labelling procedures or electron capture detectors after gas chromatography. Coppage and Cooner [1] have reported a series of testosterone levels in blood which are similar to those obtained by others. In addition, they showed a variable reduction of testosterone levels in hepatic cirrhosis and a consistent reduction after oestrogen administration.

There is general agreement on values for urinary testosterone. The levels in urine are also well correlated with the levels of plasma testosterone in the male but the situation is more complex in the female.

Both blood and urine studies show that testosterone is produced mainly by the testis with control by the pituitary. However, there are contributions from the adrenal and ovary which are normally small. Studies have been performed of testosterone levels in a wide variety of clinical conditions. In women, raised values have been found in hirsutism with and without polycystic ovaries. In the male, urinary testosterone was reduced during undernutrition; chlorpromazine treatment was also associated with lower levels [2]. Such alterations are similar to changes in ovarian function.

*Variation of androgen production in men.* Diurnal variations in plasma testosterone have been reported [3]. Day-to-day variations in male gonadal function are small compared to those of the ovary with its obvious cyclicity. However, some normal males have regular peaks of testosterone excretion in urine [2]. This investigation has now been extended to nine subjects who have been studied over 14 to 33 days; of these, four showed maximum levels at 12-day intervals and five at 5- to 6-day intervals. Three further subjects, studied for shorter times, showed no clear trends in their results which were very variable. It may also be relevant that urinary oestrone and 17-oxosteroid levels are maximal at about 8- to 10-day intervals [4] and that sperm concentration in ejaculates can show peaks at 5-day intervals [5].

Much of the above evidence only justifies tentative conclusions. However, some more definite evidence for variations in male androgen production has been obtained. After long periods of abstinence, sexual activity raised urinary testosterone levels in man [2]. This is supported by work in rats in which mating was shown to increase the weights of the accessory sex organs in males [6]. These observations may, in part, account for variations in urinary testosterone which are large before the age of 40 years in men [7, 8].

The readjustment of the urinary level of testosterone after sexual activity suggests that there may be an optimum androgen production for a given level of genital tract activity. The relationship between testosterone and the secretory activity of the male genital tract is well established [9]. Growth also requires an optimum dose of androgens in rats [10]. Thus, control mechanisms must adjust the androgen production within limits.

*The function of end organs.* Any variations in androgen production should be demonstrable at their site of action. One suitable end organ is the sebaceous gland in skin. Sebum excretion from the male skin can be used as a 'bioassay' for androgens in man, although in the mature male the gland tends to be maximally stimulated by endogenous testosterone. This 'bioassay' has a built-in delay of about 10 to 15 days and shows considerable damping [11] but it is suitable for serial studies. With careful attention to detail, especially temperature at which the subject is maintained, the assay is reasonably precise.

In collaboration with Dr Powell, sebum and testosterone excretion has been studied in two men for 33 and 47 days. Variations in sebum levels have been found which cannot be accounted for on the basis of the method used. The elevation of sebum excretion at about the 15–20th day of the investigation (Fig. 1) occurs as expected at about 10 to 15 days after the broad peak of testosterone excretion. More marked variations in sebum excretion are shown in Figure 2. Cunliffe and Shuster [12] have also noted greater variations in sebum excretion in men than can be accounted for by the errors in their method. Thus, changes in sebum excretion could be linked indirectly with the increased variability of urinary testosterone in acne patients [13].

*Oestrogen inhibition of male gonadal function by central mechanisms.* The compound or compounds which are monitored by the central receptor sites in the hypothalamus controlling male gonadal function are difficult to define precisely. Synthetic androgens do depress endogenous testos-

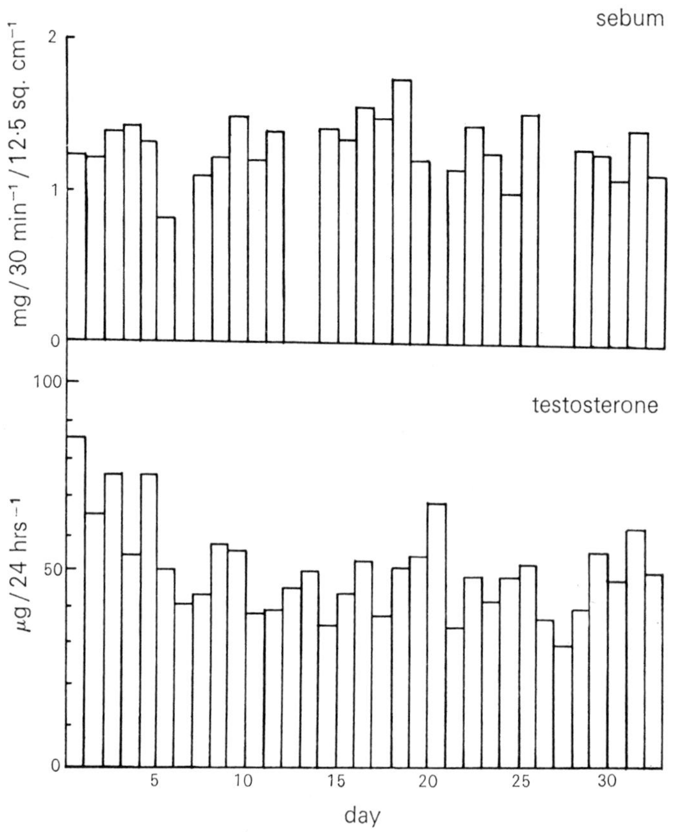


FIGURE 1
Variations of sebum excretion from the skin and of urinary testosterone levels in a normal male. Sebum was collected at 0010 to 0010.30 hr each day at 25 ± 1 °C

terone production but they are not powerful depressants. For example, physiological doses of fluoxymesterone, that is 9α-fluoro-11β-hydroxy-17α-methyltestosterone in a dose of 10 mg per day, only caused a 50 per cent depression of testosterone production [14]. Normal therapeutic doses of the weakly androgenic anabolic steroids do not depress urinary testosterone levels (Fig. 2).

A number of workers [1] have shown that oestrogens are extremely powerful depressants of Leydig cell function. Many authors have suggested that oestrogens in conjunction with secreted androgens are the agents controlling Leydig cell function through their influence on the hypothalamus and anterior pituitary. Rivarola and his colleagues [15] have shown that ACTH stimulation in normal males leads to a reduction in blood production rates of testosterone possibly due to the stimulation of oestrogen production by the adrenal.

It is possible that extra-gonadal sources of oestrogen are also significant

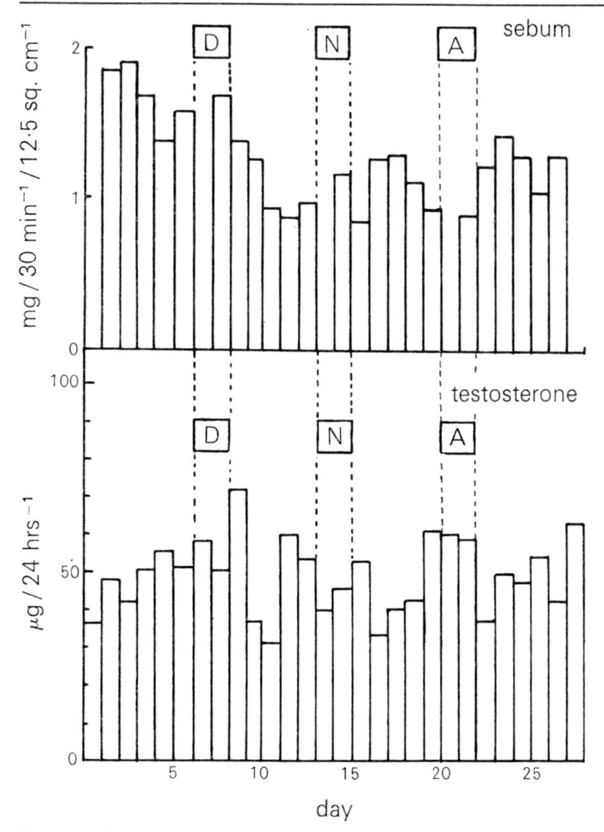


FIGURE 2
Effect of normal therapeutic doses of the anabolic steroids, methandrostenolone, norethandrolone and oxymetholone on urinary testosterone excretion in a normal man and on sebum excretion which was collected at 0010 to 0010.30 hr each day at $25 \pm 1$ °C. D = Methandrostenolone; N = Norethandrolone; A = Oxymetholone

controlling factors for the ovary. The abnormal androgen production in the polycystic ovary syndrome and in hirsutism appears to be linked in some complex way to the adrenals as well as the ovaries [16, 17]. However, the oestrogen response to ACTH stimulation is erratic [18] and this is not improved when a synthetic peptide containing 24 amino-acid residues is used in place of natural preparations (Fig. 3, Harkness and Strong, unpublished observations).

One possible explanation for this variability is the hepatic 'biosynthesis' of oestrogens from steroid precursors secreted by adrenal and gonads. This would involve initial hydroxylation. Fukushima, Bradlow, Hellman and Gallagher [19] showed that up to 10 per cent of injected androsterone could be 18-hydroxylated in adrenalectomized ovariectomized women; it seems possible that 19-hydroxylation could also occur. Chang and Dao [20] showed that 4-$^{14}$C-cortisone acetate could be converted into 11β-

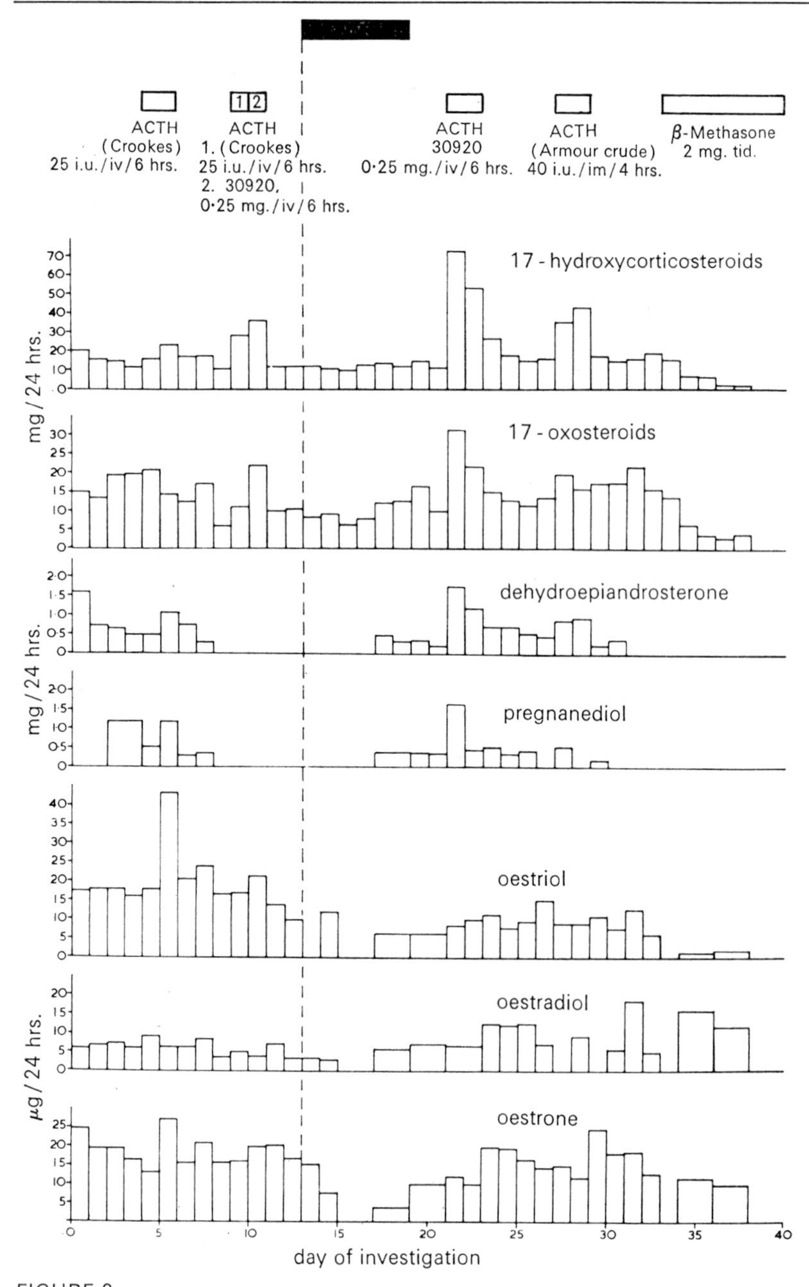


FIGURE 3

The effect of tetracosactrin (Ciba 30920) and of various ACTH preparations from natural sources on urinary levels of oestrogens and neutral steroids. The effect of Betamethasone suppression is also shown

hydroxyoestradiol and 11β-hydroxyoestrone in an adrenalectomized ovariectomized woman; other groups have reported similar findings [21, 22].

If hydroxylation is involved in oestrogen biosynthesis in the liver, it becomes easier to understand the variations in oestrogen response to ACTH because hepatic hydroxylation systems are 'induced' by many of their substrates including steroids and drugs [23]. The steroids produced by the adrenals and gonads, as well as drugs which would be given to women who had been adrenalectomized and ovariectomized for metastatic mammary carcinoma, will 'induce' hepatic hydroxylation. Since the speed of 'induction' will be slower than the rapid response of the gonads to stimulation, some disruption of the normal control mechanisms is possible. Lopez, Migeon and Jones [24] have shown an abnormality in 'feedback' in the polycystic ovary syndrome.

This hypothesis can be tested; hepatic hydroxylation can be studied using normal therapeutic doses of anabolic steroid drugs [25]; such a procedure with an almost 'physiological' substrate avoids the problems of variations in the endogenous secretion of the steroid hormones [26]. Such an assessment may help in understanding some of the problems of the control of androgen production.

## REFERENCES

[1] Coppage, W.S. and Cooner, A.E., *New Eng. J. Med.*, **273**, 902, 1965.
[2] Ismail, A.A.A. and Harkness, R.A., *Acta Endocr., Copnh.*, **56**, 469, 1967.
[3] Dray, F., Reinberg, A. and Sebaoun, J., *C. r. Acad. Sci., Paris*, **261**, 573, 1965.
[4] Corker, C.S. and Exley, D., *J. Endocr.*, **40**, 255, 1968.
[5] Zimmerman, S.J., Maude, M.B. and Moldawer, M., *Fert. Steril.*, **16**, 342, 1965.
[6] Herz, Z., Folman, Y. and Drori, D., *J. Endocr.*, **44**, 127, 1969.
[7] Ismail, A.A.A. and Harkness, R.A., *Biochem. J.*, **99**, 717, 1966.
[8] Tamm, J., Schmidt, H. and Voigt, K.D. In *Testosterone*, p. 183. Ed. J. Tamm. Stuttgart: Thieme, 1968.
[9] Mann, T. In *The Biochemistry of Semen and of the Male Reproductive Tract*, Ch. 12. London: Methuen, 1964.
[10] Joss, E.E., Zuppinger, K.A. and Sobel, E.H., *Endocrinology*, **72**, 123, 1963.
[11] Strauss, J.S. and Pochi, P.E., *Recent Prog. Hormone Res.*, **19**, 385, 1963.
[12] Cunliffe, W.J. and Shuster, S., *Br. J. Derm.*, **81**, 697, 1969.
[13] Harkness, R.A., Ismail, A.A.A., Beveridge, G.W. and Powell, E.W. In *Testosterone*, p. 192. Ed. J. Tamm. Stuttgart: Thieme, 1968.
[14] Kirschner, M.A., Lipsett, M.B. and Collins, D.R., *J. clin. Invest.*, **44**, 657, 1965.
[15] Rivarola, M.A., Saez, J.M., Meyer, W.J., Jenkins, M.E. and Migeon, C.J., *J. clin. Endocr. Metab.*, **26**, 1208, 1966.
[16] Prunty, F.T.G., *J. Endocr.*, **38**, 203, 1967.
[17] Ismail, A.A.A. and Loraine, J.A., *Clin. Obstet. Gynaec.*, **12**, 800, 1969.
[18] Barlow, J.J., *Am. J. Obstet. Gynec.*, **103**, 585, 1969.

[19] Fukushima, D.K., Bradlow, H.L., Hellman, L. and Gallagher, T.F., *J. biol. Chem.*, **237**, 3359, 1962.
[20] Chang, E. and Dao, T.L., *Biochim. Biophys. Acta*, **57**, 609, 1962.
[21] Baird, D., Horton, R., Longcope C. and Tait, J.F., *Perspectives in Biology and Medicine*, **11**, 384, 1968.
[22] Longcope, C., Kato, T. and Horton, R., *J. clin. Invest.*, **48**, 2191, 1969.
[23] Kuntzman, R., *Ann. Rev. Pharm.*, **9**, 21, 1969.
[24] Lopez, J.M., Migeon, C.J. and Jones, G.S., *Am. J. Obstet. Gynec.*, **103**, 555, 1969.
[25] Adhikary, P.M. and Harkness, R.A., *Biochem. J.*, **112**, 30 P, 1969.
[26] Thrasher, K., Werk, E.E., Choi, Y., Sholiton, L.J., Mayer, W. and Olinger, C., *Steroids*, **14**, 455, 1969.

*Discussion of paper by Dr Harkness*

*Mills* raised the question of feedback mechanisms in the control of androgen secretion; he quoted the work of Migeon (Rivarola et al., *J. clin. Endocr. Metab.*, **26**, 1208, 1966) who gave ACTH to males and females. In males, as the plasma androstenedione rose, plasma testosterone levels fell whereas in females, as the androstenedione levels rose so did the testosterone levels.

*Harkness* added that these authors had suggested that oestrogens might play a part in the control of testosterone levels.

Both *Dray* and *Ismail* had found marked variations in testosterone levels after administration of ACTH and *Ismail* suggested that there was an increase when ACTH was administered during the follicular phase to women but no change when administered during the luteal phase.

*Harkness* remarked that the findings were similar to those of Barlow in regard to oestrogen response to ACTH during the menstrual cycle.

*Grant* raised an interesting point regarding oestrogen control of the hypothalamus; he quoted the situation existing in the stallion which produces extremely large amounts of oestrogen and we do not know what this oestrogen is doing in regard to hypothalamic function.

## SESSION III. GENERAL DISCUSSION

*Mills* raised the question of induction of enzyme systems; he had shown in an investigation of a patient with 17-hydroxylase deficiency, that when she was treated with dehydroepiandrosterone sulphate intramuscularly there was only a minute conversion (about 0·1 per cent) to oestrogens but six months later when the investigation was repeated there was a much larger conversion and oestriol excretion reached 19 µg per day.

*Fotherby* criticized the use of the word 'induction' in Harkness's remarks regarding 6-hydroxylation; in many cases described as induction it was merely the activity of an enzyme which played a normal part in metabolism being increased and this certainly appeared to be the case in regard to the 6-hydroxylase. 6-hydroxylation of cortisol was increased for example by barbiturate administration but as far as progesterone was concerned, although there was a large increase in the excretion of 6-oxygenated metabolites of progesterone during pregnancy, this was mainly due to the fact that the amount of the substrate available was also increasing.

*Harkness* agreed that in many cases the word 'induction' should be qualified.

*Grant* raised the question of whether merely measuring the three classical oestrogens was satisfactory in view of the fact that many other metabolites of oestradiol had now been isolated from urine and that some of these were of considerable quantitative importance.

*Brown* agreed that other metabolites should be taken into consideration and quoted Fishman's work showing that 2-hydroxyoestrone was quantitatively as important as oestriol. The original Brown method or the total oestrogen method appeared to be quite satisfactory for applying to large populations of women and for giving an overall idea of oestrogen production but for investigating metabolic problems a more elaborate method taking into account other metabolites should certainly be used.

*Ismail* asked van der Molen about plasma testosterone levels during the normal menstrual cycle and whether the absence of a cyclical pattern was an argument against an ovarian contribution to the plasma testosterone. Lipsett and his colleagues had measured the plasma testosterone levels and production rates simultaneously and found normal plasma concentrations in hirsute women while the production rate was abnormally high so that there did not appear to be a correlation between the plasma testosterone level and the testosterone production rate.

*Van der Molen* thought that possibly the method for the measurement in plasma was not sufficiently precise to show small variations but as far as urinary excretion of testosterone was concerned, the excretion varied regularly with a peak both at midcycle and during the luteal phase.

*Ismail* thought that even if the method were made more precise, more information could be gained from measuring the production rate.

*Vermeulen* (*J. clin. Endocr. Metab.*, **29**, 1470, 1969) found high levels of testosterone in the second half of the cycle but had so far not observed a peak at the expected time of ovulation; he regarded plasma testosterone levels and production rate determinations as being complementary to each other. One other factor that had to be taken into account was the availability of testosterone to the tissues due to difference in the binding : administration of testosterone not only altered the metabolic pattern but also reduced the binding of testosterone in plasma so that patients receiving high doses of testosterone had a decreased binding capacity for testosterone. The metabolic clearance rate is also variable and both this and the binding are influenced by oestrogens. Ideally therefore one would like to measure the plasma testosterone level, degree of binding and metabolic clearance rate.

*Jeffcoate* argued that there was good evidence both from his own work and that of others that the adrenals were the source of more than 80 per cent of the plasma testosterone in normal women and that quite marked changes could take place in a small ovarian component which would not be noticeable in measuring total plasma testosterone. Levels of androstenedione in adrenal venous blood were 20 to 30 times the levels in ovarian venous blood.

*Baird* however maintained that the production of androstenedione by the ovary certainly fluctuated throughout the cycle.

*Johansson* spoke on some of the difficulties in interpreting plasma levels of progesterone; he had studied some women with short menstrual cycles (i.e., less than 25 days' duration) and following a normal LH peak and total urinary oestrogens within the normal range the oestrogen excretion then fell and was followed by only a small rise in the plasma progesterone level with menstruation occurring within 6 to 7 days from the total oestrogen peak. Although on this basis one could guess that the corpus luteum was not functioning normally did it also mean that ovulation had not occurred? In some women who have this type of cycle repeatedly he had found subnormal levels of LH and in one patient this type of cycle could be produced by taking a blood sample from the patient prior to ovulation. When blood samples were taken after the presumed date of ovulation, normal luteal phase levels of both oestrogen and pregnanediol occurred showing clearly that there were additional factors that influence ovulation and possible corpus luteum function.

*Brown* remarked that he had also seen this pattern typical of short cycles and in his view unless the luteal phase was greater than 12 days in length, it was unlikely that fertilization, if it occurred, would be followed by a successful pregnancy.

*Klopper* was of the opinion that the possibility of an unovulated follicle producing progesterone might cast doubt on the hypothesis that blood access to the granulosa cells was required before the follicle started to produce progesterone.

*Brown* agreed and quoted experiments wherein follicles which had been stimulated with HCG might not have been stimulated enough to produce an oestrogen peak but did produce progesterone, to which *Gemzell* added that if HCG was given too early, before the follicle was ripe enough for ovulation, one found an increase in progesterone for about two days reaching a level of 4 to 5 ng/ml.

*Loraine* and *Prunty* had come across menstrual cycles where there had been a midcycle peak of LH but in which the urinary steroid assays suggested that the cycles were anovulatory. In addition *Prunty* described circumstances where it had been impossible to get an oestrogen response in the follicular phase using Pergonal alone but by giving HCG with the Pergonal a good response was obtained; luteal phase activity seemed to be dependent upon the dose of HCG given early in the cycle rather than on the ovulation day.

*Gemzell* had found that when ovulation was induced with a single injection of HCG, the luteal phase in 90 cycles was shorter than normal with a range of 9 to 12 days. In cycles in which another HCG injection was given a week later, the luteal phase was 14 days. He agreed with Brown that in order to obtain a pregnancy it was important to get an oestrogen pattern which was as normal as possible.

This was confirmed by *Brown* who thought that unless there was a decrease in oestrogen excretion to 70 per cent of its peak value in three days a successful pregnancy was unlikely. In experiments carried out with Dr Burger and Dr Catt designed to define the oestrogen peak in plasma in relation to the LH peak difficulties arose when the time interval of sampling was reduced to 5 or 6 hours since the oestrogen peak became more diffuse although the LH peak still remained sharp.

*Naftolin* brought up the hypothesis that the LH peak might really consist of more than one component and that a narrow peak might be enough to cause ovulation but not to produce a functional corpus luteum or that a subnormal amount of LH might cause luteinization of an unruptured follicle. While the double peak of LH appears regularly in the human (with the development of a functional corpus luteum), such animals as the rat require coitus at this time before they form a functional corpus luteum. These preliminary data suggest that in the rat coitus is followed by a second LH release.

# Dynamics of Androgen and Oestrogen Secretion

PAUL C. MacDONALD, JAY M. GRODIN
*and* PENTTI K. SIITERI

Department of Obstetrics and Gynecology
The University of Texas (Southwestern) Medical School
Dallas, Texas

¶ A DYNAMIC interrelationship between oestrogen and androgen production in the human was postulated more than 35 years ago [1]. The first substantive evidence for this hypothesis was presented in 1956 when the conversion of testosterone to urinary oestrogen was demonstrated in an adrenalectomized, oophorectomized woman [2]. While the physiological implications of this observation were great, a critical assessment of its importance has become possible only recently by *in vivo* isotope dilution methods with which accurate estimates of total androgen and oestrogen production may be obtained easily. Nevertheless, it still is not possible to measure directly glandular secretion of these hormones in the human. Therefore, an indirect approach to the quantitative evaluation of the various possible sources of oestrogen has been developed [3].

Using this novel *in vivo* internal standard double isotope technique it has been possible to quantify not only total oestrogen production, but also the contribution of each circulating $C_{19}$ oestrogen precursor to oestrogen production. These $C_{19}$ precursors of oestrogen are produced in milligram quantities per day and therefore constitute a sizeable potential source of oestrogen, since oestrogen is produced in microgram quantities per day. Furthermore, neither adrenalectomy nor gonadectomy diminishes the extent of conversion of intravenously administered isotope-labelled $C_{19}$ precursor to oestrogen [4]. Thus, oestrogen derived from plasma steroids may be considered as an extraglandular source of oestrogen production.

To ascertain the relative contribution of both glandular secretion and extraglandular production in the case of oestrogen, a convenient approach is the simultaneous measurement of total oestrogen production and the fraction of that total which arises through the utilization of a specific $C_{19}$ steroidal precursor. For this latter purpose, however, one must clearly define (*a*) the extent of conversion of a given steroidal precursor to oestrogen; (*b*) the quantitative availability of that precursor for conversion to oestrogen; (*c*) the exact chemical nature of the product oestrogenic hormone (i.e., oestrone, oestradiol or oestriol); and (*d*) the physiologic availability of the oestrogenic hormone derived from the utilization of plasma precursor (i.e., the blood production rate of that oestrogen hormone derived from a given circulating $C_{19}$ precursor).

Utilizing the experimental design described below, a systematic survey of the origin of oestrogen from circulating $C_{19}$ steroidal precursors has been carried out in normal ovulating premenopausal women; in certain anovulatory premenopausal women; in normal postmenopausal women and in those postmenopausal women with evidence of increased endogenous oestrogen production, endometrial hyperplasia and uterine bleeding; and in normal male subjects and in certain males with gynaecomastia [4, 5].

The results of these studies strongly suggest that a sizeable portion of oestrogen production in all humans is derived from the utilization of circulating precursor(s). Specifically, the total oestrogen production in postmenopausal women can be accounted for principally if not exclusively by the extraglandular utilization of plasma androstenedione for oestrone production [5]. Furthermore, in postmenopausal women with clinical evidence of increased oestrogen production, endometrial hyperplasia and uterine bleeding, the increased oestrogen production can be attributed to either (*a*) increased conversion of androstenedione to oestrone or (*b*) by increased availability of precursor, androstenedione. But in these women with excessive endogenous oestrogen production the origin of oestrogen can be accounted for exclusively via extraglandular mechanisms.

In the normal human male, total oestrogen production is accounted for principally from (*a*) the utilization of androstenedione for oestrone production and (*b*) the utilization of plasma testosterone for oestradiol production. While these studies do not exclude the direct glandular secretion of small amounts of oestrone and/or oestradiol by the testes or adrenal, they do illustrate that direct glandular secretion of oestrogen can represent no more than a minor fraction of total production in the male. Furthermore, the results strongly suggest that alterations in the physiologic manifestation of androgen and oestrogen as occurs in certain cases of gynaecomastia, can be accounted for via alterations in the mechanism of origin of oestrogen from androgen in these subjects.

## MATERIALS AND METHODS

*Determination of the extent of conversion of $C_{19}$ precursors to product oestrogen hormone.* The extent of conversion of a given $C_{19}$ steroidal precursor circulating in plasma to a product oestrogenic hormone is measured by an *in vivo* internal standard double isotope technique. Following the simultaneous intravenous administration by constant infusion during a four-hour period of tritium labelled product oestrogenic hormone (e.g., 6,7,$H^3$-oestradiol or 6,7,$H^3$-oestrone) plus carbon-14 labelled steroidal precursor (e.g., 4-$C^{14}$-$\Delta^4$-androstenedione or 4-$C^{14}$-testosterone), plasma is sampled at 3, $3\frac{1}{2}$, 4 hours and urine is collected for 72 hours from the beginning of the infusion. The extent of conversion of a $C_{19}$ precursor to an oestrogen product hormone at the tissue site(s) of conversion can be calculated from the relationship between the isotopic ratio of infused tracers to that of the isolated urinary metabolite of the oestrogen product hormone uniquely derived from the oestrogen hormone in question. For example, the extent of conversion of androstenedione to oestrone can be calculated from the formula,

$$\% \text{androstenedione} \rightarrow E_1 = \frac{H^3/C^{14} \text{ ratio injected tracers}}{H^3/C^{14} \text{ ratio of urinary oestrone (glucuronoside)}} \times 100$$

since the internal standard, 6,7-$H^3$-oestrone will serve as the standard for the metabolism for that fraction of 4-$C^{14}$-androstenedione which behaves identically with the infused tritiated oestrone.

*Determination of the chemical nature of the product hormone derived from the utilization of circulating precursor.* In order to calculate the extent of conversion of precursor to product as described above, the exact chemical nature of the product hormone must be known. This has previously been determined from the comparison of the isotopic ratios of a large number of metabolites of the urinary oestrogens following the simultaneous administration of the combination of precursor and product hormone tracers as previously described [4]. The results of these studies have shown that androstenedione is converted exclusively to the oestrogen product hormone, oestrone; whereas testosterone is converted to oestradiol both directly and indirectly via the sequence $T \rightarrow \Delta^4 A \rightarrow E_1 \rightarrow E2$.

*Determination of quantity of precursor available for conversion to oestrogen product hormone.* Having established the extent of conversion of a given precursor to the product hormone, a quantitative assessment of this contribution to total oestrogen production can be made if the availability of the precursor for this conversion is known. In these studies, the availability of precursor has been determined from a determination of the blood production rates of the particular precursor in question. The blood production rates were calculated as a product of their rates of metabolic clearance (determined from the concentration of isotope labelled precursor in plasma during the continuous infusion of an isotope labelled tracer of that precursor) and its plasma concentration.

*Determination of the total rate of daily oestrogen production.* The total daily rates of oestrone or oestradiol production irrespective of their sources of origin (i.e., whether derived by direct glandular secretion, or from peripheral formation via the utilization of plasma androgen precursors, or from peripheral formation from another oestrogenic hormone either directly secreted or peripherally formed), were determined by the classic isotope dilution technique according to the formula,

$$\text{PRE} = \frac{R_E^I}{\text{sa } E_u \cdot t}$$

where PRE = production rate of oestrogenic hormone in question (μg/24 hr); $R_E^I$ = radioactivity (dpm) infused as the isotope labelled oestrogen tracer; sa $E_u$ = specific activity (dpm/μg) of a unique oestrogen metabolite; t = time (days of urine collection).

*Determination of the blood production rate of oestrone or oestradiol derived from circulating $C_{19}$ precursor.* As previously indicated, during the continuous infusion of the tritium labelled oestrogen end product hormone plus the carbon-14 labelled precursor hormone, blood is sampled at 3, 3½ and 4 hours. From these blood samples the tritium/carbon-14 ratios of oestrone and oestradiol are determined and compared with the tritium/carbon-14 ratio of the urinary oestrone or oestradiol.

It is theoretically possible that oestrogen formed from the utilization of plasma precursor(s) will not be available to the circulation as the product hormone oestrone or oestradiol. Rather, in the tissue site of formation it may suffer immediate metabolism and enter the blood stream as a metabolite of the parent hormone thus precluding total entry into the blood stream of the oestrogen hormone itself. An assessment of the extent of entry of the product oestrogenic hormone into the circulation can be calculated from a comparison of the tritium/carbon-14 ratio of the oestrogenic hormone in plasma with that in urine. If entry into the blood stream was total, then the tritium/carbon-14 ratio of the hormone in plasma and that of the unique metabolite in urine would be identical. Alternatively, if part of the oestrogenic hormone produced at the tissue site of conversion was immediately metabolized then the entry of $C^{14}$ labelled oestrogen derived from the circulating precursor would be less than 100 per cent. In this case, the tritium/carbon-14 ratio in plasma would exceed that which is found in urine. These determinations have been made.

*Determination of multiple precursor origin of oestrogen production in the male.* In the human female, androstenedione is the only appropriate precursor available in sufficient quantities which is converted efficiently enough to be of quantitative significance as an extraglandular source of oestrogen. However, in the male subject, while testosterone conversion to oestradiol proceeds much less efficiently than that of androstenedione to oestrone, nevertheless, the availability of large quantities of testosterone via direct secretion from the male testes constitutes a significant source of extraglandular oestradiol production that must be taken into account in the determination of total oestrogen production.

Testosterone is converted directly to oestradiol and indirectly to oestradiol via the sequence $Y \rightarrow \Delta^4A \rightarrow E_1 \rightarrow E_2$. In order to assess accurately the contribution of testosterone to oestrogen production and of androstenedione to oestrogen production, the fraction of T converted to $E_2$ via $T \rightarrow \Delta^4A \rightarrow E_1 \rightarrow E_2$ must be calculated and excluded from that fraction calculated for $\Delta^4A \rightarrow E_1$, otherwise a duplication would occur. This is carried out by determining the fraction of testosterone in plasma converted to androstenedione in plasma, of androstenedione converted to oestrone and of oestrone converted to oestradiol. Thus, the direct conversion of testosterone to oestradiol is calculated by determining total testosterone conversion to oestradiol (irrespective of its mechanism of origin) less that fraction converted to oestradiol via the indirect sequence $T \rightarrow \Delta^4A \rightarrow E_1 \rightarrow E_2$.

RESULTS AND DISCUSSION

In normal young adult cyclically ovulating women, endogenous oestrogen production arises via two mechanisms. From the utilization of circulating androstenedione, oestrone is produced in approximately 35–40 μg/day amounts via this extraglandular mechanism. Additionally, as has been pointed out by many investigators, there is cyclic secretion by the ovary of oestradiol-17β.

The extent of conversion of plasma androstenedione to oestrone during the course of the normal menstrual cycle does not fluctuate. In the same individual it is remarkably constant throughout the ovulatory cycle. As previously shown, the average extent of conversion of plasma androstenedione to oestrone in young adult women is 1·3 per cent [4].

In young adult women, the intravenous administration of isotope labelled testosterone results in its conversion to oestradiol and additionally, to oestrone via the sequence testosterone→androstenedione→oestrone; however, the efficiency of this process is much less than that observed for the conversion of androstenedione to oestrone. Specifically, the extent of conversion of testosterone directly to the product hormone oestradiol in young premenopausal women averages 0·15 per cent. Since the availability of testosterone precursor in normal young women is limited, the yield of oestrogen via this mechanism in young women is negligible.

The conversion of dehydroisoandrosterone to oestrogen is likewise limited. Free dehydroisoandrosterone is converted to oestrogen in non-pregnant women via two mechanisms. One of these is via the sequence of plasma dehydroisoandrosterone to plasma androstenedione to oestrone; while the other involves the direct conversion of dehydroisoandrosterone to oestrogen. In our studies, the yield of oestrone from the sequence, dehydroisoandrosterone→androstenedione→oestrone would have been accounted for in the quantitative assessment of androstenedione to oestrone production; additional oestrogen from circulating precursor would involve only that fraction derived from direct conversion of dehydroisoandrosterone to oestradiol or oestrone. The net conversion of dehydroisoandrosterone to either of these oestrogens is, on the average, less than 0·07 per cent, thus a quantitatively significant yield of oestrogen from circulating dehydroisoandrosterone does not appear to exist.

*Postmenopausal women.* In postmenopausal women total oestrogen production rates as well as the contribution to the total oestrogen production via the process of plasma androstenedione conversion to oestrone have been determined. Total oestrogen production rates ranging from 15 to 60 μg of oestrone per day have been found in normal postmenopausal women. The average production rate in all subjects studied is approximately 30 μg/day. Furthermore, in each of these subjects, total oestrogen production could be accounted for exclusively via the utilization of plasma androstenedione. Specifically, if one compares total oestrone production [that is, oestrone produced irrespective of its mechanism (e.g., direct secretion or formation peripherally from preformed steroid precursors or from the metabolism of oestradiol via oestrone, whether secreted directly as oestradiol or peripherally formed from other secreted precursors)] to the amount of oestrone derived from androstenedione, the two values were equivalent in all cases. Therefore, in the postmenopause, following cessation of follicular maturation, oestrogen production is accounted for primarily via the conversion of circulating androstenedione to oestrone. Accordingly, these data suggest that there is no direct secretion of oestrone or oestradiol by the ovary or the adrenal in postmenopausal women. While the nature of these studies does not absolutely exclude some small secretion by the adrenal or the ovary, nevertheless, they point out that little of the total oestrogen production in postmenopausal women can be accounted for via direct glandular secretion.

Of further interest has been the finding that with advancing age there is a tendency for an increase in the extent of conversion of plasma androstenedione to oestrone. This obtains in the case of conversion of androstenedione to oestrone and of testosterone to oestradiol in both males and females. While the extent of conversion of androstenedione to oestrone averages 1·3 per cent in young adult women, in postmenopausal women from ages 50 to 80 the extent of conversion of androstenedione to oestrone averages three times this value. There is normally a decline in the average rate of production of plasma androstenedione with advancing age. This may be accounted for, in part, by a decrease in the contribution to the plasma production rate of androstenedione by the ovaries in postmenopausal women.

In addition to an increase in the extent of conversion of plasma androstenedione to oestrone with advancing age, an increase in the conversion of androstenedione to oestrone has also been observed in the face of massive obesity and in hepatic cirrhosis.

It follows then that increased endogenous oestrogen production may result from the increased utilization of plasma androstenedione for oestrone production. Increased endogenous oestrogen production leading to endometrial hyperplasia and postmenopausal uterine bleeding may be expected if the increase in the extent of conversion of androstenedione to the product hormone oestrone is large. Indeed, this has been observed in a number of patients, production rates of oestrone derived from androstenedione exceeding 200 μg/day having been observed.

While the exact site of this increased conversion has not been determined, it appears not to be hepatic. Specifically, following the intravenous infusion of isotope labelled androstenedione plus oestrone, blood samples were obtained simultaneously in one patient from peripheral blood as well as from the hepatic vein. Analyses of these blood samples indicated that the concentration of carbon-14 labelled oestrone was not higher in the hepatic vein effluent; rather, there appeared to be a decrease in trans-splanchnic clearance of androstenedione. Thus, the mechanism of increased conversion of androstenedione to oestrone in hepatic disease appears to be related to decreased hepatic clearance of androstenedione rather than to increased conversion of androstenedione to oestrone in the liver. A decreased trans-hepatic clearance would thus make androstenedione more available to the non-hepatic aromatizing site(s).

An alternative mechanism for increased endogenous oestrogen production in the postmenopause from the utilization of plasma precursors would exist if increased amounts of the precursor were available. One patient with endometrial hyperplasia, postmenopausal uterine bleeding and increased endogenous oestrogen production has been observed in which this mechanism was operative. Specifically, this patient had an increased plasma production rate of androstenedione apparently resulting from tumour-induced ovarian stromal hyperplasia. The tumour was a pseudomucinous cystadenoma with associated ovarian stromal hyperplasia. The increased production rate of androstenedione and normal conversion to oestrone nevertheless resulted in an endogenous oestrogen production which undoubtedly led to clinical symptomatology.

*Normal males.* It is well established that there is sizeable production of both oestrone and oestradiol in normal young adult males. Average values for the production rates of oestradiol and oestrone calculated from the specific activities of the urinary oestrogen glucuronisides following the intravenous administration of isotope labelled tracers as described above are shown in Figure 1.

A presumed physiologic model for the possible origin of these oestrogens in adult males is diagramatically illustrated in Figure 2. As in women, oestrogen production in normal males may arise from direct secretion (i.e., from either the testes or the adrenal cortex); or, alternatively, it may arise from the utilization of plasma $C_{19}$ steroidal precursors. In the male, however, one must also take into account the utilization of plasma testosterone for oestrogen production. This obtains, since in the normal male a much larger amount of plasma testosterone is present and even if its utilization is less than that of androstenedione, the large amount of precursor available may yield quantitatively and physiologically significant amounts of oestradiol.

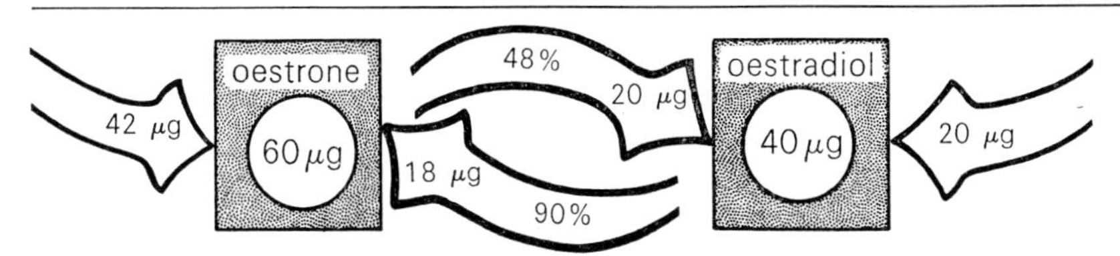


FIGURE 1
Oestrogen production in normal males

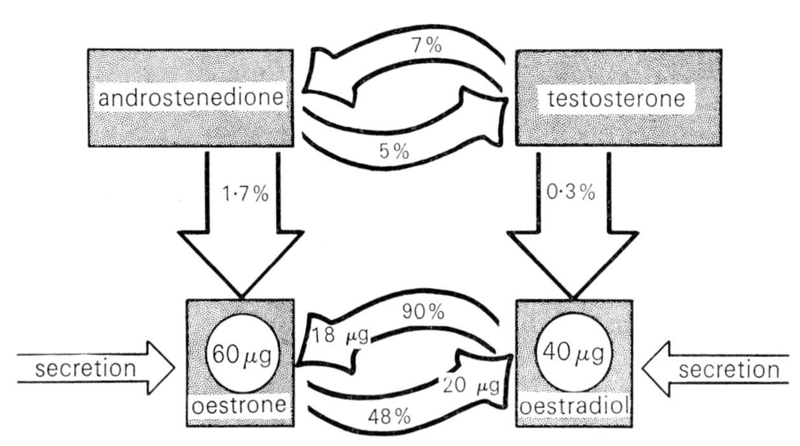


FIGURE 2
Origin of oestrogen in normal males

As shown in Figure 2, the extent of conversion of androstenedione to oestrone in the normal young adult males averages about 1·7 per cent, slightly higher than that observed in normal young women. The extent of the direct conversion of testosterone to oestradiol in young men averages 0·3 per cent. It should be pointed out that in this physiologic model, testosterone gives rise to oestrogen via two mechanisms. Specifically, testosterone is converted directly to oestradiol but additionally it is converted to oestradiol indirectly via the pathway, testosterone → androstenedione → oestrone → oestradiol. For purposes of quantitation of the origin of oestrogen from each precursor this latter pathway must be taken into account and subtracted from total conversion of testosterone to oestradiol. Thus, the conversion of testosterone directly to oestradiol is equal to the total conversion of testosterone to oestradiol minus that fraction of testosterone which is converted via the indirect pathway $T \rightarrow \Delta \rightarrow E_1 \rightarrow E_2$. For purposes of calculation of these rates of conversion and interconversion, the fraction of testosterone converted to plasma androstenedione, and the fraction of oestrone metabolized via oestradiol and of oestradiol metabolized via oestrone must be determined.

It is also readily apparent that androstenedione may be converted to oestrone via two separate pathways : (*a*) direct conversion of androstenedione to oestrone or, alternatively, (*b*) conversion of androstenedione to oestrone via the pathway, plasma androstenedione → plasma testosterone → oestradiol → oestrone. However, since the conversion both of androstenedione to testosterone in blood and of testosterone to oestradiol is extremely small, this is a quantitatively insignificant source of oestrone production and for our purposes can be ignored.

An illustrative example of the quantitative mechanism of origin of oestrogen in a normal male is shown in Figure 3. In this subject, utilizing this experimental design, there was no demonstrable secretion of oestrone or oestradiol. Specifically, total oestrogen production in this subject could be accounted for from the utilization of plasma androstenedione for oestrone production and testosterone utilization for oestradiol production.

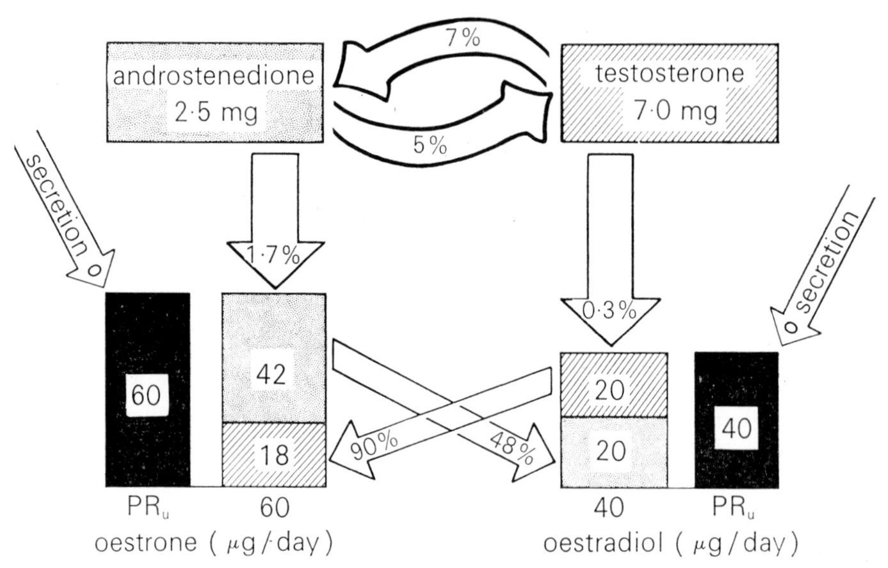


FIGURE 3
Origin of oestrogen in normal males

As illustrated in Figure 3, the blood production rates of testosterone and androstenedione as well as the extent of plasma interconversion of these two compounds were determined in this subject. The extent of conversion of androstenedione to oestrone and of testosterone directly to oestradiol is illustrated. The daily production rates of oestrone and of oestradiol were calculated from the specific activities of oestrone (glucuronoside) and oestradiol (glucuronoside) following the administration of tritium labelled oestrone or tritium labelled oestradiol, respectively.

It should be pointed out that *plasma* production rates of the precursor hormones were used to determine their contribution to oestrogen production whereas total oestrogen production was estimated from urinary production rates of the oestrogens. This is appropriate and correct since the measurement of production rates from urinary specific activities in the case of the oestrogens will reflect total production irrespective of source and irrespective of entry into blood. On the other hand, the extent of conversion of an intravenously administered isotope labelled precursor to its respective oestrogen end-product reflects that which is occurring for the endogenous precursor and therefore represents the fraction of the *plasma* production rate of precursor converted to oestrogen.

In this subject, 2·5 mg/day of plasma androstenedione was produced, 1·7 per cent of which was converted to oestrone. This represents a yield of 42 μg of oestrone per day from plasma androstenedione. At the same time this subject was producing 7 mg/day of testosterone, 0·3 per cent of which was converted directly to the product hormone, oestradiol-17β. This represents a yield of 20 μg of oestradiol production per day. Of this 20 μg of oestradiol produced from the utilization of testosterone, 90 per cent was metabolized via oestrone. Since this fraction of oestradiol had not previously appeared in the oestrone compartment, this also represents new oestrone production and would contribute to the measurement of daily oestrone production.

Accordingly, 42 μg of oestrone was derived from the utilization of plasma androstenedione and 18 μg of oestrone was derived from oestradiol which in turn had arisen directly from the conversion of testosterone. Thus, the daily production rate of oestrone from plasma precursors was 60 μg per day. Of great importance was the fact that independently measured total oestrone production in this subject was also 60 μg per day. Therefore, in this subject within the limits of this experimental design there was no evidence for direct secretion of oestrone by either the adrenal or the testes.

In the case of oestradiol production, 20 μg was derived directly from the conversion of testosterone. An additional 20 μg of new oestradiol arose via the sequence androstenedione conversion to oestrone which was subsequently metabolized via oestradiol. Therefore, 20 μg of oestradiol was derived from testosterone plus an additional 20 μg via the utilization of androstenedione for oestrone production which in turn was metabolized via oestradiol. Therefore, daily production of oestradiol from plasma precursors was a total 40 μg/day. Similarly, the total daily production rate of oestradiol in this subject independently measured from the specific activity of urinary oestradiol with respect to tritium following the administration of a tritium labelled tracer dose of oestradiol, was also 40 μg/day. Therefore, as in the case with oestrone, total daily production of oestradiol was equivalent to that derived from the utilization of plasma precursors.

Therefore, in this subject, oestradiol production could be accounted for principally if not exclusively from the utilization of circulating precursors.

Similar results have been found in a number of normal adult males, from 80 to 100 per cent of oestrone and/or oestradiol production having been accounted for via the utilization of plasma precursors. While the techniques of this study do not exclude the secretion of oestradiol or oestrone by the testes, they clearly indicate that the quantitative contribution of testicular or adrenal cortex secretion to total oestrogen production in the normal adult male is relatively small.

The results herein reported for the relative rates of production of testosterone and androstenedione as well as their respective conversions to oestrone and oestradiol are similar to those reported previously. In addition, the rates of production of oestrone and oestradiol using the urinary method are similar to those previously reported. These results are in conflict with those reported using plasma production rates of oestrone and oestradiol. It is difficult to reconcile the differences between these latter results. While it is easy to ascribe errors in technique which would lead to an overestimate with urinary methods, it is difficult to define technicologic errors which would lead to an underestimate. One is more inclined to question the validity of plasma production rates of oestrone and oestradiol which exceed those values obtained by the urinary method.

Similar studies have been carried out in a number of patients with gynaecomastia. The common finding has been that the ratio of the production rate of oestrone and/or oestradiol to that of testosterone is very elevated. This may occur with high, normal or low oestrogen production.

ACKNOWLEDGMENT

This work was supported in part by USPHS Research Grant AM-06912.

REFERENCES

[1] Zondek, B., *Nature, Lond.*, **133**, 494, 1934.

[2] West, C.D., Damast, B.L., Sarro, S.D. and Pearson, O.H., *J. biol. Chem.*, **218**, 409, 1956.

[3] Siiteri, P.K. and MacDonald, P.C., *Steroids*, **2**, 713, 1963.

[4] MacDonald, P.C., Rombaut, R.P. and Siiteri, P.K., *J. clin. Endocr. Metab.*, **27**, 1103, 1967.

[5] MacDonald, P.C., Grodin, J.M. and Siiteri, P.K. In *Proc. Int. Cong. Endocr.*, **184**, 770, 1969.

*Discussion of paper by Professor MacDonald*

*Exley* Professor MacDonald did not tell us where he thought the peripheral conversion was taking place. Has he any idea?

*MacDonald* There are many places where it does not occur—at least not exclusively. I cannot tell you at the moment where it is occurring. We have spent many years trying to determine this. It is not occurring exclusively in the liver. We have carried out studies in which there was simultaneous hepatic vein catheterization during the continuous infusion of tracers to monitor that fraction of carbon-14 oestrone from the liver as well as that which was present peripherally. It certainly was not occurring exclusively in the liver. In those patients in whom we observed increased conversion, the bulk of conversion was not in the liver. Rather, the liver appears to participate in an indirect way, that is by failure of clearing the precursor in question, i.e. if the trans-hepatic clearance of androstenedione is reduced it will ultimately contribute to increased conversion to oestrogens. It appears possible that aromatization is occurring in many sites at the same time. We have some meagre evidence, and I emphasize meagre, that it will occur in the endometrium, but removing the uterus does not change the overall conversion.

*Odell* When you calculated the absolute amount of conversion of $E_2$ to $E_1$ it appeared to me that you multiplied your $\rho$ value times the fraction of $E_2$ that came from T, not times the whole pool of $E_2$. Wouldn't that lead to an erroneous absolute amount? In other words, shouldn't you use the whole?

*MacDonald* No, because with a production rate technique, what you are measuring is the amount of compound which enters that compartment for the first time per unit time. If we were to utilize all the oestrone for say conversion to oestradiol, some of that in turn had come from oestradiol so that we would in fact be measuring it twice. If it enters a compartment and re-enters, it was labelled during the first entry so that it does not further dilute the specific activity. That which arose for the first time from androstenedione and that which arose for the first time from oestradiol contribute to total oestrone production.

*Naftolin* I would like to know about the rapidity of the interconversion.

*MacDonald* The interconversion is very fast; the ratios are the same in blood within three hours as those which ultimately appeared in urine.

*Eik-Nes* In the cases where you can show secretion of glandular origin of oestrogens in the male, is this testicular secretion, or adrenal secretion or both?

*MacDonald* Dr Eik-Nes, I can't answer that. I am assuming that it is one or the other. The only direct information we have which will support testicular secretion which has also previously been reported by others is that there is an increased amount of oestradiol in testicular vein blood in patients with testicular feminization. The only other evidence I have to support the view that it is testicular, is that adrenal suppression in one of these patients did not eradicate that portion which was of glandular origin – but this is very indirect evidence and your point is well taken.

*Baird* As I understand it, the exclusion of direct secretion of oestrogen in the male depends critically on the quantitative amounts of oestrogen produced from plasma precursor androgens, i.e., from plasma androstenedione and testosterone. There are in fact two measurements; one is a blood production rate of plasma androgen as measured by constant infusion at a particular time of the day and the other is a urinary production rate of oestrogens integrated over several days. Now if there were significant diurnal variations in the blood production rate of either testosterone or androstenedione, the amount of oestrogen produced from plasma androgen might vary throughout the 24 hours. A number of people in this room have reported a diurnal variation in plasma concentration of testosterone of approximately 25 per cent (Dray, F.A., Reinberg, A. and Sebaoun, J., *C. r. Acad. Sci.* Paris, **261**, 573, 1965, and Resko, J. and Eik-Nes, K., *J. clin. Endocr. Metab.*, **26**, 573, 1966). I know of only one study where androstenedione was measured throughout the day and this demonstrated a 60 per cent drop at night as compared to the early morning specimen (Crafts, Llerena, Guevara, Lobotsky and Lloyd, *Steroids*, **12**, 151, 1968). Thus based on a blood production rate of testosterone and androstenedione as measured in the morning, the quantity of oestrogen produced from plasma androgens might have been overestimated.

*MacDonald* It is true that we are determining metabolic clearance rate at one point of time, specifically from our infusion. It is not quite true that we are determining the blood production rate at one specific point in time. The reason that this is not precisely correct is that we have taken four blood samples during the day. I realize that this does not totally compensate for the problem. But I think it would mitigate it being a major factor here.

*Jeffcoate* Lipsett's group have shown that normal young males treated with HCG increase their oestradiol production rate many times the increase in testosterone production rate measured at the same time – the increase in testosterone production is about twofold and that of oestradiol production is about tenfold. This suggests that either HCG is increasing the peripheral aromatization or it is increasing direct secretion of oestradiol, presumably from the testes.

*MacDonald* That may be the case. I would take issue with the premise that this results from increasing peripheral aromatization. At least it does not in the female – the administration of HCG does not alter the extent of conversion of plasma precursor to oestrogen. Whether or not HCG will in fact initiate or increase oestrogen secretion, and I think Dr Baird has some evidence that there might be small amounts – if HCG were in fact administered, perhaps it would. I think that these types of measurements would have to be performed in order to determine the mechanisms of origin of the increased oestrogen.

*Deshpande* In the absence of the obvious target organ in the male, what do you see as the physiological role for the oestrogens which are produced?

*MacDonald* I would prefer that others more attuned to the problems of oestrogen in the hypothalamus for example, should answer this question.

*Prunty* Which urinary metabolite did you use for the oestrogen production rate?

*MacDonald* We used oestrone glucuronoside in the case of oestrone and oestradiol glucuronoside in the case of oestradiol and we have also measured the specific activity of oestriol glucuronoside in each of these experiments. In some model experiments we investigated the specific activity of a wide range of both sulphates and glucuronides, but routinely we use oestrone, oestradiol and oestriol derived from β-glucuronidase hydrolysis.

*Prunty* I am not clear how you handled your results : the specific activities of these urinary metabolites presumably were not identical?

*MacDonald* The specific activities of oestrone glucoronoside with respect to the administration of isotopically labelled oestrone will yield the production rate of oestrone. The specific activity of urinary oestradiol glucoronoside, following the administration of oestradiol (as in the case of testosterone yielding oestradiol) will yield the production rate of oestradiol.

*Odell* I remind the audience that the supposed antioestrogen clomiphene elevates both LH and FSH in the normal male, so possibly oestrogen does have an important role that we are missing. I should like to ask Dr MacDonald to comment on the publication of Longcope, Kato and Horton, *J. clin. Invest.*, **48**, 2191, 1969, who did a similar study and could account for about 70 per cent of the oestradiol by conversion from precursors and about 30 per cent by direct secretion. Is there an explanation of the discrepancy?

*MacDonald* There are a few points – I am not sure that we can resolve the differences. Dr Baird was involved in part of these studies originally and perhaps he would like to say more. Horton's group did not in fact measure oestrogens in the study that they undertook. Rather they measured the availability of precursor and the extent of its conversion to oestrogen, but in the same subject did not measure oestrogen. They utilized the values of Dr Baird in calculating the blood production rates of oestrogen. I don't know really where the discrepancy resides. The differences, for those of you not familiar with the particular field, are that the blood production rate of oestrogen as measured is considerably higher than that observed in urine. This is, I think, a paradox that is perhaps unique in problems of isotope dilution. How one can get a higher blood production rate than urinary production rate utilizing the same metabolites, is a little difficult to understand. There were, earlier on, some difficulties in coming to equilibrium with the infused oestrone and oestradiol in order to calculate accurately metabolic clearance rate. I personally – from a prejudiced point of view – feel that they are still having trouble getting accurate metabolic clearance rates. I have no other explanation. Perhaps Dr Baird has some comments.

*Baird* Just to say that again it depends critically as to whether there is a diurnal variation in production rate of these hormones. The concentration of oestrone in peripheral plasma of men shows a marked diurnal variation (Baird and Guevara, *J. clin. Endocr.*, **29**, 149, 1969). The concentration in the morning specimens is about two or three times higher than the specimens taken at six o'clock at night. Dr Korenman in Los Angeles using a competitive protein binding method has confirmed this finding. So again we come back to the point I raised earlier in the discussion that what we are trying to do is compare a blood production rate at a particular time of day with an integrated 24-hour specimen. This point will only be resolved when the blood production rates of androgens and oestrogens and the conversion of one to another are measured simultaneously in the same subjects.

*Ismail* Professor MacDonald, have you any direct evidence obtained by measuring oestrogens in arterial and venous testicular plasma that normal young men are not secreting oestrogens?

*MacDonald* We have very minimal evidence. We have two patients now in which the venous concentration of testicular vein blood oestrogen was compared (not with arterial, but with peripheral levels) which I think is just as valid in this case. We found relatively small differences. Dr Baird, on the other hand, has demonstrated a somewhat higher concentration of oestrone in adrenal vein blood compared with peripheral plasma. However, as I recall this is relatively small. Of course our measurements are not precise enough to exclude small secretion rates by either the testis or adrenal.

*Exley* What evidence is there for C-19-hydroxylase in adrenal and testicular tissue?

*MacDonald* Aromatization has been claimed in these tissues, so I would assume that this means that there is C-19-hydroxylation. However, the extent of conversion of any precursor in testicular or adrenal tissue to oestrogens is exceedingly small. In addition it is very difficult to establish in fact that one has radiochemical homogeneity of the oestrogen product.

*Griffiths* We recently did some incubation studies with human adrenal tissue and found the conversion of androstenedione to oestrone or oestradiol was of the order of 0·05 per cent which is very small as you say and it is very difficult to confirm the identity of the compounds which are made.

*Eik-Nes* I should just like to remind the audience that the most critical study on aromatization by the adrenal gland was done by Engel; the amount of conversion he obtained was extremely poor, if it occurred at all. I have studied oestrogen secretion by the dog testes and I have proved that this organ is secreting an oestrogen.

*Strong* Professor MacDonald, would you please comment on the mechanism of action of spirolactone?

*MacDonald* Dr P. K. Siiteri in Dallas has some preliminary evidence which suggests that in some males who have been given spironolactone there is a marked increase of plasma 17α-hydroxyprogesterone; it would appear that spironolactone *in vivo* may interfere with 17-desmolase activity. The fact that the concentration of 17α-hydroxyprogesterone was high in his incubation studies would also corroborate this. There is also evidence that the levels of testosterone and the androstenedione were reduced. This effect disappears if the drug is removed.

*Prunty* Have you any data relating to the effect of gonadotrophins on oestrogen conversion in patients with ovarian carcinoma?

*MacDonald* We found no change in the conversion of androstenedione after operation, although there was a drop in the available precursor. We did radioimmunoassays of both LH and FSH. To our surprise and chagrin the levels were within the range of the follicular phase of the normal menstrual cycle. This disturbed us because Vande Wiele in a small number of cases was unable to show an acute drop of gonadotrophin levels after the intravenous administration of oestrone. There is therefore a discrepancy between his type of experiment and these findings; possibly due to the fact that one was an acute type of experiment and the other more chronic.

*Naftolin* Can you backtrack to the premenopausal state of these patients?

*MacDonald* In women with endometrial hyperplasia there is a striking correlation with their mechanism of oestrogen production. There is an increased availability of precursor androstenedione and a decreased ovarian secretion of oestradiol. This applies equally to the postmenopausal group, and also to very obese subjects in whom there is an increased conversion of precursor to product. The human endometrium is unusual in that the metabolism is in favour of oestrone with very little conversion of oestrone to oestradiol which explains the apparent paradox of a hyperplastic endometrium with low urinary oestrogen levels. There is the possibility that adenomatous endometrial hyperplasia is a dysoestrogenic rather than a hyperoestrogenic state. Vande Wiele and also some French workers have shown that the administration of a potent oestrogen such as oestradiol may cause the histological picture of cystic glandular hyperplasia to revert to a more normal one.

*Baird* One of the most striking features of your study is the tremendous range in the conversion of precursor to product in the postmenopausal woman as compared to that in the premenopausal woman. A thought which occurs to all of us is that this may be due to the different levels of gonadotrophins. Was there any correlation between the actual levels of LH or FSH and the percentage conversion of androstenedione? If you give an infusion of LH or HCG does this affect conversion rate?

*MacDonald* Our experiments with HCG administration were only done with premenopausal women. In normal subjects there is a good correlation between gonadotrophin levels and the degree of conversion of precursor. When however you come to deal with premenopausal castrates or young subjects with gonadal dysgenesis the correlation no longer holds. In the postmenopausal woman there is a slow increase in conversion with age and a marked increase with obesity, so much so that one can almost predict what their conversion will be by their weight.

*Odell* There is no discrepancy about your findings with regard to the response of gonadotrophins to oestrogen administration. There is both a dose relationship and a time relationship. At very low levels of oestrogen administration it may take a long time to suppress castrate gonadotrophin levels down. Thus there is probably no contradiction between your findings and those of Dr Vande Wiele in acute high dosage experiments. It is explained by the time factor.

Is oestrone *per se* an oestrogen in the human female or is it oestrogenic because it is converted to oestradiol?

*MacDonald* I can't say. One can speculate that the effect of oestrone is different from that of oestradiol but whether this is due to differential conversion of oestrone to oestradiol in various target tissues is impossible to say. We are investigating this very point at present. When endogenous oestradiol is being produced the endometrium will not concentrate oestrone to a higher degree than in plasma but in the absence of oestradiol there is some slight concentration of oestrone in the endometrium. This, however, only applies to the intravenous administration of oestrone. If you administer androstenedione, the product of which is oestrone, the picture is quite different.

*Odell* Korenman in Los Angeles has shown that the binding affinity of the isolated uterine receptor protein is much higher for oestradiol than for oestrone, which could explain your findings.

*MacDonald* This may be true. Jensen has shown that after the initial stages the binding of oestradiol and oestrone is not only quantitatively but also qualitatively different. This spurs us on.

# Steroids in Blood Reflecting Ovarian Function

DAVID T. BAIRD

Department of Obstetrics and Gynaecology
University of Edinburgh

¶ UNTIL recently we depended for our assessment of ovarian function on the measurement of certain metabolites of hormones secreted by the ovary and excreted in the urine. Measurement of the urinary excretion of pregnanediol and oestriol as an index of ovarian secretion of progesterone and oestradiol respectively, has given us an enormous amount of useful information concerning ovarian function in physiological and pathological conditions [1]. However, the quantity of a metabolite of a hormone excreted in the urine is related not only to the quantity of hormone secreted by endocrine gland(s), but also to the proportion of hormone metabolized to that metabolite by the body, especially the liver and kidneys, and the clearance of the metabolite from the blood by the kidneys. Thus differences in urinary excretion may represent, not differences in secretion, but differences in metabolism. In order to differentiate between secretion and metabolism isotope dilution techniques were introduced [2]. In some circumstances however these can give a misleading impression of the production rate of hormone which is physiologically active, e.g., when a large amount of hormone is produced from a precursor in a compartment which is not in equilibrium with circulating blood. This has been shown to be the case for testosterone where a large amount of testosterone is produced in the liver from androstenedione and dehydroepiandrosterone and converted to testosterone glucuronide without mixing with blood testosterone [3].

It might be expected that the concentration of a steroid in peripheral blood would reflect ovarian secretion more directly than its excretion in urine. Since the development of micro-analytical techniques employing double isotope derivatives [4], gas chromatography with electron capture [5], fluorimetry [6] and competitive protein binding [7], the measurement of steroids in peripheral plasma of non-pregnant women has become possible.

*Steroids secreted by ovary*

It is now well established, largely as a result of the *in vitro* incubations of Ryan and Smith [8], that the ovary has the biosynthetic capacity to make progestogens, androgens and oestrogens from $^{14}C$ acetate. Until recently it was assumed that progesterone and oestradiol-17β were the two main secretory products of the ovary in physiological circumstances. This was natural because it is possible to replace many of the functions of the ovary in the oophorectomized animal by the injection of these hormones in the appropriate amounts and proportions, e.g., maintenance of pregnancy. However, comparison of the concentration of steroids present in ovarian venous plasma with that of peripheral venous plasma demonstrated that practically every steroid in the biosynthetic pathway from pregnenolone to oestradiol is *secreted* by the ovary.

It has been demonstrated, using reliable methods, that the concentration of 'free' progesterone, 17α-OH progesterone, dehydroepiandrosterone, androstenedione, testosterone, oestrone and oestradiol 17β is higher in ovarian venous than in peripheral plasma, indicating secretion by the ovary (Table 1).

Although other steroids such as pregnenolone [9], 20α-dihydroprogesterone [10], dehydroepiandrosterone sulphate [11, 12] and oestrone sulphate [13] have been measured in ovarian venous plasma, their secretion has not been established by simultaneous estimations in both peripheral and ovarian venous plasma in normal subjects. This presentation therefore will concentrate on the seven steroids listed in Table 1.

TABLE 1. Steroids present in higher concentration in human ovarian than in peripheral venous plasma

| Steroid | Author |
|---|---|
| Progesterone | Mikhail (1967) |
| 17α OH Progesterone | Mikhail (1967) |
| Dehydroepiandrosterone | Rivarola, Saez, Jones, Jones, Migeon (1967) |
| Androstenedione | Horton, Romanoff, Walker (1966) |
| Testosterone | Horton, Romanoff, Walker (1966) |
| Oestrone | Varangot and Cedard (1959) |
| Oestradiol-17β | Schild (1966) |

*Ovarian steroids in peripheral plasma*

The concentration of progesterone, 17α OH progesterone, oestrone and oestradiol-17β in peripheral plasma fluctuates markedly throughout the menstrual cycle, corresponding to the growth and regression of the follicle and corpus luteum (Fig. 1). Fluctuations in the concentration of dehydroepiandrosterone, androstenedione and testosterone have not been demonstrated, although the highest concentrations of the latter steroid occur in the middle of the cycle [14] and the urinary excretion of testosterone glucuronide is maximum at midcycle and in the luteal phase [15]. Serial studies of the concentration of these steroids in relation to the phase of the menstrual cycle are required, for Abrahams, Lobotsky and Lloyd [16] showed that the blood production rate of androstenedione was raised significantly in the luteal as compared to the follicular phase of the cycle. The range in concentration is very large: from over 1 μg/100 ml for progesterone in the luteal phase of the cycle to less than 3·0 ng/100 ml for oestradiol in the early follicular phase. This has important implications as far as the conversion of one steroid to another is concerned, e.g., the concentration of androstenedione is 25 times greater than that of oestrone. Hence a very small percentage conversion of circulating androstenedione to oestrone, e.g., 1 per cent, would make up a large fraction of circulating oestrone [17].

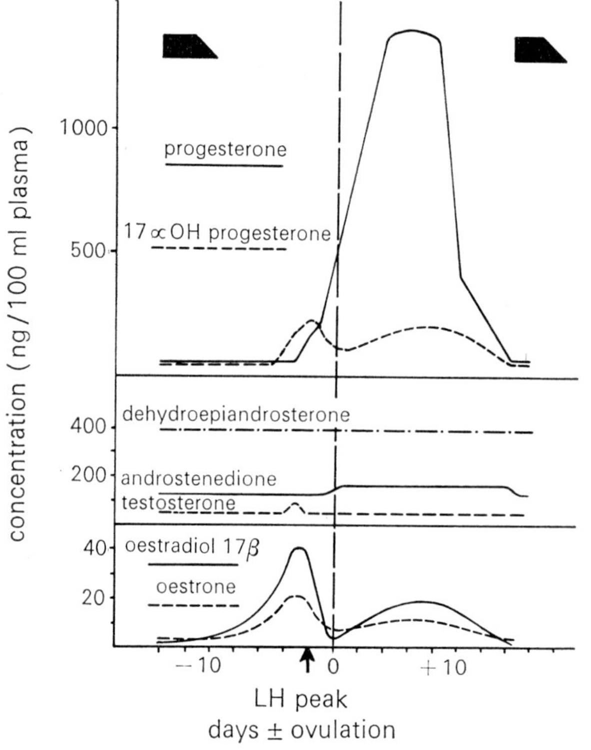


FIGURE 1
The concentration (ng/100 ml of plasma) of ovarian steroids in peripheral plasma throughout the menstrual cycle. The values are grouped ± day of ovulation, which is assumed to be the day of the LH peak + 2. The values for oestrone and oestradiol-17β are from [27]; testosterone, androstenedione and dehydroepiandrosterone are the mean of several published papers [19]; 17α-OH progesterone is from [48]; and that of progesterone from [49]

Some of these steroids originate almost exclusively by ovarian secretion, e.g., oestradiol 17β and progesterone, while the ovarian secretion of other steroids, e.g., dehydroepiandrosterone, is very small in comparison to the adrenal contribution [18]. There is considerable extraglandular production of steroids such as testosterone and oestrone [19].

*Steroids in ovarian venous blood or plasma*

As stated above, the secretion of a steroid by the ovary can be established by demonstrating that its concentration is higher in venous effluent than in arterial afferent plasma [20]. In practice it is usually assumed that the concentration of steroid is the same in peripheral venous and arterial plasma; i.e., there is negligible metabolism or secretion by the tissues of the forearm. This was confirmed for oestradiol-17β in an experiment, when 6,7$^3$H oestradiol-17β was infused at a constant rate for 180 minutes into a peripheral vein of a woman aged 33 years. A steady state was achieved after 150 minutes infusion as indicated by the constant concentration of radioactive oestradiol-17β in three samples of peripheral venous plasma taken at 15-minute intervals. There was no difference in the concentration of either oestradiol, or oestrone formed from oestradiol, between arterial and venous samples collected simultaneously (Table 2).

TABLE 2. The concentration of radioactive oestrone ($E_1$) and oestradiol-17β ($E_2$) (d.p.m./10 ml of plasma) in peripheral and pelvic venous plasma, and arterial plasma, in a 33-year-old woman undergoing hysterectomy for menorrhagia on day 17 of cycle. 6,7 $^3$H oestradiol-17β was infused at a constant rate (2μc/hour) from time 0 into a peripheral vein. Anaesthesia was induced at 140 minutes

| | D.P.M./10 ml plasma | | | | | |
|---|---|---|---|---|---|---|
| Exp. Time (min) | Peripheral venous | | Arterial | | Pelvic venous | |
| | $E_1$ | $E_2$ | $E_1$ | $E_2$ | $E_1$ | $E_2$ |
| 150 | 200 | 1,353 | 157 | 1,169 | 126 | 1,155 |
| 165 | 134 | 1,133 | 137 | 1,287 | 152 | 1,237 |
| 180 | – | – | – | – | 126 | 1,157 |
| Mean | 167 | 1,243 | 147 | 1,223 | 135 | 1,183 |

Because of its site in the pelvis and its complex blood supply, it is impossible in women to obtain ovarian venous blood in the conscious unstressed subject. Samples are collected at laparatomy when the stress of anaesthesia, surgical trauma and manipulation may alter the secretion of ovarian steroids. Owing to the complex nature of the ovarian vascular supply, venous effluent blood is usually diluted to a variable degree with blood draining the uterus and lateral pelvic wall. Thus a quantitative assessment of ovarian secretion by measuring concentration of steroids in ovarian venous effluent is virtually impossible. It is however possible to correct for many of these sources of inaccuracies by relating the concentration of a steroid to another steroid which is derived uniquely by secretion from the ovary. It is likely that virtually all the circulating oestradiol is derived by ovarian secretion (see below) so that a reasonable estimate of the ovarian contribution to the concentration in peripheral plasma of other ovarian steroids can be made by relating their concentration to that of oestradiol. Similarly by relating adrenal steroids to cortisol concentration, and testicular steroids to testosterone, the secretion rates of steroids from other endocrine glands can be calculated [21].

*Oestrogens*

In 1962 Smith and Ryan [22] found that the concentration of oestradiol-17β was higher than oestrone in follicular fluid in both halves of the menstrual cycle. When cells from follicle linings [8] and corpus luteum [23] were incubated *in vitro* with $^{14}$C acetate, oestradiol-17β was the major oestrogen formed. This indirect evidence, suggesting that oestradiol-17β was the main oestrogen secreted by the ovary, was confirmed by the analysis of the concentration of oestrogens in ovarian venous plasma [9, 10, 24–26] (see Table 3.) In all cases the concentration of oestradiol was higher than that of oestrone and the concentration of both steroids was much higher in ovarian than in peripheral plasma. The wide range in concentration can be explained partially by the fact that in some cases the blood was draining the 'inactive' ovary, i.e., the one not containing the corpus luteum or preovulatory follicle. Figure 2 illustrates that the concentration of oestradiol was much higher in the plasma collected from the active ovary ($1{\cdot}14 \pm 0{\cdot}33$ S.E. μg/100 ml plasma) than from the inactive ovary ($0{\cdot}093 \pm 0{\cdot}032$ S.E.) $P < 0{\cdot}05$. The twelvefold difference in concentration indicates that over 90 per cent of secreted oestradiol originates from the active ovary.

The difference in concentration between the two ovaries is less marked in the case of oestrone. This is reflected by the difference in ratio $E_2/E_1$ between the active and inactive ovary (Fig. 3). The $E_2/E_1$ in the plasma collected from the active ovary ($9{\cdot}3 \pm 0{\cdot}7$) was significantly higher than the ratio from the inactive ovary ($3{\cdot}6 \pm 1{\cdot}1$ $P < 0{\cdot}001$) or peripheral plasma ($1{\cdot}48 \pm 0{\cdot}27$ $P < 0{\cdot}001$). This together with the fact that the highest ratios occurred in those samples collected from women in the preovulatory and mid-luteal phases of the cycle suggests that the preovulatory follicle and corpus luteum secrete increasing amounts of oestradiol, both absolutely and relative to oestrone.

This hypothesis receives support from the finding that the ratio $E_2/E_1$ in samples of peripheral plasma changes throughout the menstrual cycle [27]. The concentration of oestradiol in peripheral plasma rises tenfold from menstruation to the preovulatory peak whereas the increase in oestrone concentration is only threefold. This is reflected by the significant change in the ratio of $E_2/E_1$ in peripheral plasma from $0{\cdot}67 \pm 0{\cdot}13$ during menstruation to a maximum of $1{\cdot}90 \pm 0{\cdot}12$ preovulatory. There is an abrupt fall in the next few days to $1{\cdot}32 \pm 0{\cdot}21$ with a smaller rise again as the corpus luteum develops ($1{\cdot}63 \pm 0{\cdot}18$).

Although the most likely explanation for this change in ratio is that the follicle and corpus luteum secrete increasing amounts of oestradiol, there are several other possibilities which must be considered:

(*a*) *Extra ovarian secretion of oestrone or oestradiol.* Adrenal venous plasma contains no detectable oestradiol-17β and very small concentrations of free oestrone [28, 29]. The concentration of the latter steroid however is so low that the maximum adrenal secretion has been calculated to be less than 10 μg per day, amounting to at most 10 per cent of the blood production rate of oestrone in normal women [21]. It is unlikely therefore that there is a significant extra ovarian secretion of oestrogen.

TABLE 3. Concentration of oestrone ($E_1$) and oestradiol-17β ($E_2$) in human ovarian venous plasma

| | Conc. ± S.E. (μg/100 ml) | | | | | | | |
|---|---|---|---|---|---|---|---|---|
| | Active | | | | Inactive | | | |
| Author | n | $E_1$ | $E_2$ | $E_2/E_1$ | n | $E_1$ | $E_2$ | $E_2/E_1$ |
| TOTAL | | | | | | | | |
| Varangot and Cedard (1959) | | 1·7 ±0·3 | 2·0 ±0·5 | 1·18 | | | | |
| Schild (1966) | 2 | 1·01 | 1·59 | 1·59 | 2 | 0·19 | 0·12 | 0·63 |
| FREE | | | | | | | | |
| Mahesh (1964) | 3 | <0·2 | 1·1 –2·8 | 10·0 (app.) | | | | |
| Mikhail (1967) | 4 | 0·065 –0·172 | 0·403 –1·76 | 6·4 | 2 | 0·071 –0·080 | 0·193 –0·359 | 3·8 |
| Lloyd, Lobotsky, Weisz, Baird, McCracken, Pupkin, Zanartu, Puga (1971) | 13 | 0·122 ±0·033 | 1·14 ±0·33 | 9·3 ±0·7 | 7 | 0·024 ±0·005 | 0·093 ±0·031 | 3·6 ±1·1 |

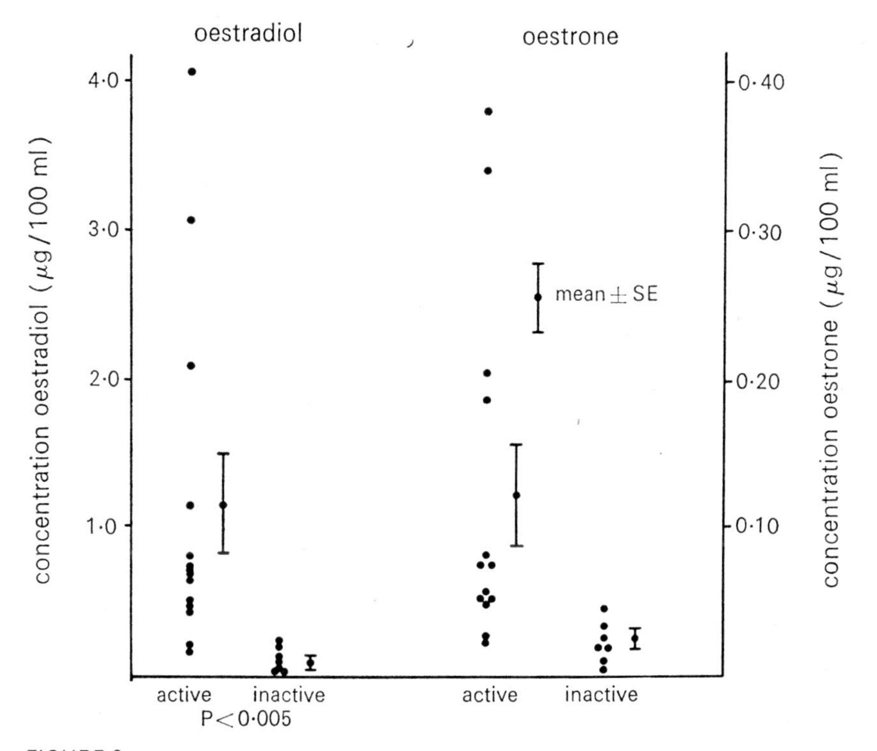


FIGURE 2

The concentration of oestrone and oestradiol-17β in ovarian venous plasma (μg/100 ml plasma) of 18 normal women at varying stages of the menstrual cycle. Note the tenfold difference in scale for the concentration of oestrone. The values have been grouped into those obtained from the 'active' ovary, i.e., the one containing the preovulatory follicle or corpus luteum, and the 'inactive' ovary (from [9])

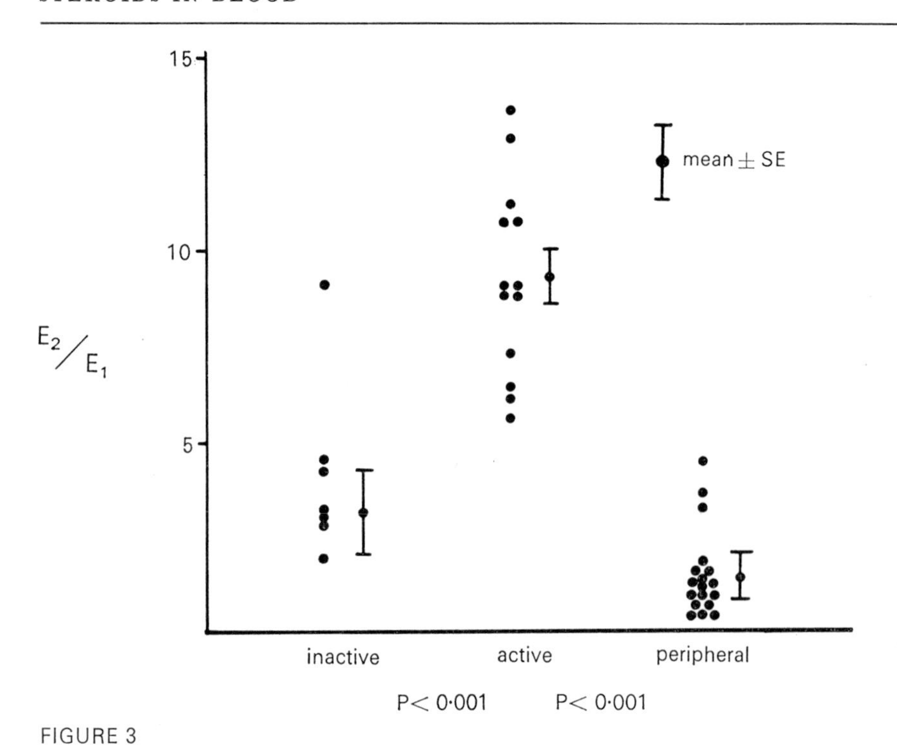


FIGURE 3

The ratio of $\frac{\text{oestradiol-17}\beta}{\text{oestrone}}$ ($E_2/E_1$) in the peripheral plasma of 18 normal women and in the ovarian venous plasma draining the 'active' (13) and 'inactive' (7) ovaries. The mean ratio ± SE in plasma from the 'active' ovary (9·3 ± 0·7) is significantly different from the 'inactive' ovary (3·6 ± 0·7 $P < 0·001$) and in peripheral plasma (1·48 ± 0·27 $P < 0·001$) (from [9])

(*b*) *Extra ovarian production of oestrone or oestradiol.* Many steriods circulating in blood are derived not only by direct secretion, but by extraglandular conversion from precursor steroids which are themselves secreted [30]. Dynamic studies have demonstrated in premenopausal women that less than 5 per cent of circulating oestradiol-17β in peripheral plasma is derived from oestrone (the only likely precursor) [19]. As the adrenal secretes no oestradiol-17β (see above) over 90 per cent of circulating oestradiol must be derived by direct secretion from the preovulatory follicle or corpus luteum. In contrast there is an appreciable extra ovarian production of oestrone. 20–35 per cent of circulating oestrone is derived by conversion in blood from oestradiol, the amount depending on the phase of the menstrual cycle [31, 32]. Although the conversion ratio of androstenedione to oestrone in blood is only 0·007 in women, the concentration of androstenedione in peripheral plasma is so much higher than that of oestrone (about 25 times) that an appreciable proportion (about 20 per cent) of circulating oestrone is derived from this steroid [33].

(*c*) *Difference in metabolism or clearance of oestrone and oestradiol in peripheral plasma.* The concentration of a steroid in peripheral blood or plasma is related not only to its secretion, or more accurately to its production rate, but also inversely to its rate of metabolism.

$$i = \frac{P_B}{M.C.R.}$$

where $i$ = concentration
$P_B$ = Blood production rate
M.C.R. = Metabolic Clearance Rate [34]

Thus if the M.C.R. of oestrone and oestradiol were different and changed relative to one another throughout the menstrual cycle, one might explain both the lower $E_2/E_1$ ratio in peripheral as compared to ovarian venous plasma, and the change in ratio throughout the cycle. However the M.C.R. of oestrone is about double that of oestradiol [31, 32] and would tend to *increase* the $E_2/E_1$ ratio in peripheral as compared to ovarian venous plasma. In addition there is no significant difference in M.C.R. of either oestrogen in the luteal as compared to the follicular phase of the cycle, although repeated studies in the same subject around ovulation have not been reported. [31]

Thus the sixfold difference in $E_2/E_1$ ratio in ovarian venous plasma as compared to peripheral plasma can be explained partially by a significant extra ovarian production of oestrone. However the combined conversions from oestradiol and androstenedione are only enough to cancel the effect of the difference in M.C.R. between oestrone and oestradiol. Even allowing for a small secretion of free oestrone from the inactive ovary and the adrenal, there remains an appreciable proportion of circulating oestrone in peripheral plasma, the source of which is unaccounted for.

It is possible that another precursor as yet unrecognized is secreted and is converted to oestrone peripherally [19]. As measured by fluorimetry Brown (1970) has recently demonstrated that the ratio of oestrone sulphate to free oestrone in peripheral plasma of normal women is approximately 5/1 [13]. Oestrone sulphate is present in higher concentrations than free oestrone in pregnancy plasma [35]. Varangot and Cedard [24] and Schild [25], measuring total hydrolyzable oestrogens, found relatively higher concentrations of oestrone in ovarian venous plasma than those authors who have measured unconjugated oestrone [9, 10, 26] suggesting that a conjugate of oestrone may be secreted by the ovary (Table 2).

*Androgens*

Turning to the androgens, we find that testosterone (Table 4) [9–11, 18, 36), dehydroepiandrosterone (Table 5) [11, 18] and in particular androstenedione (Table 6) [9–11, 18, 36, 38, 39] are present in higher

TABLE 4. Concentration of testosterone in human ovarian venous plasma

| Author | Concentration µg/100 ml ± S.E. | n | Range |
|---|---|---|---|
| Horton, Romanoff, Walker (1966) | 0·074 ± 0·006 | 5 | 0·054–0·095 |
| Mikhail (1967) | 0·209 ± 0·014 | 5 | 0·159–0·242 |
| Rivarola, Saez, Jones, Jones, Migeon (1967) | 0·130 ± 0·025 | 5 | 0·052–0·206 |
| Gandy and Peterson (1968) | 0·33 ± 0·09 | 9 | 0·12 –1.04 |
| Lloyd, Lobotsky, Weisz, Baird, McCracken, Pupkin, Zanartu, Puga (1971) | Active: 0·514 ± 0·15<br>Inactive: 0·236 ± 0·06 | 12<br>7 | 0·083–2·004 |

TABLE 5. Concentration of dehydroepiandrosterone in human ovarian venous plasma

| Author | Concentration µg/100 ml ± S.E. | n | Range |
|---|---|---|---|
| Rivarola, Saez, Jones, Jones, Migeon (1967) | 1·87 ± 0·31 | 5 | 0·72–2·51 |
| Gandy and Peterson (1968) | 1·15 ± 0·09 | 11 | 0·72–1·74 |

TABLE 6. Concentration of androstenedione in human ovarian venous plasma (µg/100 ml ± S.E.)

| Author | Mean conc. ± S.E. | n | Range |
|---|---|---|---|
| Mikhail, Allen, Zander (1963)<br>Mikhail and Allen (1966)<br>Mikhail (1967) | 4·88 ± 1·05 | 10 | 1·5–9·8 |
| Horton, Romanoff, Walker (1966) | 0·822 | 5 | 0·45–1·20 |
| Rivarola, Saez, Jones, Jones, Migeon (1967) | 1·63 ± 0·56 | 5 | 0·47–3·56 |
| Gandy and Peterson (1968) | 2·04 ± 0·51 | 11 | 0·50–5·97 |
| Lloyd, Lobotsky, Weisz, Baird, McCracken, Pupkin, Zanartu, Puga (1971) | 7·95 ± 2·12 | 17 | 1·5–30·7 |

concentration in ovarian venous than in peripheral plasma. Although the ovarian/peripheral ratio of the dehydroepiandrosterone and testosterone is only about 2/1, that of androstenedione, which is known to be an important precursor in blood of circulating testosterone [39], is very high [20/1] indicating that the ovary in normal women is an important source of this androgen. The low concentration of androstenedione in peripheral plasma in Turner's syndrome (0·047 µg/100 ml) [18], castrate women (00.88 µg/100 ml) [16] and prepubertal females [40] would support this view.

As stated above there are many factors contributing to the wide range in concentration of steroids in ovarian venous plasma. Little account appears to have been taken as to the state of the menstrual cycle although it is likely that the ovarian secretion of androstenedione would vary depending on the stage of development of the follicle or corpus luteum. In one series [36] the blood was collected from women with breast cancer, one of whom was postmenopausal. In only one of the four remaining subjects was blood collected near the middle of the cycle and may account for the rather low values reported in this series.

Lloyd et al. [9] found that the concentration of androstenedione and testosterone in ovarian venous plasma from the active ovary ($9{\cdot}39 \pm 2{\cdot}9$) was not significantly different from the inactive ovary ($3{\cdot}91 \pm 1{\cdot}09$) although the higher mean in the former was due to three very high values in preovulatory and mid-luteal samples (Fig. 4). This might indicate that the ovarian secretion and hence the total blood production rate of androstenedione might vary throughout the menstrual cycle. The higher concentration [41] and blood production rate of androstenedione [16], and urinary excretion of testosterone glucuronide in urine [15] in the luteal phase of the cycle would support this view.

The $A/E_2$ ratio in plasma from the active ovary ($10{\cdot}4 \pm 2{\cdot}5$ S.E.) is tenfold lower than that from the inactive ovary ($97{\cdot}7 \pm 40$ $P < 0{\cdot}005$),

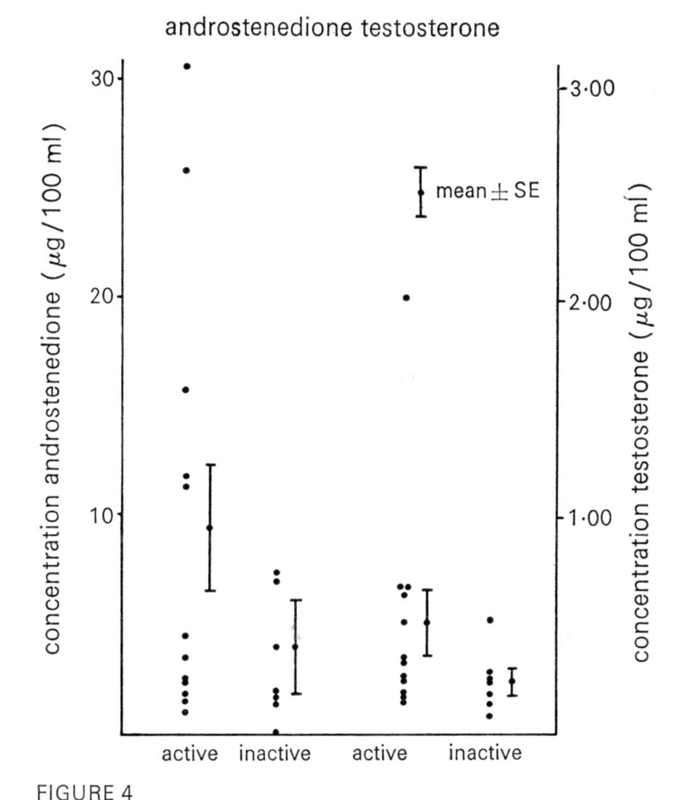


FIGURE 4

The concentration (μg/100 ml plasma) of androstenedione and testosterone in ovarian venous plasma from 18 normal women throughout the menstrual cycle. Note the tenfold difference in scale for testosterone (from [9])

indicating that relatively more A than $E_2$ is secreted by the inactive ovary (Fig. 5). We can conclude therefore that the interstitial tissue in the inactive ovary as well as in the follicle and corpus luteum secretes significant amounts of androstenedione [42].

In peripheral plasma the A/$E_2$ ratio ($18{\cdot}8 \pm 5{\cdot}0$) is nearly double that in plasma from the active ovary. The M.C.R. of androstenedione is about double that of oestradiol [27] and would tend to *decrease* the A/$E_2$ ratio in peripheral as compared to ovarian venous plasma. Thus ovarian secre-

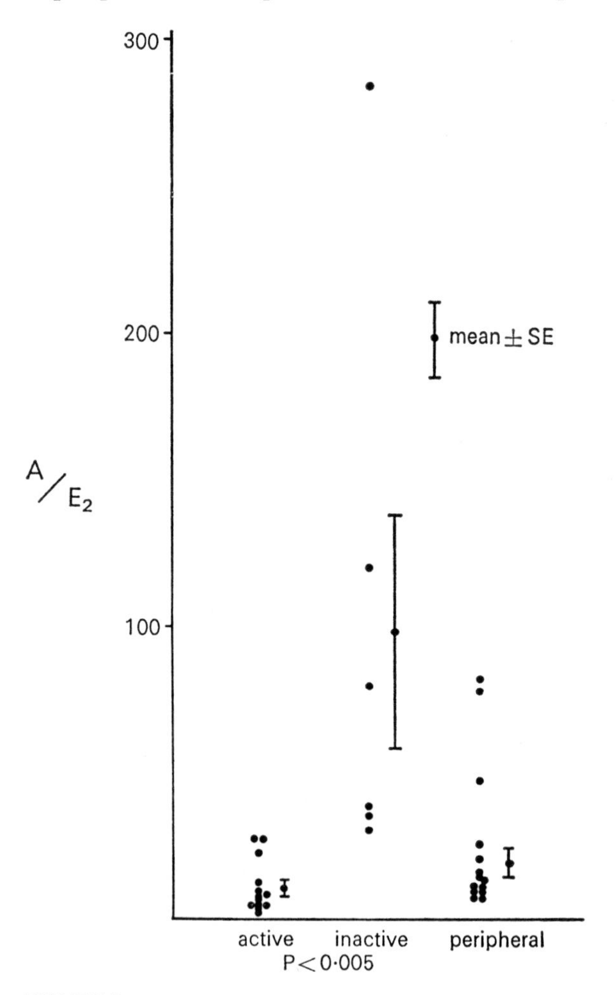


FIGURE 5

The mean ratio (± SE) of $\frac{\text{androstenedione}}{\text{oestradiol-17}\beta}$ (A/$E_2$) in ovarian venous plasma draining the 'active' and 'inactive' ovaries and in peripheral plasma of 14 normal women at different stages of the menstrual cycle. The mean ratio A/$E_2$ in plasma from the 'inactive' ovary ($97{\cdot}7 \pm 40$) is significantly higher than the ratio in plasma draining the 'active' ovary ($10{\cdot}4 \pm 2{\cdot}5$ $P < 0{\cdot}005$) (from [9])

tion from the active ovary can only account for about 25 per cent of the circulating androstenedione. If we assume a similar amount arises from the inactive ovary and about 10 per cent from dehydroepiandrosterone [43] there remains about 40 per cent to be secreted by the adrenal glands. This corresponds fairly well with the amount calculated on the basis of analysis of androstenedione in adrenal venous plasma [21].

## CONCLUSION

It might be expected that the concentration of a steroid in peripheral blood would bear some relationship to the concentration of steroid in the cytoplasm of the cells of the target organ. However, steroids exist in blood bound in varying proportions to proteins, e.g., transcortin, and to red blood cells. The affinity with which a steroid is bound to a specific plasma protein is probably important in determining not only its rate of clearance [30] but also its uptake by the cells of the target organ [44].

It is probably relevant that those steroids of highest biological activity, i.e., cortisol, testosterone and oestradiol-17β, are bound to specific plasma proteins with high affinity, which may limit their biological potency [44]. It is not known whether the bound steroid can be taken up by the tissues of the target organ as has been suggested for thyroxine [45]. If this were so it would provide a means of providing high concentrations of steroid in the target organ while limiting the concentration in other tissues. Studies of the alterations in clearance [46] and in protein binding [47] of testosterone have revealed abnormalities in hirsutism which were not obvious from the concentration of circulating hormones. The function of 17α-OH progesterone, androstenedione, dehydroepiandrosterone and oestrone secreted by the ovary are unknown, although by serving as pre-hormones in specific tissues they may provide high concentrations of potent hormone usually without high circulating levels. Application of micro-analytical methods for measuring the concentration, metabolism and physical state ovarian steroids in blood to abnormalities of ovarian function, should give us further insight into the pathogenesis of these conditions.

## ACKNOWLEDGMENTS

The author is grateful to grants from Population Council, Lalor Foundation and MRC Great Britain during the course of this work.

## REFERENCES


[1] Brown, J.B. and Matthew, G.D., *Recent Prog. Hormone Res.*, **18**, 337, 1962.

[2] Vande Wiele, R., MacDonald, P., Gurpide, E. and Lieberman, S., *Recent Prog. Hormone Res.*, **19**, 275, 1963.

[3] Korenman, S.G. and Lipsett, M.B., *J. clin. Invest.*, **43**, 2125, 1964.

[4] Kliman, B. and Peterson, R., *J. biol. Chem.*, **235**, 1639, 1960.

[5] Brooks, C.J.W., Zabkiewicz, J.A. In *Hormones in Blood*, p. 51. Eds. C.H. Gray and A.L. Bacharach. London/New York: Academic Press, 1967.

[6] Brown, J.B., MacNaughton, C., Smith, M.A. and Smythe, B., *J. Endocr.*, **40**, 175, 1968.

[7] Murphy, B.E.P., *J. clin. Endocr. Metab.*, **27**, 973, 1967.

[8] Ryan, K.J. and Smith, O.W., *J. biol. Chem.*, **236**, 705, 1961.

[9] Lloyd, C.W., Lobotsky, J., Weisz, J., Baird, D.T., McCracken, J.A., Pupkin, M., Zanartu, J. and Puga, J., *J. clin. Endocr. Metab.*, **32**, 155, 1971.

[10] Mikhail, G., *Clin. Obstet. Gynaec.*, **10**, 29, 1967.

[11] Rivarola, M.A., Saez, J.M., Jones, H.W., Jones, G.S. and Migeon, C.J., *Johns Hopkins med. J.*, **121**, 82, 1967.

[12] Aakvaag, A., and Fylling, P., *Acta Endocr., Copnh.*, **57**, 447, 1968.

[13] Brown, J.B., Personal communication, 1970.

[14] Lobotsky, J.A., Wyss, I.H., Segre, E.J. and Lloyd, C.W., *J. clin. Endocr. Metab.*, **24**, 1261, 1964.

[15] Ismail, A.A.A., Harkness, R.A. and Loraine, J.A., *Acta endocr., Copnh.*, **58**, 685, 1968.

[16] Abrahams, G., Lobotsky, J.H. and Lloyd, C.W., *J. clin. Invest.*, **48**, 696, 1969.

[17] MacDonald, P.C., Rombaut, R.P. and Siiteri, P.K., *J. clin. Endocr. Metab.*, **27**, 1103, 1967.

[18] Gandy, H.M. and Peterson, R.E., *J. clin. Endocr. Metab.*, **28**, 949, 1968.

[19] Baird, D.T., Horton, R., Longcope, C. and Tait, J.F., *Perspectives Biol. Med.*, **11**, 384, 1968.

[20] Eik-Nes, K.B. and Hall, P.F., *Vitam. Hormones*, **23**, 153, 1965.

[21] Baird, D.T. In *Reproductive Endocrinology*, p. 95. Ed. W.J. Irvine. Edinburgh/London: E. & S. Livingstone, 1970.

[22] Smith, O.W. and Ryan, K.J., *Am. J. Obstet. Gynec.*, **84**, 141, 1962.

[23] Huang, W.Y. and Pearlman, W.H., *J. biol. Chem.*, **238**, 1308, 1963.

[24] Varangot, J. and Cedard, L., *C. r. Soc. Biol.*, **153**, 1701, 1959.

[25] Schild, W., *Geburtsh Frauenheilk*, **26**, 607, 1966.

[26] Mahesh, V.B. In *Proceedings of the Second International Congress of Endocrinology*, London 1964, p. 945. Ed. S. Taylor. Excerpta Medica Found. Amsterdam, New York, London.

[27] Baird, D.T. and Guevara, A., *J. clin. Endocr. Metab.*, **29**, 149, 1969.

[28] Roy, E. and Brown, J.B., Quoted by J.K. Grant, *Br. med. Bull.*, **18**, 100, 1961.

[29] Baird, D.T., Uno, A. and Melby, J., *J. Endocr.*, **45**, 135, 1969.

[30] Baird, D.T., Horton, R., Longcope, C. and Tait, J.F., *Recent Prog. Hormone Res.*, **25**, 611, 1969.

[31] Longcope, C., Layne, D.S. and Tait, J.F., *J. clin. Invest.*, **47**, 93, 1968.

[32] Hembree, W.C., Bardin, C.W. and Lipsett, M.B., *J. clin. Invest.*, **48**, 1809, 1969.

[33] Longcope, C., Kato, T. and Horton, R., *J. clin. Invest.*, **48**, 2191, 1969.

[34] Tait, J.F. and Burstein, S. In *The Hormones*, vol. 5, p. 441. Eds. G. Pincus, K.V. Thimann and E.B. Astwood. New York: Academic Press. 1964.

[35] Purdy, R.H., Engel, L.L. and Oncley, J.L., *J. biol. Chem.*, **236,** 1043, 1961.
[36] Horton, R., Romanoff, E. and Walker, J., *J. clin. Endocr. Metab.*, **24,** 1267, 1966.
[37] Mikhail, G., Zander, T. and Allen, W.M., *J. clin. Endocr. Metab.*, **23,** 1267, 1963.
[38] Mikhail, G. and Allen, W.M., *Proceedings Second International Congress Hormone Steroids*, Milan, 1966, p. 150. Eds. E.B. Romanoff and L. Martin. Excerpta Medica Found., Amsterdam/New York.
[39] Horton, R. and Tait, J.F., *J. clin. Invest.*, **45,** 301, 1966.
[40] Frasier, S.D. and Horton, R., *Steroids*, **8,** 777, 1966.
[41] Rosenfeld, R.L., *Steroids*, **14,** 251, 1969.
[42] Leymarie, P. and Savard, K., *J. clin. Endocr. Metab.*, **28,** 1547, 1968.
[43] Horton, R. and Tait. J.F. *J. clin. Endocr. Metab.*, **27,** 79, 1967.
[44] Rosner, W., *New Engl. J. Med.*, **281,** 658, 1969.
[45] Oppenheimer, J.H., Surks, M.I. and Schwartz, H.L., *Recent Prog. Hormone Res.*, **25,** 381, 1969.
[46] Bardin, C.W. and Lipsett, M.B., *J. clin. Invest.*, **46,** 891, 1967.
[47] Dray, F., Monszowiez, I., Ledru, M.J., Crépy, O., Delzant, G. and Sebaoun, *J. Annal. d'Endocrinol. Paris*, **30,** 223, 1969.
[48] Strott, C.A., Yoshimi, T., Ross, G.T. and Lipsett, M.B., *J. clin. Endocr. Metab.*, **29,** 1157, 1969.
[49] Johansson, E.D.B. and Wide, L., *Acta endocr., Copnh.*, **62,** 82, 1969.

## *Discussion of paper by Dr Baird*

*Gemzell* We measured the ratio between oestrone and oestradiol just before induction of ovulation with gonadotrophin and four days later we found in the urine twice as much oestrone as oestradiol. After ovulation there was a very marked increase in oestradiol as compared to just before ovulation.
*Baird* You and Dr Brown have noticed that there are probably significant differences in the ratio of the three metabolites in the different parts of the cycle. One of the reasons that it wasn't very obvious is that the interconversion of oestrone and oestradiol is so extensive in the body that it obscures any difference in the pattern of secretion.
*Loraine* Another situation in which differences occur is in the administration of clomiphene citrate which produces a preferential increase in oestrone output as compared with that for the other classical oestrogens. A further interesting point about clomiphene is the fact that the rise in oestriol output as a result of its administration lags well behind that for oestrone and oestradiol. It is now known that clomiphene citrate consists of a mixture of two isomers, designated *cis* and *trans*, and that the former compound is the more active in relation to ovarian stimulation (Charles, D., Klein, T., Lunn, S.F. and Loraine, J.A., *J. Obstet. Gynaec. Br. Commw.* **76**, 1100, 1969). Preliminary evidence indicates that the preferential effect on oestrone output appears to be more pronounced with the normally used clomiphene citrate than with the *cis* isomer.

*Naftolin* Can Dr Loraine tell us whether he thinks this is an effect of the clomiphene on the ovary or on the pituitary?

*Loraine* The site of action of clomiphene has been a controversial point for some time, some workers believing that it acts through the pituitary-hypothalamic axis and others that it has a direct effect on the ovaries. In the research which our Unit conducted in the field of clomiphene isomers gonadotrophins were not estimated, and accordingly a definite conclusion with respect to the site of action of such compounds could not be drawn.

*Newton* Concerning the site of action of clomiphene, we have some considerable experience with monitoring patients with LH, FSH and oestrogens and I would like to confirm Professor Odell's comments. We also believe it does act on the hypothalamic-pituitary axis because in all our patients, bar two, the FSH and the LH was shown to increase prior to the increase in oestrogens.

*Loraine* In our experience clomiphene had little or no effect on urinary LH output as measured by the bioassay depending on ventral prostatic weight increase in hypophysectomized rats (Papanicolaou, A.D., Loraine, J.A. and Lunn, S.F., in : *Reproductive Endocrinology*. Ed. Irvine, W.J. Edinburgh: Livingstone, p. 60, 1970). It is however possible that the bioassay employed was insufficiently precise to detect the small degree of fluctuation which it would be necessary to demonstrate under such circumstances.

*Van der Molen* It was evident from your data that there was a large overlap between what you call the 'active' and 'inactive' ovaries.

*Baird* Only on three occasions in this group of women was blood collected simultaneously from both ovaries. I am glad you gave me the opportunity to discuss in a little more detail the reasons for the wide range of concentration. The anatomy of the venous drainage from the ovary in the human is extremely complex. If you cannulate the vessel that appears to be draining the ovary, *in situ* at operation, you can be collecting blood draining the uterus as well as the ovary, and the lateral pelvic walls. We have a preliminary study where we measured the concentration of oestradiol before and after clamping the vein which joined the ovarian from the lateral pelvic wall. The concentration after clamping was 25 times greater. For this reason, I think that you have to relate the concentration of any steroid ovarian venous blood to a steroid like oestradiol which is uniquely secreted by the ovary before any quantitative statements can be made.

*Brown* I would confirm Dr Baird's difficulties about getting ovarian vein blood from the human. I would like to ask him just how he did it, but before that I would like to comment on our work on ovarian vein blood in the sheep. This is much easier to collect. We estimated these samples without knowing which ovary they came from. Our progesterone and oestradiol results fitted in perfectly with the structure in that particular ovary. Can I

ask Dr Baird just how much blood he was able to collect by this procedure?
*Baird* I would like to emphasize that this is a procedure in which you have to be prepared to accept some failures. I think probably in the work we have done we have had about a 50 per cent success rate. In those we have managed to collect from, we have obtained from 15 to 55 ml.
*Macnaughton* I just wanted to confirm the source of the blood that was used for the testosterone and androstenedione measurements in your Figure 1. We had this problem of clamping veins too and think you have to make sure that you do clamp the uterine vein and lateral pelvic wall veins before you can get blood that really comes from the ovary alone.
*Baird* I assume that you are referring to the work published by Horton, Romanoff and Walker. I must say that the concentrations of androstenedione and testosterone in that publication (*J. clin. Endocr. Metab.*, **24**, 1267, 1966) are much lower than other published data (see text).

# *In Vitro* and *in Vivo* Studies of Testosterone Production

J. K. GRANT

University Department of Steroid Biochemistry
Royal Infirmary, Glasgow

¶ It is of interest to observe the changing fashions in steroid research. In recent years androgens have returned to popularity. From their earliest days these substances have presented difficult problems. Like onions, when one layer is removed another appears beneath bringing tears of frustration to the eyes. Forty years ago Butenandt [1] isolated androsterone from urine and thought that he had found the male sex hormone. A few years later, he was proved to be wrong by Laquer [2] who obtained the compound which he called testosterone from the testes of cattle. Thirty-five years later, uncertainty is still with us. We are not sure that we know all the tissues which can make testosterone, either *de novo* or from steroids carried in the blood. We are faced with the complicated situation in which not all of this hormone is produced by direct secretion. As a result there has, during the past decade, been much discussion about different methods of measuring the production rate as distinct from the secretion rate of testosterone [3, 4]. The latter would now appear to be only a fraction of the former. One wonders if attempts to measure testosterone production rates are really of any value. Do we really know, at the present day, how best to assess the androgenic status of the individual animal or human subject? We have in recent years learned how to measure *reliably* the concentration of testosterone in plasma [5–7], but is this enough? We should not assume that the concentration of testosterone in any body fluid is indeed the main factor in determining androgenic status. We are uncertain of the role of testosterone conjugated with glucuronic and sulphuric acids. These conjugates eventually appear in the urine in which they have been measured. They have not been reliably measured in plasma. They are probably mostly (70 per cent) derived in normal women from plasma androstenedione [8] which can and should be measured. Testosterone is also present in plasma bound to a specific plasma protein [9]. The methods referred to above [5–7] measure the total amount of plasma testosterone present in the protein bound and free state. Special procedures must, however, be adopted to distinguish the protein bound from the free testosterone [10]. The suggestion of Yates [11] that binding of steroid hormones to specific plasma proteins modifies the hormonal message must be considered here.

While we have no hesitation in describing testosterone as a hormone, how are we to regard 5α-dihydrotestosterone [12]? It is possible that testosterone and 5α-dihydrotestosterone are produced within certain cells for 'local' use, and that they are not released into body fluids before they are oxidized and reduced to what may be relatively innocuous compounds such as androsterone.

In view of so many uncertainties, it seems important to obtain as much evidence as possible about the tissues and cells which can and do make testosterone under normal or pathological conditions, and whether in fact this testosterone ever leaves these tissues. In Glasgow we have from time to time been able to add to this evidence. Many years ago, Dr O'Donnell [13] showed for the first time that fresh surgically removed ovarian tissue was able to make testosterone *de novo* from $^{14}C$ acetate. The ovaries were polycystic. The ovarian compartment involved in this biosynthesis is uncertain since corpus luteum cells which possess 3β-hydroxysteroid dehydrogenase activity were not present in this tissue. Direct evidence for the secretion of testosterone by the normal human ovary is lacking.

Following on the histological demonstration of 3β-hydroxysteroid dehydrogenase in the sebaceous glands of the skin of normal human subjects [14], Dr Cameron and his colleagues in Glasgow showed that $^{3}H$ dehydroepiandrosterone was converted to labelled testosterone by the skin of normal men [15]. Even although the percentage transformation appears to be small, the fact that there are from 60 to almost 1,000 sebaceous glands per square cm of skin surface [16] suggests that the overall production of testosterone in these glands may be considerable. It does not, of course, follow that any of this testosterone enters the systemic circulation.

Much more attention has been paid to the adrenal cortex in man as a source of testosterone and/or its precursors. The observation *in vitro* that adrenal tissue possesses the enzymes for the formation of testosterone from progesterone was made in our laboratory by Dr Pamela Ward [17] (Table 1). In two cases the adrenals investigated were hyperplastic. In a third

TABLE 1. Testosterone production *in vitro* by adrenocortical tissue [17]

| Patient | Adr. Wt. g | µg Testo. | 17 OH.P | 11 OH.A /g/h |
|---|---|---|---|---|
| ♂ gastric ca. | 7·6 | 8 | 50 | – |
| ♀ adr. hyper. | 5·7 | 11 | 46 | – |
| ♀ adr. ca. | 139 | 11 | – | 28 |
| ♀ br. ca. | 4·7 (N) | 5 | – | – |

Tissue slices incubated with 4-$^{14}C$ progesterone (30µCi/g tissue)

case the tissue was from a tumour, and one adrenal was removed from a patient with carcinoma of the breast. It showed no histological abnormality. No distinction could be made between the ability of the zona fasciculata and the zona reticularis to effect *in vitro* biosynthesis. Prior to this it had been known that the human adrenal, particularly under pathological conditions, produced androgenic steroids, but the formation of testosterone by adrenal tissue had not been reported. The isolation of testosterone from an adrenal tumour [18] does not in itself prove that the tissue can produce this substance.

A considerable time passed before it was possible to make direct measurements of testosterone on adrenal venous blood in human subjects. In the interim, indirect evidence for the production of testosterone or testosterone precursors by the adrenal continued to accumulate. Patients with congenital adrenal hyperplasia, in which ACTH secretion is elevated, have increased plasma concentrations of androstenedione and testosterone, the latter probably arising from peripheral conversion of the former. These concentrations may be decreased by corticosteroid and raised further by ACTH administration [19]. In idiopathic hirsutism the concentration of plasma testosterone, which may be raised, is suppressed by corticosteroid administration [20].

In 1968 we observed a rise in plasma testosterone concentration in women in late pregnancy [21]. Similar results were reported by others [10, 22, 23]. The excellent agreement of these results, obtained by three different methods (Table 2) is very gratifying. The testosterone concentration returns to normal within a few days of delivery. Women who were having their third or subsequent baby appeared to have a significantly higher concentration of plasma testosterone (Table 3). No explanation

TABLE 2. Mean values of plasma testosterone (ng/100 ml $\pm$ S.D.). Figures in parentheses are the numbers of individuals studied

| | Women | | Umbilical | Reference |
|---|---|---|---|---|
| Method | Non-preg. | Preg. | venous | |
| DID | 37 $\pm$ 17 (77) | 127 $\pm$ 25 (12) | 48 $\pm$ 28 (22) | [23] |
| DID | 49 $\pm$ 13 (23) | 114 $\pm$ 38 (17) | 46 $\pm$ 24 (9) | [22] |
| CPB | 45 $\pm$ 17 (9) | 140 $\pm$ 41 (4) | 56 $\pm$ 15 (12) | [10] |
| GLC | 38 $\pm$ 20 (10) | 114 $\pm$ 64 (16) | – | [21] |

TABLE 3. Plasma testosterone before and after delivery

| | ng Testo./100 ml | |
|---|---|---|
| No previous pregnancies | In late pregnancy | After delivery |
| 0 or 1 (10) | 104 | 46 |
| 3 or more (6) | 131 | 56 |
| | $P < 0.05$ | |

can be offered for this. It may be of interest that we found no correlation between plasma testosterone concentration and baby sex. Others, who measured umbilical cord arterial and venous blood, observed the same. Mizuno et al. [23], however, reported a bias towards a higher venous concentration of the hormone, whereas August et al. [10] found a bias towards higher arterial concentration. The latter observation, should it prove to be significant, would be in keeping with other evidence [24] that there is a transfer of androstenedione from the placenta to the foetus, where the liver converts this steroid to testosterone for return to the placenta. Bertrand and Saez [25] have recently reported in abstract that the average plasma concentration of testosterone and testosterone sulphate is significantly higher in pregnant than in non-pregnant women, but there is no difference dependent on the sex of the foetus. However, when the foetus is male the mean testosterone concentration in the umbilical artery ($171 \pm 17$ S.D. ng/100 ml) is greater than that in the umbilical vein ($83 \pm 12$ ng/100 ml $P < 0{\cdot}001$). A double isotope derivative method was used. Harkness [26] has also reported briefly in discussion that the urinary testosterone glucuronide excretion of the adrenalectomized pregnant woman is extremely low. The significance of this observation can only be interpreted with knowledge of the limit of sensitivity of the method used. One cannot confidently conclude that the maternal plasma testosterone in late pregnancy is of adrenal origin. Nor would it be wise to conclude that the Leydig cells of the foetal testes make no significant contribution. More work must be done.

We have used the method of Eik-Nes [6], with minor modifications, for the measurement of plasma testosterone. This involves thin-layer chromatography of the plasma extract, chloroacetylation and further chromatographic purification before gas-liquid chromatography on a 1 per cent XE-60 column in a Pye Series 104 instrument with $^{63}$Ni electron capture detector. The method is very demanding and calls for extreme care and attention to detail. Satisfactory results have, however, been obtained by four out of five workers in our laboratory. The evaluation of the method by one of the successful workers is shown in Table 4. We have experience of

TABLE 4. Evaluation of GLC method

| | | | |
|---|---|---|---|
| Pye Series 104 | $^{63}$Ni e.c. detector | 250° 150μ sec/min | |
| 3 ft. 1% XE-60 | Gas-Chrom S | 210° argon-methane 60 ml/min | |
| *Accuracy* | Mean recovery before GLC 50% | | (74) |
| *Precis ion* | $2{\cdot}4 \pm 0{\cdot}684$ (SD) ng/10 ml plasma | | (8) |
| | $7{\cdot}1 \pm 1{\cdot}65$ (SD) ng/10 ml plasma | | (10) |
| *Specificity* | Retention time, peak shape, e.c. selectivity | | |

both competitive protein binding (CPB) methods (for other steroids) and GLC. In my opinion, GLC is preferable for testosterone, at least where extreme sensitivity is not called for. It is impossible to evaluate a method under all the circumstances in which it may be used. It is therefore desirable that a method should have no poorly understood steps. It should also have as many built-in safeguards as possible. In the GLC procedure for testosterone, a satisfactory worker will obtain, with biological extracts, recorder traces which are as good as those obtained with standards of pure steroids. While it is readily admitted that a good-looking peak on the recorder may in fact be due to steroid chloroacetate with an unknown contaminant, one can obtain unsatisfactory peaks which give warning that the determination must be repeated. Does one have similar warnings that something has interfered with the CPB method? For a time we almost began to think that Glasgow tap water, used to spread thin-layer media, contained a progesterone-like substance, as London water has been reputed, not too seriously, to contain oestrogen. The blank was high. This problem was surmounted, but what if the same interfering substance should appear in the plasma measured? In the GLC method it should be remembered that use of the electron capture detector itself provides some additional measure of specificity. In some earlier reports it was suggested that the method might not separate testosterone from epitestosterone. The separation obtained is shown in Figure 1. The CPB method suffers from the disadvantage that it employs more steps and reagents than the GLC method, which are not clearly defined chemically and may thus be less susceptible to control.

Baird [27], using a double isotope derivative method, has recently reported a few direct measurements of testosterone in the adrenal venous plasma of conscious human subjects with a cannula placed near the adrenal vein. Since the observations (Table 5) are very limited in number and since conflicting results were obtained on administration of ACTH, I am taking the opportunity of reporting a few measurements which we were able to make on specimens of adrenal venous blood of women undergoing adrenalectomy for treatment of carcinoma of the breast. These results are shown in Table 6. The plasmas had been stored frozen at −15°C for

TABLE 5. Plasma testosterone ng/100 ml [27]

| | | Adrenal venous | |
|---|---|---|---|
| | Peripheral | Control | ACTH* |
| 44 yr ♂ PUO | – | 307 | 252 |
| 33 yr ♀ hirsute | 23 | 145 | 119 |
| 51 yr ♀ hypertensive | 10 | 21 | – |
| 21 yr ♀ CAH | – | 227 | 720 |

*15 min. post 250 μg ACTH i.v.

TABLE 6. Adrenal and peripheral venous plasma testosterone in females with carcinoma of the breast

| | Vol. | | Testosterone (ng/100 ml) | |
|---|---|---|---|---|
| Patient | ml | ACTH | Adrenal venous | Peripheral |
| 1 | 8 | – | 170 | – |
| 2 | 6 | + | 307 | – |
| | 10 | – | 127 | – |
| 3 | 10 | + | 300 | – |
| 4 | 10 | + | 316 | 72 |
| | | | Normal females (10) | 38 ± 20 SD |

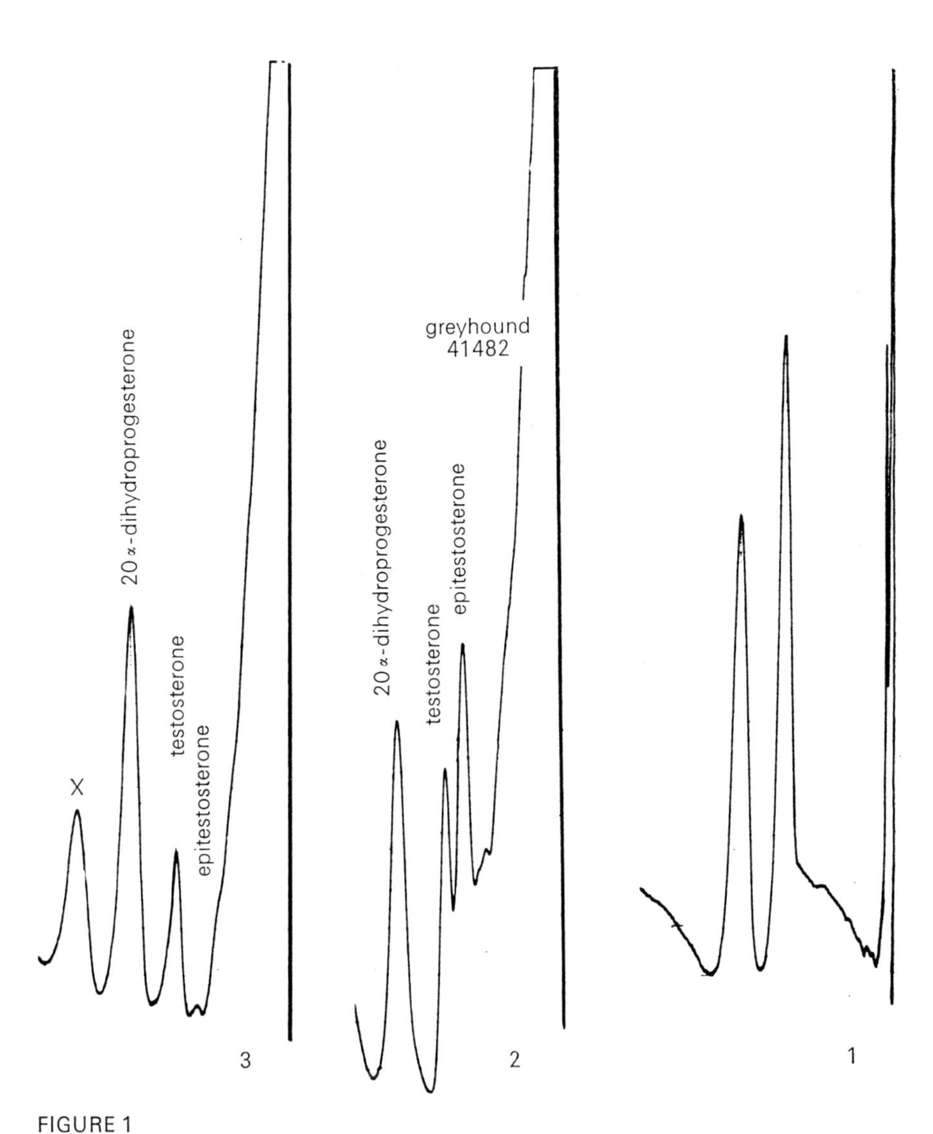


FIGURE 1

Recorder tracings obtained with (1) standard testosterone and 20α-dihydroprogesterone (internal standard), (2) steroids extracted from dog plasma showing the separation of testosterone from epitestosterone, (3) steroids extracted from the plasma of a hirsute woman showing a peak due to an unknown substance X. All steroids are as chloroacetates. The chromatograph is Pye Series 104 with $^{63}Ni$ electron capture detector operated at 260°C. Columns were packed with 1% XE-60 on gas chrome Q, and were operated at 225°C. The carrier gas was nitrogen 50 ml/min and the detector was given 5 volt pulses for periods of 150μ sec. No purge gas was used

some time and a peripheral blood plasma specimen was available in one case only. The cannula was placed in the main adrenal vein and blood was collected in heparinized containers. It is evident that concentrations well above those found in peripheral plasma of normal women are observed with the unstimulated adrenals. The concentrations are similar to those reported by Dr Baird and his colleagues. Administration of ACTH results in a marked rise in testosterone concentration. It should be noted that no account is taken of the increase in adrenal venous blood flow which occurs when ACTH is administered [28]. This would, of course, further increase the amount of testosterone secreted in a given time. Attention should also be paid to the fact that cannulation near or in the main adrenal vein need not necessarily result in collection of all the blood draining from the gland. Other minor adrenal veins may enter the renal vein at points remote from the main vein [29].

In conclusion, it appears that several tissues other than the testes possess enzymes for the production of testosterone. Polycystic ovarian tissue from women can produce testosterone *de novo* from acetate. There is some direct evidence that the adrenal cortex in man secretes testosterone and that this is increased by corticotrophin.

## ACKNOWLEDGMENTS

I acknowledge gratefully the assistance of Dr K. Demisch, Dr N. Fanchenko, Dr Irene Gavras, Miss L. C. Cunningham and Mr J. McCallum with various aspects of this work, and the generous financial support of the British Medical Research Council and the Deutsche Forschungsgemeinschaft.

## REFERENCES

[1] Butenandt, A., *Z. angew. Chem.*, **44**, 905, 1931.

[2] David, K., Dingemanse, E., Freud, J. and Laquer, E., *Z. physiol. Chem.*, **233**, 281, 1935.

[3] Baird, D., Horton, R., Longscope, C. and Tait, J. F., *Perspectives in Biology and Medicine*, **11**, 384, 1968.

[4] Migeon, C. J., Saez, J. M. and Rivarola, M. A. In *Testosterone*, p. 42. Ed. J. Tamm. Stuttgart: Thieme Verlag, 1968.

[5] Riondel, A., Tait, J. F., Gut, M., Tait, S. A. S., Joachim, E. and Little, B., *J. clin. Endocr. Metab.*, **23**, 620, 1963 (double isotope derivative).

[6] Brownie, A. C., van der Molen, H. J., Nishizawa, E. E. and Eik-Nes, K. B., *J. clin. Endocr. Metab.*, **24**, 1091, 1964 (gas chromatography).

[7] Pearlman, W. H., Cr py, O. and Murphy, B. E. P., *J. clin. Endocr. Metab.*, **27**, 1012, 1967 (competitive protein binding).

[8] Horton, R. In *Testosterone*, p. 220. Ed. J. Tamm. Stuttgart: Thieme Verlag, 1968.

[9] Pearlman, W.H. and Crépy, O., *J. biol. Chem.*, **243**, 182, 1967.
[10] August, G.P., Tkachuk, M. and Grumbach, M.M., *J. clin. Endocr. Metab.*, **29**, 891, 1969.
[11] Keller, N., Richardson, U.I. and Yates, F.E., *Endocrinology*, **84**, 49, 1969.
[12] Gloyna, R.E. and Wilson, J.D., *J. clin. Endocr. Metab.*, **29**, 970, 1969.
[13] O'Donnell, V.J. and McCaig, J., *Biochem. J.*, **71**, 9P, 1959.
[14] Baillie, A.H., Calman, K.C. and Milne, J.A., *Br. J. Derm.* **77**, 610, 1965.
[15] Cameron, E.H.D., Baillie, A.H., Grant, J.K., Milne, J.A. and Thomson, J., *J. Endocr.*, **35**, xix, 1966.
[16] Montagna, W. In *Advances in Biology of Skin*, vol. 4, p. 19. Eds. W. Montagna, R.A. Ellis and A.L. Silver. London: Pergamon Press, 1963.
[17] Ward, P.J. and Grant, J.K., *J. Endocr.*, **26**, 139, 1963.
[18] Anlicker, R., Rohr, O. and Masti, M., *Helv. Chim. Acta*, **39**, 1100, 1956.
[19] Horton, R. and Frasier, S.D., *J. clin. Invest.*, **46**, 1003, 1967.
[20] Nichols, T., Nugent, C.A. and Tyler, F.H., *J. clin. Endocr. Metab.*, **26**, 79, 1966.
[21] Demisch, K., Black, W.P. and Grant, J.K. *J. Endocr.*, **42**, 477, 1968.
[22] Rivarola, M.A., Forest, M.G. and Migeon, C.J., *J. clin. Endocr. Metab.*, **28**, 34, 1968.
[23] Mizuno, M., Lobotsky, J., Lloyd, C.W., Kobayashi, T. and Murasawa, Y., *J. clin. Endocr. Metab.*, **28**, 1133, 1968.
[24] Benagiano, G., Kincl, F.A., Zielske, F., Wiqvist, N. and Diczfalusy, E., *Acta endocr., Copnh.*, **56**, 203, 1967.
[25] Bertrand, J. and Saez, J.M., *Biochem. J.*, **112**, 22P, 1969.
[26] Harkness, A. In discussion in *Testosterone*, p. 209. Ed. J. Tamm. Stuttgart: Thieme Verlag, 1968.
[27] Baird, D.T., Uno, A. and Melby, J.C., *J. Endocr.*, **45**, 135, 1969.
[28] Grant, J.K., Forrest, A.P.M. and Symington, T., *Acta endocr., Copnh.*, **26**, 195, 1957.
[29] Dobbie, J.W., M.D. (Thesis) University of Glasgow, 1968.

## *Discussion of paper by Dr Grant*

*Macnaughton* With reference to your data suggesting a relationship between parity and plasma testosterone – could this be due to a correlation with the increasing age of the women and not the number of children they have had?

*Grant* It might be, but we have not measured the correlation. On the other hand, one woman of only 22 years had four previous pregnancies and a plasma testosterone of 192 ng/100 ml, whereas another of 19 years with no previous pregnancies had 53 ng testosterone/100 ml plasma.

*Harkness* I can confirm that levels of urinary testosterone glucuronide in an adrenalectomized pregnant woman are very low.

*Mills* There is an increase in the amount of plasma testosterone binding during pregnancy. Does the amount of unbound testosterone actually increase?

*Vermeulen* About 0·3 per cent of the testosterone is free in pregnancy and 0·9 per cent in non-pregnancy plasma.

*Griffiths* In Cardiff, my colleagues, Drs Anne Anderson, Colin Pierrepoint and Professor Turnbull, have been carrying out studies in the sheep on the control of parturition. We have found, as Liggins has reported, that ACTH will induce parturition. We have also found that substance S and epi-testosterone have the same effect.

*Klopper* I suspect that Dr Griffiths would have us believe that these results can be extrapolated to man – this is certainly not so. If it were true, it would also spoil one of my pet theories about the control of onset of labour in man. Are you suggesting, Dr Griffiths, that these effects are controlling normal parturition in the sheep?

*Griffiths* I should perhaps refer to these effects as premature expulsion of the foetus and not parturition.

*Grant* Has anyone measured testosterone levels throughout human pregnancy?

*Vermeulen* The testosterone levels do not fall before parturition but the binding capacity for testosterone does appear to fall before the onset of labour. We recently published these results in *J. clin. Endocr. Metab.*, **29**, 1470, 1969. The apparent fall of binding capacity may however be related to methodological problems and this finding should be controlled.

## SESSION IV. GENERAL DISCUSSION

*Bulbrook* I have been waiting for the light on how dehydroepiandrosterone and dehydroepiandrosterone sulphate secretion is controlled but everybody has skirted round these two problems. Dr van der Molen, you put up as part of your evidence for the cyclicity of ovarian androgens and oestrogens the evidence that the excretion of androgens and oestrogens in the urine correlated in man. So they do, but this is a correlation mainly with androsterone-aetiocholanolone and DHA with oestrone, oestradiol and oestriol. Most of these particular C-19 metabolites would be coming from DHAS and DHA not from androstenedione and testosterone, so that the cyclicity must be due to DHAS and DHA.

*Van der Molen* Part of the evidence might be derived from the correlation between androsterone and aetiocholanolone with the oestrogen but this was not a full story because I think that the correlation between testosterone glucuronide and androstenedione in urine with oestrogens is better evidence.

*Bulbrook* Dr MacDonald, when you were talking about the occasional man who was producing more oestrogen than could be accounted for by conversion from testosterone and androstenedione, which you explained by postulating glandular secretion, why shouldn't this small amount come from conversion from DHAS or DHA?

*MacDonald* Of course DHA or DHAS is a possible source. However, if it went via the pathway DHA to testosterone we would have measured it, since we measured the yield of oestrogen from testosterone. So the critical question is, is conversion of DHA or its sulphate directed to oestrogen circumventing blood androstenedione and testosterone? The evidence that we have accumulated is as follows : the DHA is converted to oestradiol to the extent of about 0·1 per cent only; approximately 50 per cent of that, however, is via the pathway DHA → blood androstenedione → oestrone → oestradiol. The other 0·05 per cent appears to go directly to oestradiol but this is pretty small quantitatively, in terms of total oestrogen production. The DHAS in our hands is even less well converted in the non-pregnant subject.

*Mills* With regard to the conversion of DHAS to either androgen or oestrogen, the patient I quoted with the 17-hydroxylase deficiency was given 80 mg of DHAS three times a week and she put out at maximum about 90 μg oestriol. We could not find any testosterone glucuronide in the urine at that time and I think it might be possible therefore that she was converting the DHAS to oestrogen without going through androstenedione or testosterone. The conversion figure is about the same as Professor MacDonald suggests, i.e., about 0·1 per cent.

*MacDonald* I would agree with you whole-heartedly although I would not think that the absence of testosterone glucuronide in the urine necessarily excludes this pathway, but I think our numbers appear relatively similar.

*Vermeulen* During the discussion of Dr MacDonald's paper, Dr Baird brought up the question of whether a diurnal variation exists in plasma testosterone. Ever since Dr Dray showed it, it has been confirmed by almost everybody working in this field. We measured plasma testosterone levels and in ten out of eleven patients the 9 p.m. value was definitely lower than the 9 a.m. value and the mean difference was 33 per cent. The value at noon is on the average slightly higher than the value at 9 a.m. and this corresponds exactly I believe with the results obtained both by Dr Dray and by Dr Ismail. In another series, the 8 p.m. values in the elderly were 44 per cent of the morning value compared with 70 per cent for younger people.

*Van der Molen* Is there anybody who has information about the diurnal variations in women? If it does exist then this implies an adrenal source. Until now we were not able to find any constant pattern in the female and I believe that Dr Dray didn't find any pattern either.

*Dray* I observed these variations in 1967 and I didn't find variation in female subjects. I have now found variation of testosterone glucuronide in urine of men with the low value at three o'clock in the morning.

*Baird* Our Chairman has suggested that a diurnal variation implies an adrenal source. It has been shown however that a marked diurnal variation of 17α-hydroxyprogesterone in men persists after treating the subject with dexamethazone. This would imply that in men the testis may have a diurnal variation in secretion of 17α-OH progesterone. I raise the question again of the diurnal variation of the androstenedione concentration. The only published data are those of Lloyd's group, which were published in *Steroids* about two years ago (Crafts et al., *Steroids*, 1969). Could we go round the people here who are measuring androstenedione and ask them if they have looked for this and if they have observed it?

*MacDonald* We have not looked consistently for diurnal variation. We have done some measurements with respect to cyclic variation but not diurnal variation.

*Eik-Nes* We looked for a diurnal variation in androstenedione in young male subjects in the same plasma samples as we found a diurnal variation for testosterone in 1966–7. There was a similar variation in androstenedione. What that means, I don't know.

*Bulbrook* The answer I got didn't really satisfy me. David Baird said about 20 per cent of his $\Delta^4$-steroids in women came from the DHA. If that happens it means that some of the oestrogens have got to come via DHA. Dr MacDonald said the conversion of DHA to oestrogens was one-tenth of one per cent; that sounds insignificant but when you think of the secretion rate of DHA which might be as high as 10 mg in some cases, then you are up to the 10 μg level a day at that sort of conversion rate which is a substantial proportion of the oestrogen that you are measuring. What I would like to ask Dr MacDonald is, are you sure that the number of counts that you get from perfusing radioactive DHA would be enough to tell you whether it was a good source or not, or could there be a methodological artifact in this work?

*MacDonald* I think there are several objections to the hypothesis you are raising. Firstly, in our hands, the DHA conversion to the blood androstenedione does not approach 20 per cent, it is in the order of 2–5 per cent. Secondly, of this 0·1 per cent conversion, half of it is already being accounted for via androstenedione. The remaining 0·05 per cent conversion of DHA to oestrone accounts for 5 μg per day only. We have administered sufficient radioactively labelled DHA to be confident that the conversion of DHA to oestrone does not exceed 0·1 per cent. I wouldn't for a moment have you believe that that might not be a source of oestrogen, but within the framework of the techniques we have available, it must be a very tiny source.

*Bulbrook* I am still puzzled about the discrepancy. Dr Baird said 20 per cent.

*Baird* I meant to say that about 10 per cent of blood androstenedione arises by conversion from dehydroepiandrosterone.

*Mills* In our patient we injected with DHAS, it was the DHAS that she was converting to oestrogen. It is possible that the presence of the sulphate may limit the conversion to androstenedione and testosterone. Certainly the sulphate in that case was being converted.

*Grant* Could I return to this question of diurnal rhythm? Dr Ismail, the German colleague you had in Edinburgh – didn't he read a paper at a meeting of the Endocrine Society about hirsute or virilized women and some modifications of some sort of rhythm in these individuals in urinary testosterone, because if we have the rhythm in men as Dr Vermeulen says and no rhythm in women, where is the drive coming from?

*Ismail* Dr Nieschlag from Mainz and I initially studied the circadian rhythm in testosterone in 9 normal healthy men, with regular waking and sleeping habits. Six blood samples were taken from each subject at 4-hour intervals, and the results of these experiments are in print (Nieschlag and Ismail, *Klin. Wschr.*, **48**, 53, 1970). The main points were that firstly, there was a circadian rhythm in plasma testosterone in all subjects investigated with values higher in the morning (between 4 a.m. and 12 noon) and low in the evening (8 p.m.–12 midnight). More experiments were carried out and confirmed our findings. Another point which came out of this study was that a poor correlation was found between the sum of the six readings during the day and any of the individual readings. However, the mean of three plasma samples taken at 8-hour intervals or two taken at 8 a.m. and 8 p.m. were found to reflect adequately plasma concentration. We adapted initially the protocol of three plasma samples taken at 12 noon, 8 p.m. and 4 a.m. and it is this study which Dr Grant is referring to. We noted elevated values in women with mild hirsutism at the 4 a.m. sample but not in the sample taken at 12 noon or 8 p.m. However, I would like to reconsider our findings since we are now investigating the hormone levels during sleep, and we noted fluctuations in plasma testosterone levels during the 8-hour sleep period with peaks during or around the so-called REM sleep or rapid eye movement stage I, when the person seems to be dreaming (Ismail, Evans, Love and Loraine, unpublished data). These REM periods are longer and more frequent in the second half of the sleep period. It is therefore possible that the elevated values noted in these subjects could well be due to the fact that the sample was taken around the REM phase of sleep. I must admit that when we carried out these experiments and put forward this possibility we were not aware of the fact that testosterone levels change with various stages of sleep.

*Jeffcoate* On the question of diurnal variation in the plasma testosterone one should not forget the fact that variations in the rate of clearance of testosterone will also result in changes in the plasma steroid level. There is some evidence that the metabolic clearance rate of testosterone changes with posture.

*Grant* I have heard the story that the plasma testosterone in man will change when he bends down to tie his shoes. Is that what you are mentioning? If you alter the scrotal circulation you get a change in plasma testosterone. Is that the same?

*Jeffcoate* No, I am referring to the data of Lipsett et al. (*Recent Prog. Hormone Res.*, **22**, 245, 1966) who showed by a constant infusion technique that a patient lying down had reached a constant level of radioactive testosterone. When the patient stood up, the level rose and reached a new level indicating a change in the metabolic clearance rate with a change of posture.

*Ismail* We are actually looking for the effect of change of posture on plasma testosterone : Firstly, taking plasma from people in the morning before they get out of bed and also half an hour or one hour after they assume their upright posture. We have also studied the opposite way : standing and then lying on the bed. I must say that the results are very inconsistent. There is no definite pattern with changing posture.

*Deshpande* How did Dr Baird manage to persuade 18 young healthy women to give ovarian venous blood?

*Baird* The data on the first slide were women having elective tubal ligation in Santiago, Chile. Some other data which I presented were collected in this country. These were mainly patients undergoing hysterectomy for Stage 0 carcinoma of the cervix.

*Van der Molen* Professor MacDonald, could you have obtained any information about your possible ovarian or testicular contribution to oestrogens by administering gonadotrophins to your subjects? Did you consider it or have you done it?

*MacDonald* We have not done it and the reason is that it is very difficult when you alter secretory rates to achieve a new steady state, and for that reason we have been hesitant to try for fear of failure. We have gone in the opposite direction in women, namely to try to reduce the production rates by suppression of androstenedione. In postmenopausal women we have not administered gonadotrophins. We have administered gonadotrophin for purposes of inducing ovulation to see if this in normal women would alter the extent of conversion of androstenedione or other precursors, i.e., would the large multiple follicular apparatus not utilize plasma precursors – they do not.

*Mills* This may be a very important point. Patients with carcinoma of the bronchus that have been shown to produce gonadotrophin produce predominately FSH and these people convert a higher percentage of testosterone to oestrogen than normal. I wonder whether it is possible that the FSH production from the carcinoma of the bronchus might be playing a part in this conversion?

*MacDonald* I am not familiar with the study. I wonder if it could not be accounted for by ageing?

*Brown* It was Ginsburg and Brown's study. Have any experiments been done in this type of patient with carcinoma of the bronchus where there is an actual increase in production rates? Is this due to increased conversion or is it actually secretion?

*MacDonald* No, we have not studied such a patient.

*Brown* You also said there is no increase in production in the man with bronchial carcinoma.

*MacDonald* No. There is a marked increase but we could account for it principally via the utilization of the DHAS, by the neoplastic trophoblast. This is on one of the examples I listed in which you could not account for increased oestrogen from androstenedione and testosterone. The oestrogen production rates were, in the one individual that we studied, more than half a milligramme a day.

# A Study of Pituitary Control of Ovarian Function using Gonadotrophin Therapy

J.B.BROWN
J.H.EVANS
F.D.ADEY
H.P.TAFT *and*
S.L.TOWNSEND

Department of Obstetrics and Gynaecology, University of Melbourne
and the Endocrine Clinic, Royal Women's Hospital, Melbourne

¶ THE present study, in which human gonadotrophins have been used therapeutically, has been conducted on two planes. The first has been to achieve pregnancies in women with infertility due to abnormal ovarian function. The second has been to obtain information on the quantitative changes in gonadotrophin output from the pituitary whereby normal cyclical ovarian activity is maintained. The aim has been to determine minimum therapeutic doses of human pituitary gonadotrophin (HPG) and of human chorionic gonadotrophin (HCG) in the hope that the use of these would maintain normal levels of ovarian activity and eliminate the hazards of hyperstimulation and of multiple pregnancies. Fertility has been related to the ovarian responses as judged by the measurement of oestrogens and pregnanediol in the urine, and the achievement of a successful pregnancy has provided irrefutable evidence that a fertile ovulation has been induced. The present paper is based on work which has already been published [1, 2].

## MATERIALS AND METHODS

*Gonadotrophins.* HPG was prepared by fractional alcohol precipitation of material extracted from acetone-dried glands [3]. The yield per pituitary processed averaged 250 i.u. of follicle stimulating hormone (FSH) and 1,500 i.u. of luteinizing hormone (LH) (second IRP). The dosages in FSH units used in this paper were calculated from this average yield and from the fraction or multiple of a pituitary which the dose represented. Provided the numbers of pituitaries in each batch of HPG were sufficiently large (at least 750), calculations of potency from the numbers of pituitaries processed gave more reproducible responses in patients from batch to batch than was obtained by using the actual bioassay figures. This is probably because most bioassays lack the precision required to distinguish between the small dosage increments which are effective in the human.

The HPG was relatively rich in LH and its potency in stimulating follicular development in the human female was not enhanced by giving additional HCG (100 to 600 i.u.) daily along with the HPG [1]. However, additional HCG was required to achieve maximum spermatogenesis in men [4]. The HCG was 'Pregnyl' manufactured by Organon.

*Assay methods.* 'Total' urinary oestrogens were measured by the rapid method of Brown et al. [5], which provides results the same morning that the urines are received and therefore in time for making decisions on therapy that day. Urinary pregnanediol was measured by gas-liquid chromatography by the method of Cox [6]. The results were usually available on the day after the urines were received.

*Collection of urine.* Urines were collected daily throughout treatment with HPG and for six days after the ovulating dose of HCG was given. Thereafter, they were collected every three days until menstruation occurred or until a positive pregnancy test was obtained, then weekly throughout the first trimester and then monthly until delivery. Total urinary oestrogens were measured on all specimens. Pregnanediol was measured occasionally during HPG therapy and then on all specimens collected after giving HCG. Such a schedule in which urine or blood is collected for assay, particularly daily over the periods before and for five to six days after ovulation, is the only means at present available for assessing exactly how the ovaries have responded.

*Dosage schedules.* HPG was not started until urinary oestrogen and pregnanediol excretion were both at established base-line levels. As a result of initial experience, HPG was administered daily each morning starting at a low dose (usually 125 i.u. FSH) and increasing every five days until an ovarian response, as judged by urinary oestrogen excretion, was obtained. A single dose of HCG, usually 3,000 i.u., was given for ovulation, and this was increased in subsequent cycles if the 3,000 i.u. had failed to induce ovulation. Additional smaller doses of HCG were given during the luteal phase.

The gonadotrophins were dissolved in saline (1 ml) and injected deeply into the gluteal muscle.

*Insemination.* The lowest sperm count accepted from any husband was 17 million per ml. Intercourse was recommended as near as was convenient to the time of the ovulating dose of HCG and for several days afterwards.

## PATIENTS STUDIED

The study now includes 60 infertile women desiring pregnancy in whom abnormal ovarian function was the only apparent cause of their complaint. The majority (46) had either primary amenorrhoea without chromosomal defects, or secondary amenorrhoea of 1½ to 17 years duration, and the remainder had oligomenorrhoea, defined as infrequent or irregular menses occurring at intervals of 42 days to 6 months, or had persistently anovulatory cycles (Table 1). Clomiphene had been given earlier to 39 of these patients; 19 had failed to respond and 20 had responded by ovulating but had not conceived. The study does not include women with persistently high urinary gonadotrophin excretion, nor does it include two women with

TABLE 1. Classification of patients for gonadotrophin therapy (60 patients). Figures in parentheses show the number of patients who conceived

| Urinary gonadotrophins | Clomiphene therapy | Amenorrhoea | | Oligomenorrhoea | Anovulatory cycles |
|---|---|---|---|---|---|
| | | Primary | Secondary | | |
| Low | Not tested | 4 (3) | 3 (3) | | |
| Normal | Not tested | 1 (1) | 13 (12) | | |
| Normal | Failed | | 18 (15) | | 1 (0) |
| Normal | Responded | | 7 (5) | 12 (7) | 1 (0) |

fluctuating normal to high gonadotrophin excretion who failed to respond to doses of up to 1,000 i.u. FSH per day.

## RESULTS

A total of 273 treatment cycles has been studied. The important findings are illustrated in Figures 1 to 9, which are taken mainly from the earlier phases of the work when experience was being gained and mistakes were common. Subsequent experience has repeatedly confirmed the validity of these findings.

### *Steroid excretion patterns in conceptual cycles*

The treatment schedule adopted and the patterns of oestrogen and pregnanediol excretion obtained during conceptual cycles are illustrated in Figure 1. Before commencing therapy, urinary oestrogen and pregnanediol levels were at established base-line values. In this example, HPG was given at a daily dose of 125 i.u. FSH. Changes in oestrogen output are minimal at first, and then the values increase logarithmically (see also Figs. 5, 6, and 7). Because of this initial delay, it is our usual practice to start treatment on a Thursday and not be concerned about the response until the Sunday to Monday collection of urine four days later. Under correct stimulation, the oestrogen levels should reach approximately 60 μg per 24 hours (the mean value for the midcycle peak of the normal cycle) about nine days after starting therapy or six days after increasing the dose. The HPG is then discontinued and HCG (5,000 i.u. in this case) is given to induce ovulation which is indicated by an abrupt fall in oestrogen values followed by a rise in both oestrogen and pregnanediol values. This sequence of steroid response is precisely the pattern of the normal ovulatory cycle [7] and was found in all but one of the 56 conceptual cycles induced in this study. The preovulatory peak values of oestrogen excretion often exceed those of the normal cycle (maximum of 100 μg per 24 hours) as illustrated in many of the figures shown. The luteal phase increases in oestrogen and pregnanediol excretion are also usually in excess of normal because of the additional HCG given at this time. These high luteal phase values are maintained for some time after the HCG has been discontinued, thus giving an early indication of pregnancy, but they eventually fall four to five weeks after ovulation to the values normally found at this time of pregnancy and thereafter increase at normal rates.

The pattern of a follicular rise in oestrogens reaching a well-defined peak, followed by an abrupt fall at ovulation and a subsequent rise in oestrogen and pregnanediol excretion appears to be basic to fertility and a successful pregnancy, since only one conception occurred in its absence and this ended in abortion at 10 weeks [1]. Therefore, an important aim of this

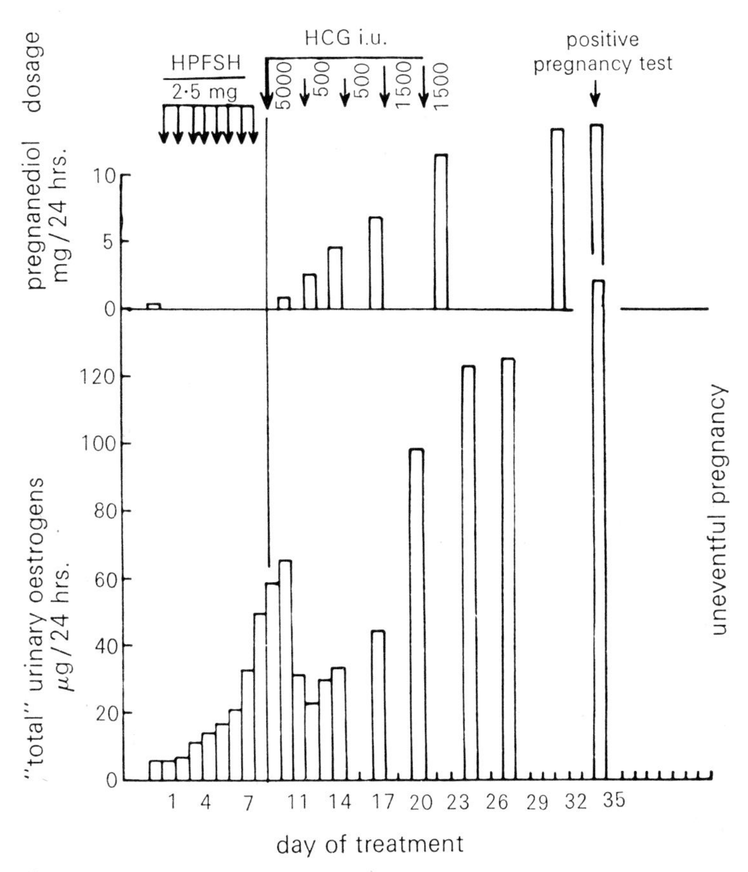


FIGURE 1
The treatment schedule showing an ovulatory response and conception (from Townsend et al. [2])

investigation has been to determine the factors which produce this pattern and which ensure that the steroid levels do not rise excessively above those found during the normal cycle.

*Factors involved in achieving 'correct' steroid excretion patterns*
(1) *Dosage of HPG*. Figure 2 illustrates the very narrow limits in the dosages of HPG which are required to obtain satisfactory follicular responses. During the first treatment cycle shown, a dose of 250 i.u. FSH per day led to a rapid increase in urinary oestrogens which exceeded 200 μg per 24 hours within seven days. HCG (2,000 i.u.) given on the eighth day failed to induce ovulation but 'synergized' with the response to HPG giving values which reached 1,200 μg per 24 hours before returning to base-line levels. Such

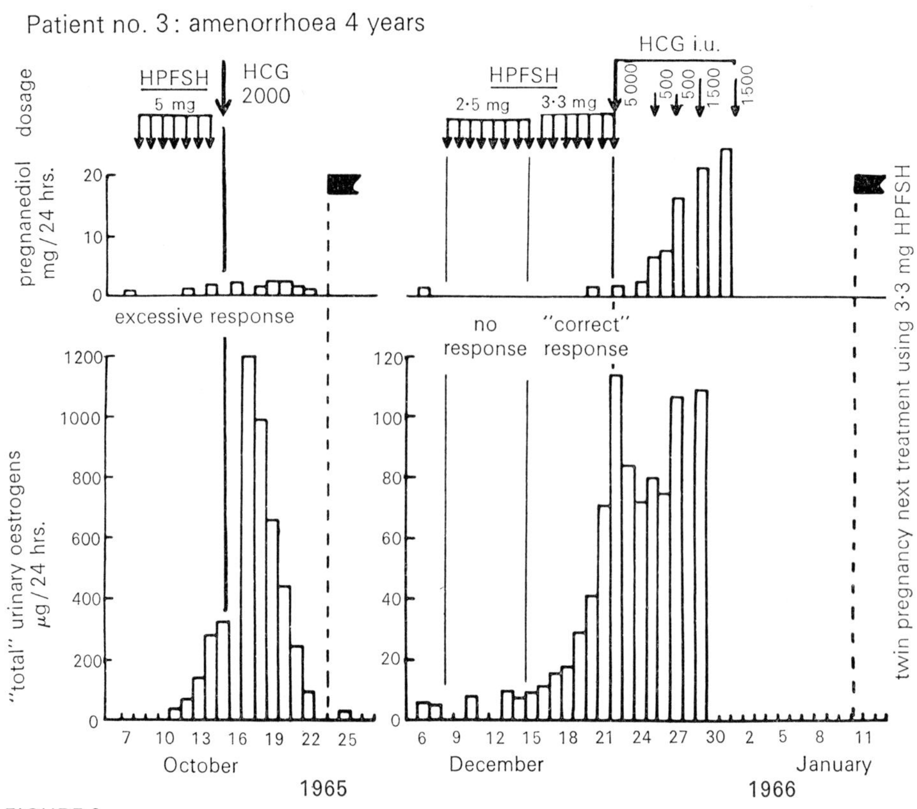


FIGURE 2
Effect of dosage of HPG showing an excessive response to 250 i.u. FSH per day, no response to 125 i.u. and a 'correct' response to 165 i.u. per day (from [2])

vigorous reactions were common during the early phases of the study when even marginally excessive doses of HPG were combined with doses of HCG which failed to induce ovulation (Figs. 5, 6 and 7). Providing ovulation did not occur with such responses, clinical symptoms of overstimulation were absent or present only to a minor degree. However, the quintuplet pregnancy reported from New Zealand [8] occurred under such conditions of follicular stimulation. Following this report, it has been our practice to withhold HCG whenever such an over-response has been obtained.

In the second treatment cycle shown in Figure 2, the commencing dose was half that of the first cycle (125 i.u. FSH using the same batch of HPG). After eight days, no increase in oestrogen excretion has been detected. The dose was then increased by a factor of 1·3 to 165 i.u. and the oestrogen levels rose in six days to 70 μg per 24 hours. HCG (5,000 i.u.) administered next day induced ovulation. A similar response was obtained in the next cycle and the patient conceived.

Subsequent experience has confirmed that each patient has a threshold dosage requirement for HPG. Doses below this, even when continued for long periods of time, do not stimulate oestrogen production. Doses of up to 30 per cent above the threshold lead to normal responses, whereas increases of more than 30 per cent produce excessive responses (Figs. 2, 7b and 8b). Other workers have reported the same phenomenon and Crooke and colleagues [9, 10] also concluded that the maximum allowable increment in the dosage of HPG to avoid over-responses is 30 per cent. However, sub-threshold doses of FSH appear to have some conditioning effect on the ovaries because the time taken to reach a specified response in oestrogen excretion is less (five to six days) when a sub-threshold dose has been given first than when the effective dose has been given from the beginning (eight to nine days).

These studies show that a precisely defined elevation in FSH levels is necessary to initiate follicular development in women with absent ovarian function. It is therefore likely that a similar situation exists naturally during the normal menstrual cycle. Earlier studies failed to demonstrate a significant increase in FSH during the early part of the cycle. Eventually, Stevens and co-workers [11], using bioassays on urine, succeeded in demonstrating a small increase and this has since been substantiated by several careful studies in which FSH has been measured in plasma by radioimmunoassay. These recent studies have been reviewed in this symposium by Odell [12] who concluded that the increases in FSH during the early part of the cycle are no more than 30 per cent above the general levels found at other times of the cycle apart from the ovulatory peak area. This figure of 30 per cent agrees exactly with the changes which would be predicted from the present studies.

The minimum effective dose of HPG differs for different patients. It can be determined during the first treatment cycle by commencing at a low dosage and increasing gradually until a response is obtained. To maintain increments within the maximum of 30 per cent, three basic units containing 75, 100 and 125 i.u. FSH, equivalent to 0·3, 0·4 and 0·5 of a pituitary, are required. Except for the most sensitive patients, our starting dose is 125 i.u. FSH, and after five days, this is increased to 150, then 175, 200, 250 i.u. etc. until a sustained increase in oestrogen excretion is obtained (see Fig. 8b). This effective dose is then continued until the oestrogen values exceed 50 μg per 24 hours, the HPG is then discontinued and HCG is given for ovulation. In patients with high FSH requirements, the effective dose may not be reached until after four or five weeks. The process may therefore be tedious and wasteful of HPG. However, no alternative method which avoids over-responses and provides the answer during the first treatment cycle has yet been devised. Once the dose has been determined, it is sufficiently reproducible in that patient to be used directly in subsequent cycles, or alternatively treatment is started at the next lower dose. The doses of HPG required for the first 45 patients to be treated in this study are summarized in Figure 3. The range was ninefold and the distribution of doses was similar to that reported by Crooke and co-workers [10].

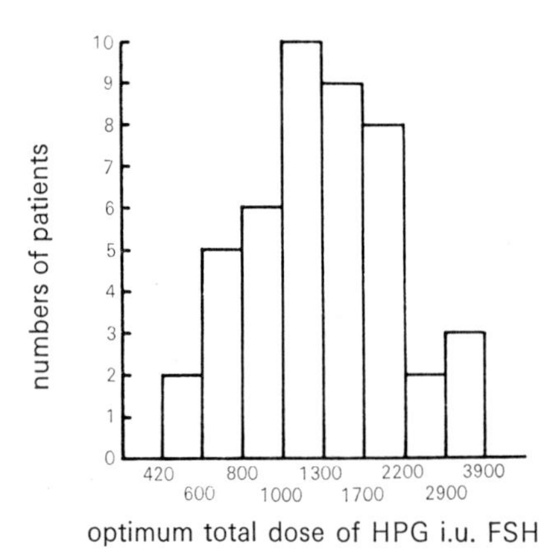


FIGURE 3
HPG dosage in total i.u. FSH required to produce optimum follicular responses in 45 women, showing the number of patients in each dose range (from [1])

(2) *Short luteal phases.* Short luteal phases of less than 12 days, as measured from the oestrogen peak to menstruation, occurred when doses of 2,000 to 5,000 i.u. HCG were used for ovulation. The phenomenon is illustrated in Figure 4 which shows a luteal phase of nine days in a patient who ovulated when given a dose of 3,000 i.u. HCG. This deficiency, which would interfere with implantation, was corrected by giving additional doses of HCG during the luteal phase, and it is now our practice to give 1,000 i.u. six days after the ovulating dose and 1,500 i.u. on days nine and twelve. As the ovulating dose of HCG is increased above 5,000 i.u., the luteal phases become more normal in duration and additional HCG is unnecessary when the ovulating dose is 10,000 i.u. or more (Fig. 5).

Vande Wiele and co-workers [13] have found that short luteal phases are the rule when pituitary LH is used instead of HCG to induce ovulation. This is presumably because LH is cleared more rapidly than HCG. Under these conditions, it was found that luteal phases of normal duration could be obtained by giving further doses of LH. However, although the doses were continued, there was a limit beyond which they were no longer effective in prolonging the luteal phase. These studies indicate that the life span of the corpus luteum in the human is under the control of LH.

In another experiment to prolong the luteal phase, HPG (160 i.u. FSH)

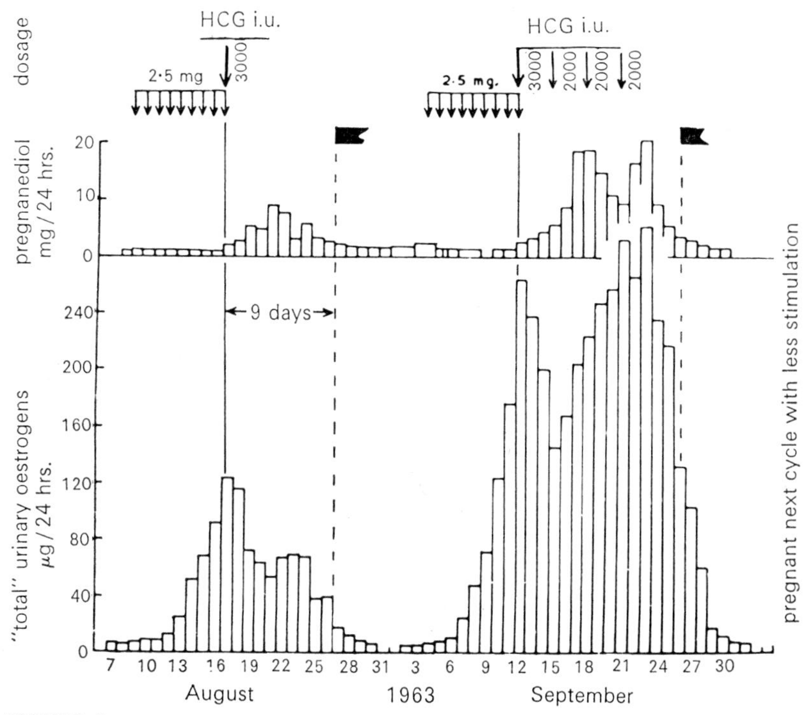


FIGURE 4
A short luteal phase of 9 days followed an ovulating dose of 3,000 i.u. HCG. In the next cycle, the luteal phase was prolonged and steroidogenesis was enhanced by giving three additional doses of 2,000 i.u. HCG (from [2])

was given along with the maintenance doses of HCG (3,000 i.u.) [1]. This caused a dramatic increase in oestrogen and pregnanediol excretion, with pregnanediol values reaching 100 mg per 24 hours. Treatment was discontinued immediately, but hyperstimulation occurred reaching clinical grade 3 of Rabau et al. [14]. HPG has not been given again during a luteal phase and no other instance of such hyperstimulation has been encountered. It would appear from the literature that clinically severe hyperstimulation is a phenomenon which occurs only after the patient has ovulated.

(3) *Dosage of HCG for ovulation.* The factors which determine the minimum dosage of HCG required for ovulation are more complicated than those for HPG. Single doses of 3,000 to 5,000 i.u. HCG proved to be effective in the first patients to be treated, but patients were then encountered in whom these doses failed to induce ovulation. Such a patient is illustrated in Figure 5. HCG (5,000 i.u.) given in cycle (a) failed to induce ovulation but synergized with the HPG to give oestrogen values which reached 900 µg

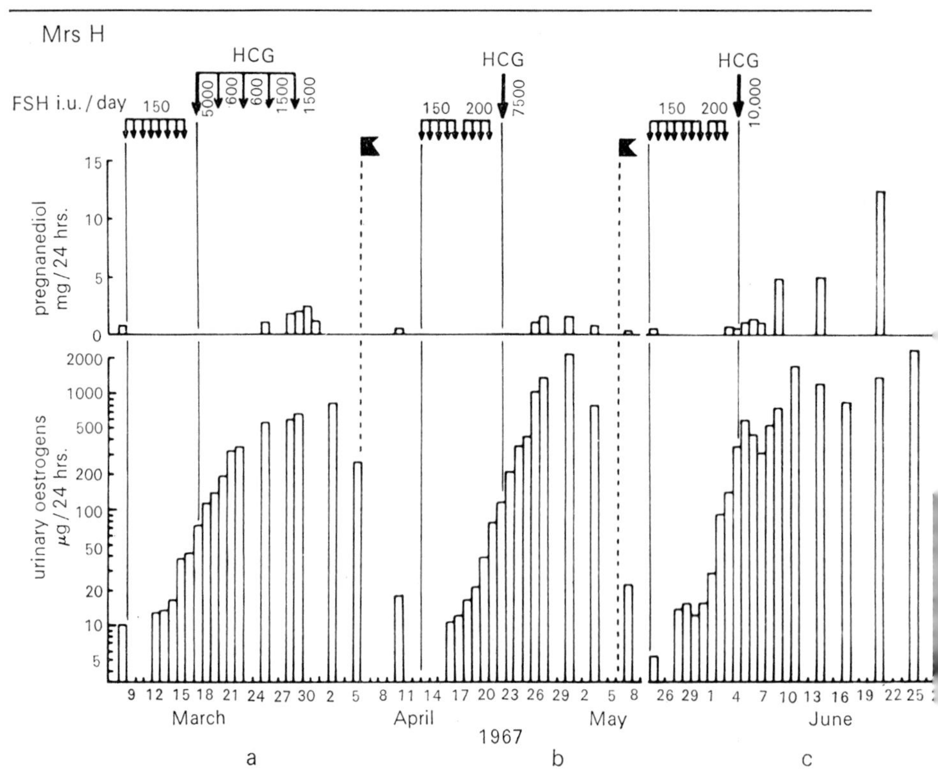


FIGURE 5

Achieving ovulation by increasing the dose of HCG. The oestrogen responses are shown on a logarithmic scale (from [1])

per 24 hours. In cycle (b), 7,500 i.u. were given after a greater stimulation with HPG, this also failed to induce ovulation and the oestrogen levels reached 2,000 μg per 24 hours. In cycle (c), the dose was increased to 10,000 i.u., ovulation followed and, although the oestrogen levels were excessively high, a single pregnancy resulted. The decision to increase the dose of HCG in spite of the over-responses to smaller doses had therefore produced the desired result. However, subsequent experience has shown that this is not the only means of achieving ovulation under these circumstances. Furthermore, in a period in which high doses of HCG were used indiscriminately, there was a sharp increase in the incidence of multiple pregnancies which included quadruplets and two sets of triplets [1]. These pregnancies were not associated with excessive follicular stimulation because HCG was withheld when this occurred. We considered that unnecessarily high doses of HCG were the cause of these multiple pregnancies and therefore should be avoided.

Other factors which influence the ovulatory responses to HCG are illustrated in Figures 6, 7 and 8. Figure 6 shows that the period of time elapsing between completing the course of HPG and giving the ovulating dose of HCG is important. Cycle (a) shows high levels of urinary oestrogens without an ovulatory peak (synergism) when HCG (7,500 i.u.) was given with the last dose of HPG. Progressively less marked responses occurred as the doses were separated by 10 hours (c) and 24 hours (b). Ovulation was achieved when the interval was 34 hours (d) and in subsequent cycles ovulation was achieved regularly using doses as low as 3,000 i.u. combined with more careful adjustment of follicular responses and using time intervals of up to 48 hours, a period first recommended by Crooke et al. [10]. This patient also demonstrates that pregnanediol levels can increase after giving HCG without ovulation (cycles a, b and c) but that the responses are less marked than those which occur after ovulation (cycle d).

The rate at which the oestrogen values are rising under stimulation with HPG is another factor which influences response to HCG. This is illustrated in Figure 7 which shows two cycles (a and c) in which a dose of 5,000 i.u. HCG given after an oestrogen rise from approximately 10 to 70 μg per 24

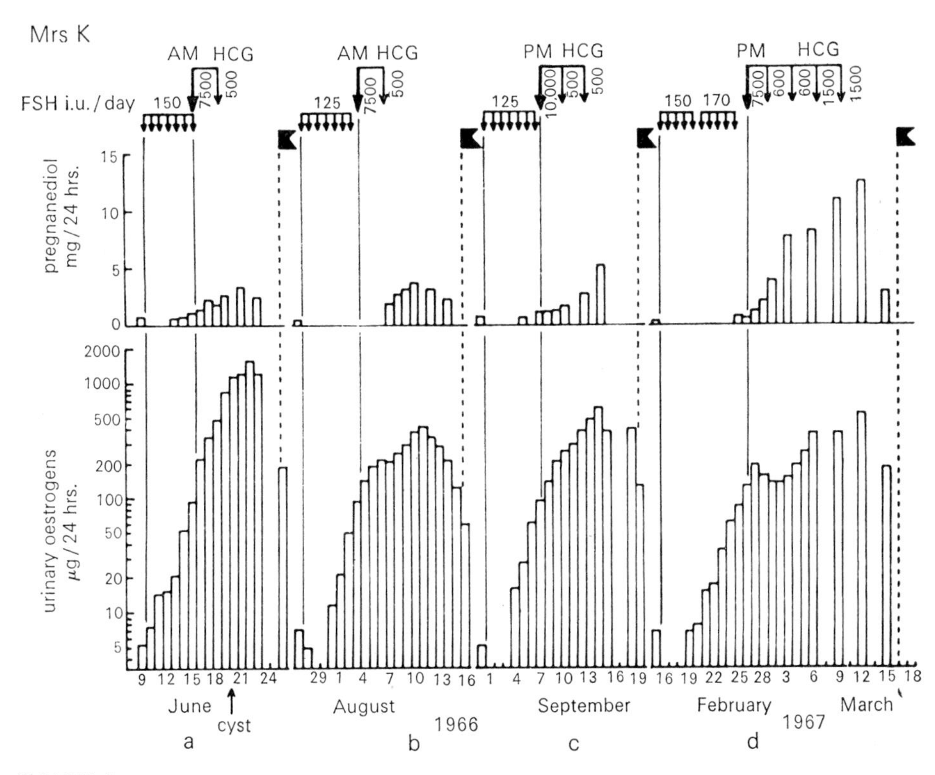


FIGURE 6
The effect on the ovulatory response of separating the ovulating dose of HCG from the last dose of HPG. The oestrogen responses are shown on a logarithmic scale (from [1])

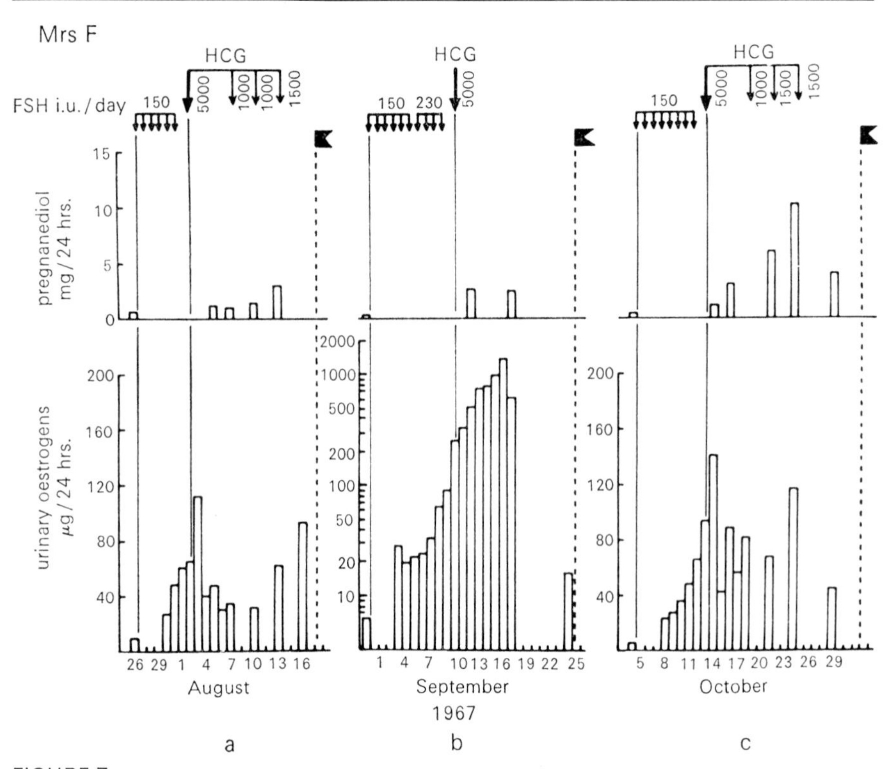


FIGURE 7
The effect on the ovulatory response of the preceding rate of follicular stimulation (from [1])

hours in six to seven days induced ovulation but failed to do so when given after the more rapid oestrogen rise from 30 to 90 µg in three days, which followed a dosage increment in HPG of 1·5 (cycle b).

The oestrogen levels reached at the time the HCG is given are also important. Sometimes, when marginally effective doses of HPG are used, the oestrogen levels rise initially but plateau at between 20 and 40 µg per 24 hours. HCG given during such stationary conditions is without effect (Fig. 8, cycle a). Oestrogen levels rising towards a peak seem to be essential before ovulation can occur. Furthermore, it is preferable that the oestrogen values reach at least 50 µg per 24 hours before the ovulating dose of HCG is given. Five pregnancies occurred in this series when the oestrogen value was less than 50 µg on the day before the HCG was given; three of these ended in first-trimester abortions, one yielded triplets and only one was a normal single pregnancy [1]. This value of 50 µg compares with the range of 45 to 100 µg per 24 hours found at the midcycle peak of the normal cycle [7].

In the majority of ovulatory cycles induced in this study, the HCG was given as the oestrogen levels were rising. This was followed by a further rise in oestrogen values, the peak being reached either within the same 24-hour period as the HCG was given or up to two days later. However, in nine conceptual cycles, the oestrogen values had risen initially but were falling when the HCG was administered so that the result for the day the HCG was given was lower than that of the previous day. In six of these nine cycles, the levels then rose again to reach a peak one or two days later (Fig. 9b). In the other three, the administration of HCG did not influence oestrogen excretion, and the values continued to fall before rising again into the luteal phase (Fig. 9a). It was unlikely that ovulation was spontaneous in these latter three patients because one had primary amenorrhoea associated with hypogonadotrophic hypogonadism (Fig. 9a). Eight of these nine pregnancies have delivered, four were multiple (twins) and three of these occurred with doses of 3,000 i.u. HCG, indicating an increased sensitivity to HCG under these conditions.

All these findings can be explained on the assumptions that the minimum effective ovulating dose of HCG depends on the state of maturity of the follicle upon which it acts, and that maturity can be defined by the trends

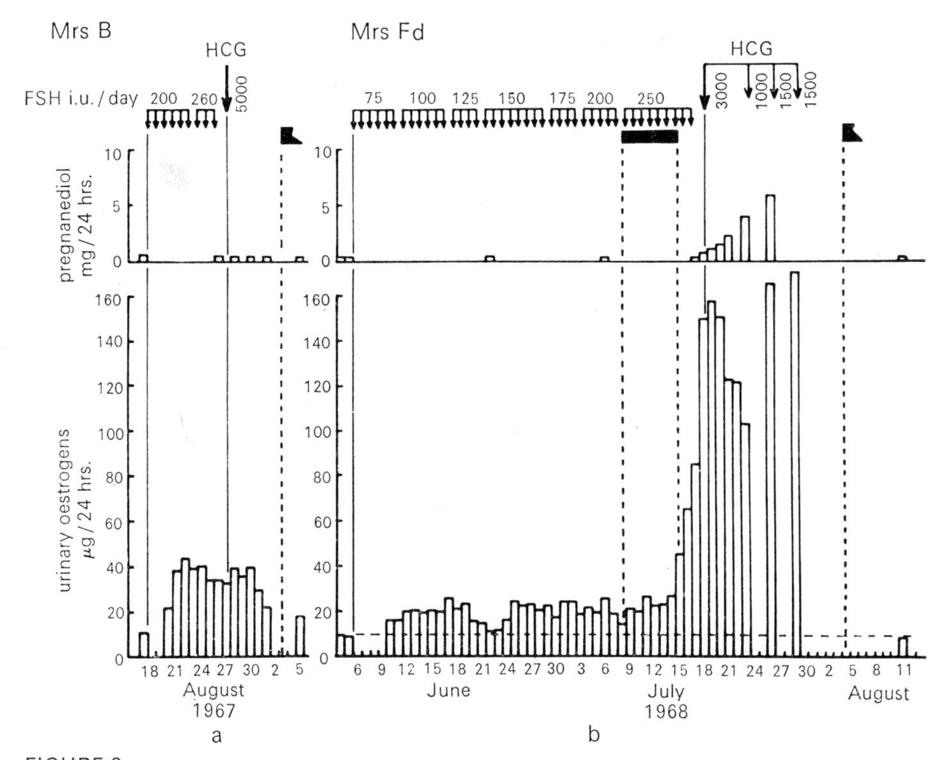


FIGURE 8
Plateau effects and dosage increments (from [1])

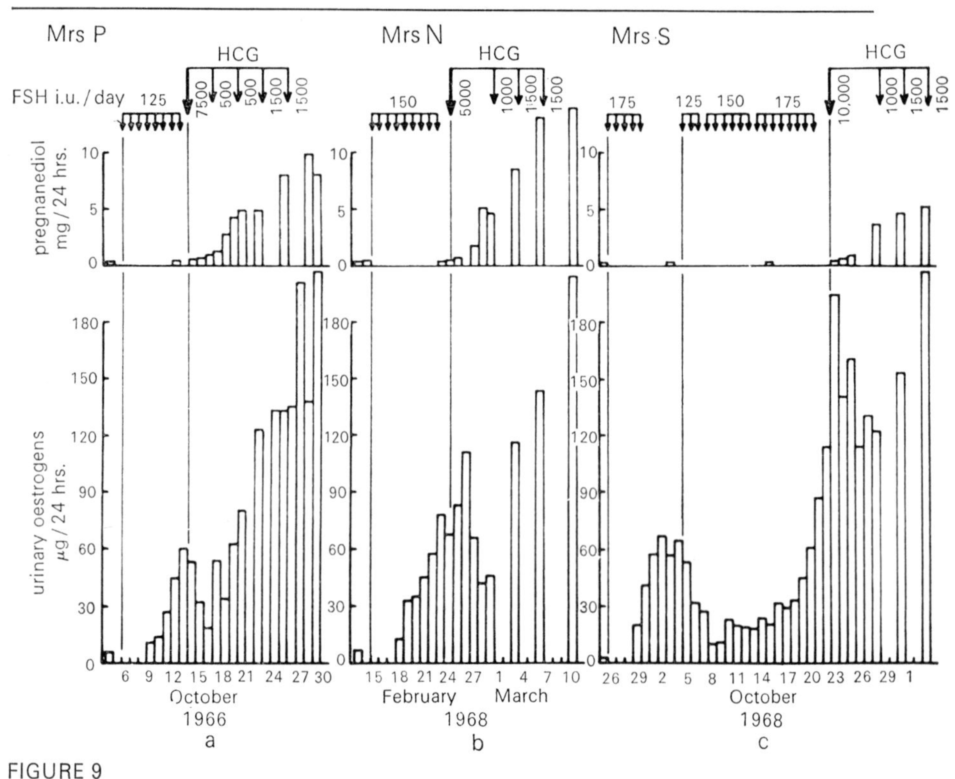


FIGURE 9

Responses to ovulating doses of HCG. Cycle (a), HCG given after the oestrogen peak did not produce an additional follicular response. Cycle (b), HCG given as the oestrogen values were falling caused an additional rise to a peak two days later. Cycle (c) shows an attempt to obtain maximum follicular sensitivity to HCG in a patient who had previously required a dose of 40,000 i.u. (from [1])

and levels of urinary oestrogen excretion. The immature follicle is not susceptible to ovulation until the urinary oestrogen levels rise above 40 µg per 24 hours. Above this, high doses of HCG are required as oestrogen output is rising rapidly. The requirement decreases as the rate of growth slackens and this is achieved by stopping the HPG and allowing the follicle to 'coast'. Maximum sensitivity is reached during this coasting period at approximately 48 hours after the last dose of HPG has been given. However, the optimum time interval depends on many variables which include the rate at which the follicle is being stimulated at the time the HPG is withdrawn. It might be more accurate to specify the period of optimum susceptibility to HCG as the 24 to 48 hours after the oestrogen peak while the values are falling. After that, it would appear that the ageing follicle rapidly becomes refractory to the action of HCG. Besides these differences in response due to different degrees of follicular maturation, the doses of HCG required by different patients under similar conditions may differ by twentyfold [1]. It is therefore not surprising that difficulties have been encountered in correlating responses with the dosage of HCG.

*Relevance to the events of the normal menstrual cycle*

The agreement between the quantitative changes in HPG dosage required to obtain normal follicular responses and rises in FSH levels measured during the early part of the menstrual cycle has already been considered. After the initial elevation, the FSH levels fall as the follicular phase progresses, then rise in parallel with the LH to a midcycle peak and then fall again during the luteal phase [12]. The fall before the LH peak occurs at the time when the oestrogen levels are rising rapidly. It corresponds in the induced cycles to the coasting period which ends the rise in oestrogen output and decreases the dose of HCG required for ovulation. However, the midcycle peak has no counterpart in the induced cycles where in fact HCG seems to be more effective in inducing ovulation in the complete absence of HPG. However, the experiment in which HPG is given along with the HCG after the coasting period has not yet been performed.

The relationship between oestrogen production, follicular maturation, onset of oestrus and ovulation has been studied in the sheep (Fig. 10)

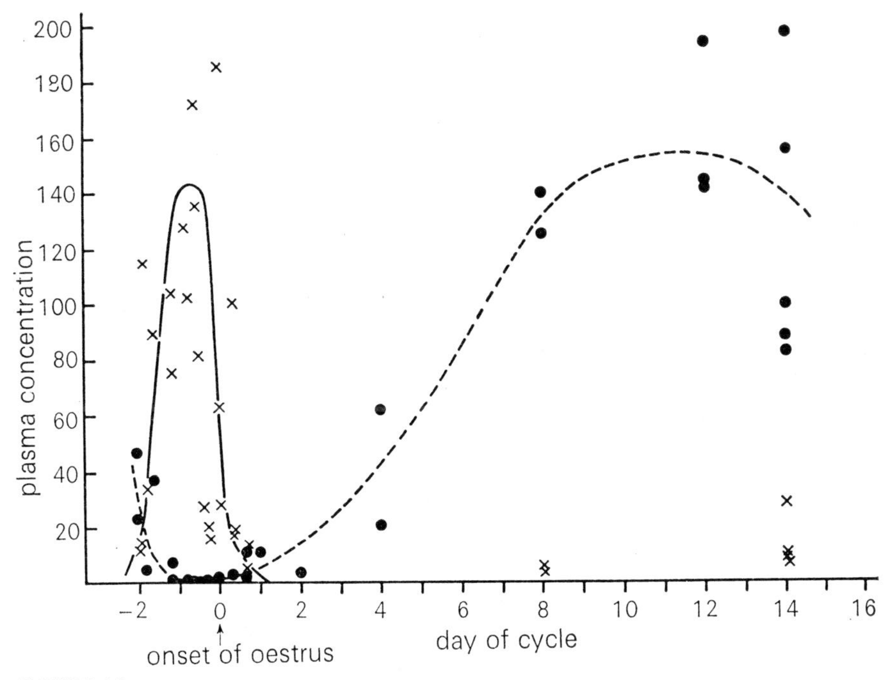


FIGURE 10
Levels of oestradiol and progesterone in ovarian vein blood of the ewe throughout the oestrous cycle (from [15])

[15]. In this animal, ovulation occurs on the average 25 hours after onset of oestrus. Oestradiol levels in the ovarian vein blood reached a maximum just before onset of oestrus, fell during the oestrous period and were undetectable at the time of ovulation. The ovulatory release of LH occurs a few hours after onset of oestrus [16] as the oestrogen levels are falling. This precise information in the sheep would seem to be translatable, at least in part, to the human. Clearly, ovulation must come after the dose of HCG or the midcycle surge of LH, but its timing is likely to be more closely related to the nadir in oestrogen excretion. In the majority of the induced cycles, the administration of HCG caused a further rise in oestrogen excretion before it reached the peak, and this probably accounted for the increased peak values encountered. However, in the normal cycle, the LH peak occurs after the oestrogen peak [12, 17] at a time when the follicle no longer responds by an increase in oestrogen secretion. This normal situation was apparently reproduced in the three cycles illustrated by Figure 9a in which HCG was given after the oestrogen peak and had no immediate effect on oestrogen output. This situation appeared to produce follicles which were maximally sensitive to HCG and a further reduction in dosage below 3,000 i.u. needs to be tested. However, there is no proof that a carefully graded release of LH to match the sensitivity of the dominant follicle is a factor in preventing multiple pregnancies during the normal cycle. It can be seen that the information derived from the therapeutic use of gonadotrophins agrees in most of the essential details with the more direct measurements performed during the normal menstrual cycle and thus provides important confirmatory data.

*Pregnancies achieved*

Table 1 includes the clinical results of this study. Ovulation was achieved in all the patients who responded to HPG. Of the 60 women in the series, 46 have already conceived (77 per cent), nine of them twice and one of them three times, making a total of 56 pregnancies. Of these, eight ended in abortion (14 per cent). The pregnancy rate was higher (85 per cent) in patients with amenorrhoea than those with oligomenorrhoea and anovulatory cycles (50 per cent). However, only one of the failures had persisted with treatment and failure was accepted only after 21 treatment cycles, 11 of which had been ovulatory (Mrs K, Fig. 6). There was only one instance of clinical hyperstimulation which caused concern and this was in the first patient to be treated. Of the 46 delivered pregnancies, including three of the abortions, 32 were singleton, nine were twin, three were triplet and two were quadruplet, making a multiple pregnancy rate of 30 per cent. These multiple pregnancies were concentrated into two periods, one in which high doses of HCG were being used indiscriminately, and the other more recently in which optimum conditions for ovulation were aimed at and often achieved, yet the doses of HCG were not correspondingly reduced below 3,000 i.u.

This study, which is an extension of the classical work of Gemzell [18], demonstrates that with present knowledge and refinements in techniques, treatment with gonadotrophins is now a safe and highly effective method of treating infertility in women with deficient ovarian function, and the main problem remaining is a further reduction in the incidence of multiple pregnancies.

## REFERENCES

[1] Brown, J.B., Evans, J.H., Adey, F.D., Taft, H.P. and Townsend, L., *J. Obstet. Gynaec. Br. Commonw.*, **76,** 289, 1969.

[2] Townsend, S.L., Brown, J.B., Johnstone, J.W., Adey, F.D., Evans, J.H. and Taft, H.P., *J. Obstet. Gynaec. Br. Commonw.*, **73,** 529, 1966.

[3] Brown, J.B., Catt, K.J. and Martin, F.I.R., *J. Endocr.*, **38,** 451, 1967.

[4] De Kretser, D.M., Taft, H.P., Brown, J.B., Evans, J.H. and Hudson, B., *J. Endocr.*, **40,** 107, 1968.

[5] Brown, J.B., MacLeod, S.C., Macnaughtan, C., Smith, M.A. and Smyth, B., *J. Endocr.*, **42,** 5, 1968.

[6] Cox, R.I., *J. Chromatog.*, **12,** 242, 1963.

[7] Brown, J.B. This volume p. 131.

[8] Liggins, G.C. and Ibbertson, H.K., *Lancet*, **1,** 114, 1966.

[9] Crooke, A.C. This volume p. 230.

[10] Crooke, A.C., Butt, W.R. and Bertrand, P.V., *Acta endocr., Copnh., Suppl.* **111.**

[11] Fukushima, M., Stevens, V.C., Gantt, C.L. and Vorys, N., *J. clin. Endocr. Metab.*, **24,** 205, 1964.

[12] Odell, W.D. This volume p. 32.

[13] Vande Wiele, R.L., Bogumil, J., Dyrenfurth, I., Ferin, M., Jewelewicz, R., Warren, M., Rizkallah, T. and Mikhail, G., *Recent Prog. Hormone Res.*, **26,** 63, 1970

[14] Rabau, E., David, A., Serr, D.M., Mashiach, S. and Lunenfeld, B., *Am. J. Obstet. Gynec.*, **98,** 92, 1967.

[15] Moore, N.W., Barrett, S., Brown, J.B., Schindler, I., Smith, M.A. and Smyth, B., *J. Endocr.*, **44,** 55, 1969.

[16] Goding, J.R., Catt, K.J. and Brown, J.M., *Endocrinology*, **85,** 133, 1969.

[17] Burger, H.G., Catt, K.J. and Brown, J.B., *J. clin. Endocr. Metab.*, **28,** 1508, 1968.

[18] Gemzell, C. In *Proceedings of Fifth World Congress of Gynaecology and Obstetrics.* Ed. C. Wood. Sydney: Butterworths, p. 240.

*Discussion of paper by Dr Brown*

*Donovan* What do the ovaries look like when they are hyperstimulated?
*Gemzell* The result of this type of stimulation shows conglomerations of big follicles. If the follicles become luteinized they fill with blood and form luteal cysts. Sometimes these rupture and then blood and follicle fluid are found in the abdomen. Cases of thrombosis have been reported with this overstimulation syndrome.
*Donovan* Are the multiple pregnancies due to HCG or to overtreatment with FSH?
*Brown* Obviously, more than one follicle is required to produce more than one egg. However, the ovulatory peak of oestrogen excretion in cases of multiple pregnancies may be quite low and in one of our cases of triplets only reached 40 μg per 24 hours, so that excess stimulation with FSH was not a likely factor in this case. We believe that if a certain amount of HCG is given it will rupture only the major follicle, i.e., that which has reached the greatest sensitivity to HCG. However, if a massive dose of HCG is given, it will also rupture marginal follicles. This seems to be just as important a cause of multiple pregnancies as giving too much HPG but as the two effects are interrelated it is very difficult to design experiments to separate them.
*Johansson* Dr Brown, is it not dangerous to look only at oestrogens? You have previously suggested that there was considerable variation and that an ovulatory peak in the menstrual cycle could be 15 μg. Sometimes an ovulatory peak of over 100 μg was necessary to stimulate one follicle. Is it not difficult to judge ovulation from the dose because several follicles might go on and produce oestrogen?
*Brown* I emphasize again that the main value of monitoring ovarian response by oestrogen assay is in titrating the patient's dosage requirement for HPG, that is, in determining the threshold dose and ensuring that an increment does not exceed this by more than 30 per cent. We quickly found that otherwise we had no control over achieving specified oestrogen levels. I agree that, in many cycles demonstrated, the oestrogen peak exceeded that ever found during the normal cycle. Many of these were taken from our early studies when we were gaining experience. We now aim at a level of between 50 and 100 μg for the ovulatory peak but still often exceed this. This is because an increment of 30 per cent is still excessive for some patients and because the HCG often causes an extra rise in oestrogen levels which does not occur during the normal cycle. Ovulatory peaks of less than 50 μg occur sufficiently often during spontaneous cycles to be considered normal. We settled on this lower figure because of the higher incidence of abortions and the lower incidence of conception at lower oestrogen peaks. Very little information is available on oestrogen levels in conceptual cycles

in normal individuals. We are now trying to obtain this information and I feel that there is a good chance that a similar relationship between oestrogen levels, fertility and abortion will be found.

*Naftolin* Would the use of LH rather than HCG, as an ovulatory trigger, be more beneficial and also the use of progesterone rather than HCG or LH to support the inadequate corpus luteum syndrome?

*Brown* We have not had pure LH to work with. Vande Wiele has achieved ovulation with pure LH but his patients showed the deficient corpus luteum effect that we obtained with the low doses of HCG. This seems to be a bigger problem with LH than with HCG. It could be due to differences in clearance rates. With regard to using progesterone instead of HCG, we considered that as the corpus luteum produces both oestrogens and progesterone it was better to use a stimulus which caused the corpus luteum to produce the natural hormones rather than investigate optimum mixtures of synthetic oestrogens and progestogens.

*Grant* Is the type of fluorimeter used important? We have used your corrections and had negative oestrogen values for the base line. We have had little success with regard to stimulating pregnancies and I wonder whether the figure of 50 μg that you suggested as the optimum might not be too low. Do you really feel the correction factor is necessary?

*Brown* In treatment with gonadotrophin the patient acts as her own control. The correction obtained by applying the correction factor to fluorimetric measurement amounts to approximately 6 μg per 24 hour urine. Such an overestimate would make no difference to the interpretation in this type of application. In fact there are some centres using simple filter type fluorimeters without spectrophotofluorimetric correction for monitoring gonadotrophin therapy by oestrogen assay. I would not wish to be dogmatic about the level of 50 μg but would just say that stimulation above a certain level, which for most individuals approximates this figure, is necessary before ovulation and a pregnancy will occur.

*Gemzell* I agree with what Dr Brown has said. In order to reduce multiple births during 1969 we were very careful with the rise in oestrogens and induced ovulation at a total oestrogen level of around 60 μg. When we induced ovulation at about 50 μg the rise in plasma progesterone twenty-four hours later was around 3 ng which corresponds with the level we have found following normal spontaneous ovulation. If ovulation was induced at about 100 μg the rise in plasma progesterone was 5 to 6 ng and when we induced ovulation at 200 μg the rise was 9 to 19 ng. We have now tended to stimulate the oestrogen level to 50 or 60 μg and then induce ovulation. In 1961–64 we took a hundred women who ovulated at 300 μg total oestrogen level. The pregnancy rate was 43 per cent and the multiple birth rate 29 per cent. In 1968 we reduced the ovulation level to 127 μg and had the same pregnancy and multiple birth rate. In 1969 we induced ovulation at up to 80 μg. The pregnancy rate was 26 per cent and there was only one case of twin pregnancy. We are now stimulating to the lower level and have found that although this gives a lower pregnancy rate it also gives a very small incidence of multiple births. We are also now treating a lot of women who are not very suitable for treatment and this might account for the low rates.

# Induction of Ovulation with Human Gonadotrophins

A. C. CROOKE *and* P. V. BERTRAND

Department of Clinical Endocrinology, Birmingham and Midland Hospital for Women, Birmingham

¶ THERE are many variables involved in the treatment of infertile women with failure of ovulation by injections of gonadotrophic hormones. We have investigated these systematically in a long series of factorial experiments during the past nine years. The most important are the patients themselves, the total dose of follicle-stimulating hormone (FSH) and the magnitude of the response which, in our experience, is best judged by the excretion of urinary oestrogens [1]. Next we find that the duration of treatment with the ovulating dose of human chorionic gonadotrophin (HCG) is important in relation to the incidence of multiple pregnancies and we recommend a single injection after completion of treatment with FSH [2–4]. We likewise find that the ratio of FSH to luteinizing hormone (LH) in the mixture has a bearing on the incidence of multiple pregnancies and we recommend a ratio of about 5:1 [5]. We do not find that the size of the ovulating dose of HCG when it is given as a single injection after treatment with FSH has any bearing on the incidence of multiple pregnancies [6]. Nor do we find any difference in the magnitude of the response when the total dose of FSH is given in equally divided daily doses or in twice-weekly doses [6]. Since the latter is more convenient for both patients and staff and adequate control can be obtained with twice-weekly estimations of urinary oestrogens done at the time of the visits for treatment, this system has now become standardized in our department.

In our earlier work using factorial experiments it was necessary to use rigid systems of treatment increasing the total dosage of FSH at monthly intervals when necessary, but we found that there was, on average, a steady loss of sensitivity to FSH by patients [7]. This varied between patients but was sometimes so striking that it was difficult to increase dosage fast enough. Some two years ago, we started to use a system of treatment in which we increased the dosage of FSH at twice-weekly intervals, that is at each injection, until a satisfactory oestrogen response occurred. An example of this system is shown in Figure 1, in which the dose of FSH is proportional to the shaded area. This patient ovulated as judged by the satisfactory rise in excretion of oestriol and pregnanediol. The main problem now was to decide what increase in dose of FSH was optimal. Figure 2 shows in the first and third columns the amount of oestriol excreted at the time of the first positive oestrogen response by two groups of patients. The second and fourth columns show the amount excreted by the same patients at the next visit after a further injection of FSH. The straight lines join the means for both groups. In the first group, the dosage of FSH was increased by a factor of 50 per cent and in five of the ten patients the excretion of oestriol rose to above 100 μg/24 hours at the next visit. In the second group, the dosage was increased by a factor of 30 per cent and none of the seven patients showed a rise to above 100 μg/24 hours. This difference is signifi-

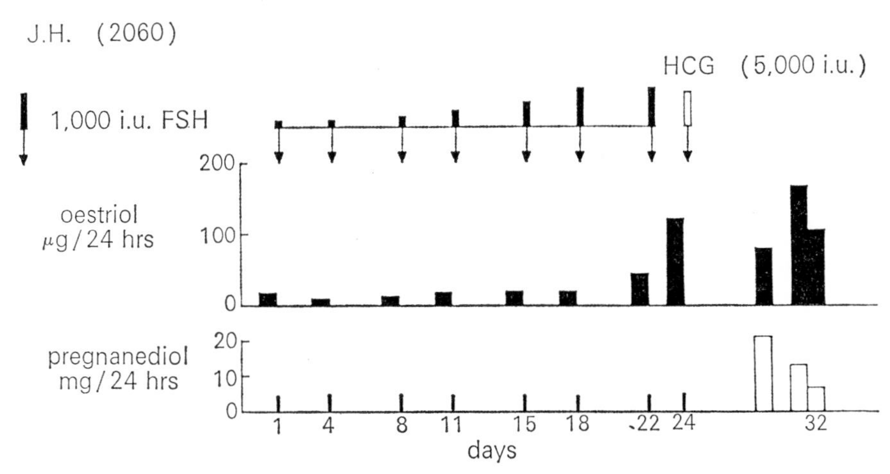


FIGURE 1
The excretion of oestriol and pregnanediol of a patient given dosages of FSH increased by 50 per cent at twice-weekly intervals.

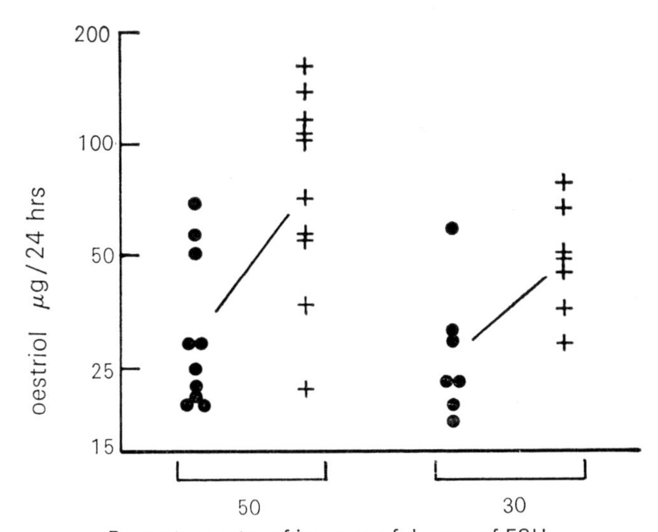


FIGURE 2
The amount of oestriol excreted by patients treated with increasing dosages of FSH at twice-weekly intervals. In ten patients FSH dosage was increased by a factor of 50 per cent and in seven by a factor of 30 per cent. • The excretion of oestriol at the time of the first positive oestriol response; + The excretion of oestriol at the time of giving HCG

cant at the 5 per cent level. The figure of 100 μg/24 hours is critical since in four of our five patients who gave birth to triplets or more, the excretion of oestriol had risen above this figure on the day when the ovulating dose of HCG was given [5]. If HCG had been withheld when this occurred, none would have conceived and the incidence of grand multiple pregnancies, that is of triplets or more, would have been greatly reduced. Obviously, therefore, an increment in dosage of FSH of 30 per cent at twice-weekly intervals is satisfactory and has become our standard practice.

For convenience the incremental dosages in terms of ampoules of FSH each containing 75 i.u. are shown in Table 1. The first positive response is taken as an increase in excretion of total oestrogen of 35 μg/24 hours above the control value on day one. When the response at the next visit is between 35 and 125 μg/24 hours above the control value the last dose of FSH is repeated. When it is between 125 and 250 μg above the control value, the last dose but one is given, and when it is more than 250 μg above the control value, no more FSH is given. HCG is given in a single injection 2 to 4 days later provided the total oestrogen excretion does not exceed 250 μg/24 hours on that day – otherwise treatment is suspended for that month.

TABLE 1. Dosage Schedule. The 24-hourly excretion of total oestrogen is measured on each of the days shown below. The corresponding dosage of FSH is then given if the amount of total oestrogen is less than 35 μg/24 hours greater than the control amount on day one

| Day | No. of ampoules | FSH dosage (i.u.) | Day | No. of ampoules | FSH dosage (i.u.) |
|---|---|---|---|---|---|
| 1 | 2 | 150 | 22 | 9 | 675 |
| 4 | 2 | 150 | 25 | 12 | 900 |
| 8 | 3 | 225 | 29 | 16 | 1,200 |
| 11 | 4 | 300 | 32 | 22 | 1,650 |
| 15 | 5 | 375 | 36 | 30 | 2,250 |
| 18 | 7 | 525 | 39 | 40 | 3,000 |

If the patient shows a positive response to treatment but fails to conceive another course is begun two weeks after the last injection but the starting dose of FSH is adjusted by reference to the previous course of treatment. The starting dose which is given on day one is one-third of the total dosage given in the last three injections of the previous course. The same dosage is given on day four and thereafter the procedure is the same as that shown in Table 1 and described above.

This system has been in regular use in all experiments carried out since we reviewed our first fifty-six pregnancies which were completed by November 1968 [5]. There have been sixteen more pregnancies with only one case of triplets since then and this occurred in a patient given a preparation with FSH to LH ratio of 1:1.

To facilitate usage of the dosage schedule shown in Table I we would recommend that commercial preparations of FSH should be ampouled in two dosages, namely in ampoules containing 75 i.u. as at present, and in ampoules containing five times this amount, i.e., 375 i.u.

ACKNOWLEDGMENTS

This work was carried out under block grants from the Medical Research Council and the Ford Foundation.

REFERENCES

[1] Crooke, A.C., Butt, W.R. and Bertrand, P.V., *Acta endocr., Copnh., Suppl.* **111**, 1966.
[2] Crooke, A.C., Butt, W.R., Palmer, R.F., Morris, R., Edwards, L.R. and Anson, C.J., *J. Obstet. Gynaec. Br. Commonw.*, **70**, 604, 1963.
[3] Crooke, A.C., Butt, W.R., Palmer, R.F., Bertrand, P.V., Carrington, S.P., Edwards, L.R. and .Anson, C.J., *J. Obstet. Gynaec. Br. Commonw.*, **71**, 571, 1964.
[4] Crooke, A.C., *Proc. R. Soc. Med.*, **57**, 111, 1964.
[5] Crooke, A.C., Eleftheriadis, G. and Bertrand, P.V., *Hormones: Eur. Rev. Endocr.* **1**, 46, 1970.
[6] Awaiting publication.
[7] Crooke, A.C., Bertrand, P.V., Butt, W.R. and Morris, R. In *Reproductive Endocrinology*, p. 47. Ed. W.J. Irvine. Edinburgh: E. & S. Livingstone, 1970.

*Discussion of paper by Dr Crooke*

*Brown* In your comparisons between the effects of different doses of HCG for ovulation, when you gave more than 5,000 i.u., had you already tried to ovulate these patients with doses of less than 5,000 i.u. and failed? In this case your results would support our view, or were these two separate experiments with different patients?

*Crooke* This was an overall survey, but a factorial experiment now in progress should show this.

*Odell* Dr Crooke, could you summarize the concept as to whether more than one injection was needed or what was the optimum number of injections of FSH?

*Crooke* We have been particularly interested in the single injection of FSH as an academic problem and we have data on the results of single compared with multiple injections. We have had twelve pregnancies following single injections but the pregnancy rate per number of ovulations was about half with single injections compared with multiple injections. We now give twice-weekly injections with increasing doses until a satisfactory response occurs as judged by the excretion of oestrogens. The optimum number of injections depends, therefore, on how soon we get a response and this in turn depends on the dose that an individual patient requires. Some have responded and conceived after only three injections and a total dose of 500 i.u. FSH. Our most insensitive patient failed to respond to 8,000 i.u. FSH. This was a woman with primary amenorrhoea aged 36. We gave her 16,000 i.u. eventually and she ovulated and conceived, having a single pregnancy.

*Mills* Have you analyzed your data into different groups of presenting problems to see if there is any difference in response or any other characteristics?

*Crooke* A paper on this subject will appear shortly in *Hormones : European Review of Endocrinology*. I agree with Dr Brown that patients with primary amenorrhoea generally require a larger dose of FSH. Patients with secondary amenorrhoea generally require the next largest dose and women with anovular cycles and the Stein-Leventhal syndrome require the lowest dose.

*Gemzell* We have a number of women with both primary and secondary amenorrhoea from whom we have taken ovarian biopsies and were not able to find any follicles in the ovary. These women already have a high FSH excretion. We have been very reluctant to treat these women with FSH levels in the postmenopausal range but I agree with Dr Crooke that there may be cases who respond to this although I think it is very difficult to treat these women because they seem to require larger doses of FSH and longer terms of treatment. We have one patient who had been treated with daily injections for three weeks before she responded. I think the reason for this might be that these women have only one or two available follicles and that it takes time to stimulate them. Concerning the reproducibility of treatment, we have several women with primary amenorrhoea who have been treated over periods of four or five years. These women have been pregnant two or three times and we found that comparing the amounts of FSH given during the first treatment and then three or four years later there was a considerable increase in the amounts required. I wonder if this could be due to antibodies produced to the FSH but we have not been able to demonstrate any circulating antibodies to FSH in these women. We have treated one patient with primary amenorrhoea each month during the year for ten months before she became pregnant. We have also been interested to find how FSH should be given and we have followed Dr Crooke's suggestion about giving a single injection on days 1, 5 and 8. We have given this treatment to a woman who was a hypopituitary dwarf, who had been treated with growth hormone for about five or six years. We could not get her to grow any more so we stimulated her ovaries. When we gave a single injection of 1,000 i.u. to this woman we got a total oestrogen rise of about 15 μg on the seventh day but when we repeated this the next month we got a rise of 10 μg. When we gave 100 units a day we got a good response of about 40 μg. If you give single injections of FSH you have to give much more FSH activity. You have to give three to four times as much FSH activity if you give it in a single injection. The object is to give as little as possible and I think that you can get the best response by a daily injection.

*Crooke* We have done a number of laparotomies on patients with high gonadotrophin excretion and in general we find no primordial follicles. We have, however, obtained three pregnancies in such patients and I think that this indicates that they do occasionally have primordial follicles.

*Odell* What bioassay was used for measuring the gonadotrophins?

*Crooke* In our early work the mouse uterus test was used but in the last eight years the specific augmentation test. I would like to bring up the question of isolated case reports and say that the case reports as shown by Dr Brown were to me rather unconvincing. I think they could be made to show anything.

*Brown* Before publishing our work, we had an accumulated experience of over 230 completely studied cycles. It was very difficult to present this in one intelligible paper and yet it made a complete story. We considered that it was better to demonstrate individual cycles which showed a point clearly and then to state how many times this particular experience occurred rather than combine the information and blurr the message that it contained. Another question I would like to discuss is the maximum dose of FSH which should be reached before concluding that the patient has reached the menopause. We go up to 1,250 i.u. per day for five days which is a total dose of 6,250 i.u. but some workers have gone up to a total dose of only 650 i.u. spread over three injections before diagnosing an early menopause.

*Crooke* I am sure this is not true. I think that the average dose for pregnancy is much above this figure. We have had patients who have not responded until 16,000 units were given as I mentioned before.

*Butt* I would like to refer to Professor Odell's question of yesterday about the mechanism of action of a single injection of FSH. Professor Odell suggested that the single injection might trigger off a follicle which might then grow and I wonder whether in fact endogenous FSH might play a part here.

*Brown* Dr Crooke, if a patient does not become pregnant in the first treatment cycle, do you completely titrate the patient with gonadotrophin a second time until you get a response or do you start further up the dose ladder? If you do the latter, there is not much difference between the practices in our two centres.

*Crooke* We start further up the dose ladder. We use the mean of the last three injections as the starting dose in the next month if conception has not occurred.

# Suppression of Ovulation

JOHN A. LORAINE *and* D. A. ADAMOPOULOS

Medical Research Council Clinical Endocrinology Unit
Edinburgh

¶ OVULATION is the final step in a chain of events which commences with the growth of the ovarian follicle, continues with the formation of the stigma and follicular rupture, and culminates with the expulsion of the ovum. Although the morphological changes occurring in the ovary prior to ovulation are now reasonably well established [16, 28, 41], the same cannot be said for the precise physiological, biochemical and endocrinological mechanisms underlying this process. Accordingly, although the last two decades have seen a great intensification of research in this field, including such classical contributions as that of Harris and his co-workers in Oxford [18] emphasizing the role of the hypothalamus in the production of ovulation, much remains to be discovered before definite conclusions can be drawn.

This paper deals firstly with substances capable of suppressing ovulation in human subjects, concentrating particularly on the steroid contraceptives. The second topic concerns possible mechanisms of action of the latter group of compounds, and under this heading some of their short and longer term effects on endocrine function are described. Mention is also made of the so-called 'over-suppression syndrome', while the final subject considered is the importance of ovarian suppression within the world context as a method of combating one of the most serious problems facing our universe in the twentieth century, namely that of overpopulation. For those especially interested in the topics of ovarian suppression and the population crisis a number of recent reviews and monographs should be consulted [7, 10, 22, 26, 29, 31, 45].

## SUBSTANCES CAPABLE OF SUPPRESSING OVULATION

A large number of compounds have been described with the potential for suppressing ovulation in human subjects. These can be divided into two main groups – *non-steroidal* and *steroidal*.

1. *Non-steroidal substances.* Included in this category are the following:

(a) *Depressants of the central nervous system*, e.g., morphine, barbiturates and chlorpromazine [17, 43, 51]. Such compounds are most unlikely to be used as contraceptive agents in human subjects because of the formidable difficulties associated with the separation of their antiovulatory effects from their other pharmacological actions.

(b) *Drugs affecting the cardiovascular system* – e.g., reserpine [6]. The same comment is relevant as in the case of (a).

(c) *Inhibitory substances produced by the hypothalamus and suppressing gonadotrophin production* [39]. Recent research in this field reviewed by Segal and Tietze [45] suggests that, in addition to the secretion of gonadotrophin-releasing factors, the hypothalamus may elaborate inhibitory substances capable of suppressing the production of these hormones. It is of interest to note that inhibitors of this type have been demonstrated in the brain of infants and of children prior to puberty. Whether or not such substances will have an important part to play in contraceptive practice in human subjects remains to be established.

(d) *Antibodies to gonadotrophins of pituitary and placental origin.* The control of human fertility by immunological means, e.g., by the administration of antibodies to gonadotrophic hormones, is attractive on a theoretical basis [44, 45]. However, as in the case of hypothalamic inhibitors, such an approach is not practicable at the present time although research in this area is proceeding apace and is likely to expand in the future.

(e) *Natural plant products*, e.g., extracts of North America prairie grass [40]. From time to time products of this type have been claimed to be effective in the control of fertility by inactivating circulating gonadotrophins. It must however be admitted that until now this line of investigation has not yielded promising results.

(f) *Derivatives of dithiocarbamoylhydrazine*, e.g., ICI 22, 365 and ICI 33, 828. In the early 1960s our Unit investigated the effects of these compounds on endocrine function in human subjects [1, 2]. It was found that both substances suppressed pituitary gonadotrophic activity in postmenopausal subjects and that the latter had a marked antiovulatory effect in women during reproductive life. Unfortunately compounds of this general series proved too toxic for routine clinical use in the human female, although they have proved to be of considerable value in the control of fertility in a number of animal species [50].

2. *Steroid contraceptives.* These fall into four main categories – *'classical' contraception by the combined Pill, sequential contraception, progestogens administered alone* and *long-acting contraceptive preparations.*

(a) *'Classical' contraception by the combined Pill.* This will always be associated with the names of Pincus and Rock who were its pioneers. The classical Pill, which is generally administered from day 5 of the cycle for a period of 20 or 21 days, consists of a mixture of an oestrogen and a progestogen. The two major oestrogens which have been used since the introduction of this form of birth control have been *ethinyl oestradiol* and its *3-methyl ether* commonly known as mestranol. The progestogens which have been most widely employed have been derivatives of *19-nortestosterone* and *17α-hydroxyprogesterone.* The chemical composition of the many types of combined Pill currently available for clinical use has been discussed in numerous articles in recent years and for those particularly interested in this field reviews by Mears [36], Diczfalusy [7], Jeffery and Klopper [21] and Klopper [22] merit attention.

(i) *Mechanism of action.* There is now little doubt that the major effect of this form of medication is to suppress ovulation, and data supporting this view have been derived from a large number of investigations including those involving laparotomy, histological examination of ovarian biopsies and hormone assays in blood and urine [7]. Furthermore, the consensus of opinion is that the antiovulatory effect of the Pill is due mainly to its oestrogenic component.

It has been generally assumed that one of the major actions of the combined Pill in women is to suppress pituitary LH secretion, this being evidenced by the obliteration of the LH peak at midcycle [7, 42]. Recently, however, Dufau et al. [9] have put forward the alternative hypothesis that the major action of progestogen-oestrogen mixtures is to suppress pituitary FSH secretion. This would in turn cause failure of follicular development and a diminution in oestradiol secretion by the follicle. These workers believe that the secretion of the latter hormone, working through a positive feedback mechanism, is the main stimulus to pituitary LH release and consider that in the absence of such secretion ovulation is unlikely to occur. The hypothesis of Dufau et al. [9] is challenging but must at present be accepted with reserve, firstly because assays of plasma FSH were not reported in their paper, and secondly because there remains considerable doubt as to whether FSH alone is capable of affecting steroidogenesis in the human ovary.

(ii) *Short-term effects on endocrine function.* These have been studied by various investigators over the past decade [5, 46, 47, 49). The early papers of Shearman [46] and of Buchholz et al. [5] showed that administration of the combined Pill resulted in suppression of ovarian steroid excretion, while Stevens et al. [48], using bioassay methods, reported that such medication suppressed the midcycle peaks of FSH and LH output. A similar conclusion to that of Stevens et al. [48] was reached by Swerdloff and Odell [49] who employed radioimmunoassays for FSH and LH and conducted their estimations in serum rather than in urine.

(iii) *Longer-term effects on endocrine function.* Investigations in this field have also been made by a number of workers including Loraine et al. [32, 33], Shearman [46], Bell et al. [3] and Papanicolaou et al. [42]. The studies reported by the Unit in Edinburgh during the 1960s were conducted in 18 women who, prior to cessation of medication, had been treated with various types of combined Pill for periods of time ranging from 10 to 80 calendar months. The main conclusions to emerge from such studies were firstly, that following cessation of long-term treatment ovulatory cycles rapidly reappeared, and secondly, that the effects produced on urinary FSH and LH output varied greatly depending on such factors as the type of contraceptive administered, its dosage and the duration of therapy [31].

Figure 1, taken from the paper of Papanicolaou et al. [42], shows the long-term effect of the progestogen-oestrogen mixture Ovulen (G. D. Searle

& Co.) on urinary LH and pregnanediol output; the former substance was measured biologically by the hypophysectomized rat prostate test and the latter by the technique of Klopper et al. [23].

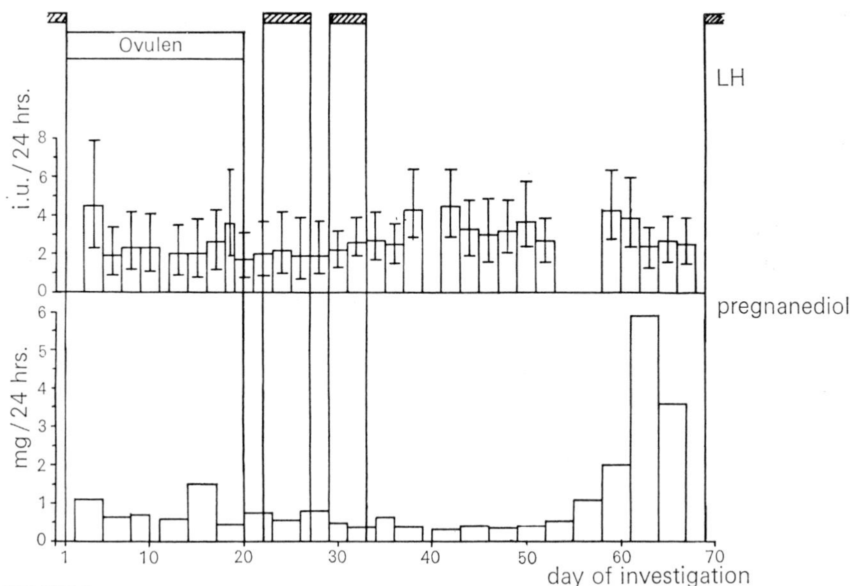


FIGURE 1
Pattern of LH and pregnanediol output in a subject during and following treatment with Ovulen (R) (from [42])
Hatched areas indicate duration of menstrual bleeding
I = fiducial limits (P = 0·95) of individual assays

Prior to the period of study the subject had been treated for 51 cycles. Assays were performed during the 52nd cycle of treatment and in the first cycle immediately following withdrawal of medication.

It will be noted that the last cycle on treatment was anovular in character as judged by urinary pregnanediol assays; however the pattern of excretion of this steroid was atypical. The first post-treatment cycle was definitely ovulatory in type, pregnanediol readings being maximal from days 60 to 62 of the investigation.

Throughout the period of observation LH activity was present, and readings expressed in terms of the Second International Reference Preparation for Human Menopausal Gonadotrophin (2nd IRP-HMG) ranged from 1·7 to 4·5 i.u. per 24 hours. The fiducial limits of error ($P = 0{\cdot}95$) of all assays overlapped indicating the lack of any significant difference between individual estimates. The overall mean value (2·8 i.u. per 24 hours) was significantly lower ($P < 0{\cdot}001$) than that found in normally menstruating women [27].

(b) *Sequential contraception.* This involves the administration of an oestrogen alone for a varying number of days followed by combined therapy by an oestrogen and a progestogen. Such a regime would appear to have certain theoretical advantages over the combined Pill in that it would more closely mimic the endocrine background of the normal menstrual cycle. Garcia [14] has classified sequential contraception into three categories – '*classical*' when the progestogen is given from days 20 to 25, *modified* when the progestogen is given from days 16 to 25, and *step-up sequential* when there is a progressive increase in oestrogen dosage from days 1 to 20, the progestogen being given from days 21 to 25.

(i) *Mechanism of action.* The consensus of opinion remains that this form of contraception, particularly when given on a long-term basis, produces its effects mainly by the suppression of ovulation [7]. It must however be emphasized that other modes of action have been postulated for sequential therapy, including suppression of FSH production and the occurrence of a dysrhythmia between FSH and LH secretion.

(ii) *Effects on endocrine function.* At the time of writing these have been investigated to a much smaller extent than in the case of the combined Pill. Short-term effects on pituitary gonadotrophic function have been examined by Stevens and Vorys [47], Mishell et al. [38] and Swerdloff and Odell [49]. The results reported have varied considerably and have included suppression of the midcycle FSH and LH peaks, no effect on the levels of either hormone, and obliteration of the midcycle FSH peak in association with normal or raised LH levels.

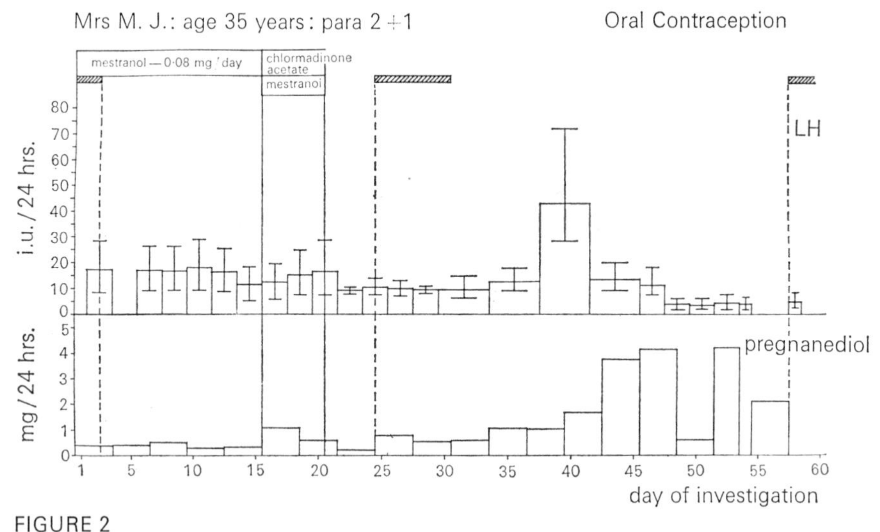


FIGURE 2

Pattern of LH and pregnanediol output in a subject treated with a sequential regime (from [42]). Notation as in Figure 1

Long-term effects of sequential therapy on endocrine function have been investigated by Papanicolaou et al. [42] and Figure 2 is taken from this paper. Prior to the study the subject had been treated with a sequential regime consisting of mestranol and chlormadinone acetate for 13 cycles. Assays of urinary LH and pregnanediol were performed during the 14th cycle of treatment and in the first cycle following withdrawal of medication.

It will be noted that the last cycle of treatment was probably anovulatory in character as judged by the pattern of pregnanediol output. LH activity was present during this time, but a midcycle peak of excretion was not observed. The cycle immediately following cessation of medication was definitely ovulatory in type, the midcycle peak of LH excretion and the luteal phase rise in pregnanediol output being the main features.

So-called 'breakthrough ovulation' is a recognized complication of sequential therapy [30], and the subject shown in Figure 3 illustrates this

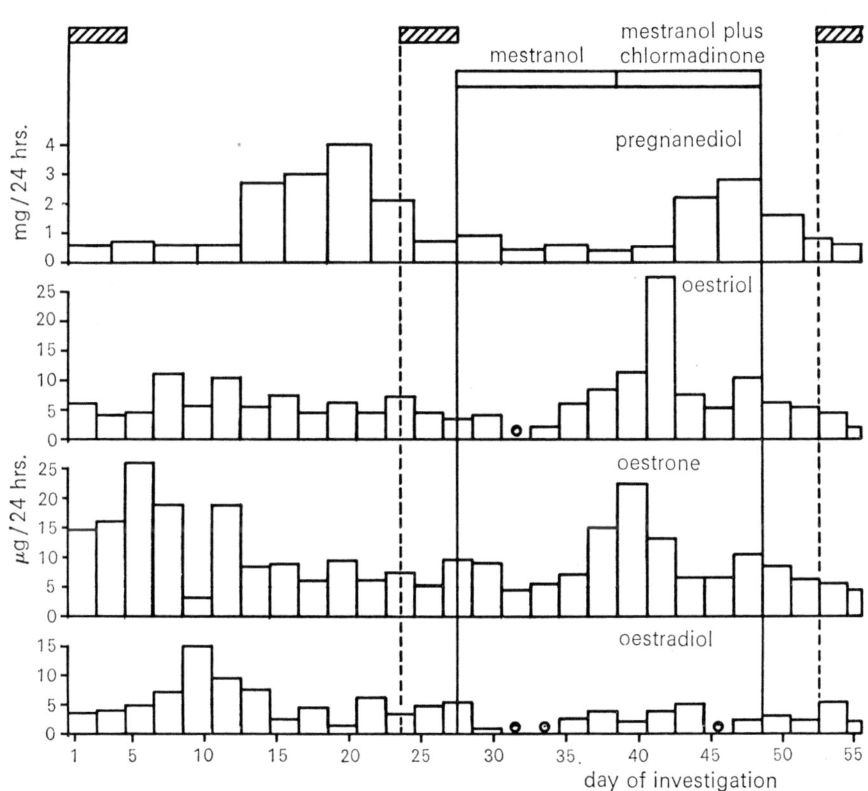


FIGURE 3
Steroid excretion pattern in a subject receiving a sequential regime. Notation as in Figure 1

point. It will be noted that both the pretreatment cycle and the cycle during which a regime of mestranol and chlormadinone was administered were of an ovulatory character as judged by the pattern of urinary oestrogen and pregnanediol output.

(c) *Progestogens administered alone.* (i) *Mechanism of action.* Possible modes of action of such compounds have been discussed by numerous investigators including Diczfalusy [7], Diczfalusy et al. [8], Klopper [22] and Larsson-Cohn et al. [24, 25]. Suggestions have been made that progestogens may inhibit ovulation, that they may have a direct effect upon the endometrium preventing nidation of the ovum, and that they may act directly on the consistency of the cervical mucus rendering the latter more hostile than previously to penetration by spermatozoa.

When in the early days of oral contraception progestogens were administered cyclically in relatively high dosage, e.g., 5–10 mg per day, inhibition of ovulation occurred quite frequently [4]. On the other hand, with the more modern therapeutic regimes in which the compounds are given continuously at a dose level of less than 1·0 mg per day, inhibition of ovulation occurs much less often, and according to Martinez-Manautou [35] does not constitute the major mechanism by which such materials produce their contraceptive effect.

(ii) *Effects on endocrine function.* Short and somewhat longer term effects of low dose progestogens on endocrine function have recently been reported [8, 11, 20, 24, 25]. In the study of Diczfalusy et al. [8] chlormadinone acetate was administered at a dose level of 0·5 mg per day to three normally menstruating women. Estimations of urinary LH by a radio-immunoassay and of 'total oestrogens' and pregnanediol by conventional methods were performed during the pretreatment cycle and in the first and fourth cycles of medication. One of the major findings to emerge from this investigation was the variability in hormone excretion patterns in cycles during which the treatment was being given. Another interesting observation was the apparent dissociation between the LH peak on the one hand and the urinary steroid pattern on the other as indices of ovulation. Thus in some of the treatment cycles the peak of LH excretion was absent, while the pattern of urinary oestrogen and pregnanediol output was compatible with the presence of an ovulatory menstrual cycle.

A somewhat similar investigation has recently been reported by Larsson-Cohn et al. [24]. These investigators studied four women, employed continuous treatment with norethindrone at a dose level of 0·5 mg per day, and performed assays of plasma progesterone and of urinary LH, 'total oestrogens' and pregnanediol. As in the paper of Diczfalusy et al. [8] considerable variability in hormone patterns during the treatment cycles was noted, the only consistent finding being the obliteration of the LH peak at midcycle. In some of the subjects luteal activity as evidenced by estimations of plasma progesterone and urinary pregnanediol was abolished by the medication, while in others such activity persisted. Excretion values for 'total oestrogens' tended to increase during the treatment, but the pattern characteristic of the ovulatory menstrual cycle was not observed.

That ovulation can occur during therapy by low dosage progestogens is now well documented both by purely clinical parameters and by studies involving hormone assay. Figure 4 is a good example of this fact. The subject was treated by chlormadinone acetate, and it will be noted that both the pretreatment and treatment cycles were of a normal ovulatory character as judged by the pattern of urinary steroid excretion.

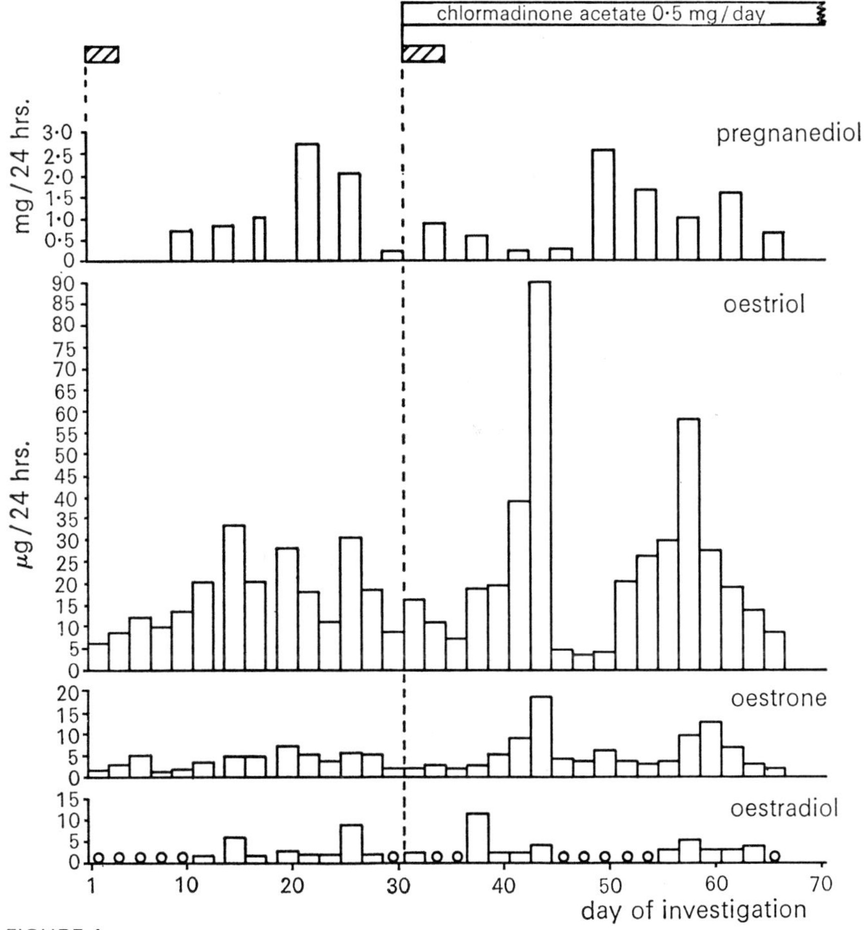


FIGURE 4

Steroid excretion pattern in a subject receiving chlormadinone acetate. Notation as in Figure 1

(d) *Long-acting contraceptive preparations.* These fall into two main groups – the *long-acting Pill* and *long-acting preparations administered parenterally.*

The long-acting Pill is currently being studied on a limited scale in centres in the USA and elsewhere [7, 45]. Most preparations in use are progestogen-oestrogen mixtures, and it is probable that they produce their effects by suppressing ovulation. In this form of medication the steroids are absorbed from the gastrointestinal tract, stored in adipose tissue and released gradually over a period of time. Various progestogens, e.g., chlormadinone acetate, medrogestone or dydrogesterone, have been employed, while the major oestrogen used until now has been the 3-cyclopentyl ether of ethinyl oestradiol (quinestrol). Further research on this form of contraception with particular reference to its efficacy will be awaited with considerable interest.

In addition to pills given by mouth, contraceptive preparations are now available which can be administered parenterally, either by injection [37] or by the implantation of capsules or pellets. With the latter type of medication the contraceptive effect is likely to last for a relatively long period of time [45]. A so-called 'once-a-month' injection has been described [12], this generally being administered as a progestogen-oestrogen mixture. One of the more popular of such preparations has been the material known as Deladroxate (16α-dihydroxyprogesterone acetophenide); this is given intramuscularly together with oestradiol oenanthate. According to Felton et al. [12] and others such medication constitutes an effective form of contraception; however, its major disadvantage is its tendency to produce cycles of variable length. More recently Mishell et al. [37] reported on the use of a progestogen alone as a long-acting injection. They used 6α-methyl-17α-hydroxyprogesterone acetate at a dose level of 150 mg once every three months and reported very satisfactory clinical results.

It appears probable that the majority of parenterally administered contraceptives produce their effect by suppressing ovulation. However, it must be emphasized that at the time of writing detailed hormone assay studies in women receiving these forms of medication have not yet been reported, and until such investigations have been carried out definite conclusions with respect to their mode of action cannot be drawn.

## THE OVER-SUPPRESSION SYNDROME

In recent years the side effects of steroid contraceptives have been intensively studied, and most of these are now well documented [22, 26, 29, 45]. However, quite recently, a condition known as the 'over-suppression syndrome' has come to be recognized [19]. The main feature of this condition, the incidence of which is relatively low [34], is prolonged amenorrhoea or oligomenorrhoea following withdrawal of long-term therapy by oral contraceptives. The aetiology of the syndrome remains obscure, although the suggestion has been made that it may arise as a result of dysfunction of the hypothalamic centres regulating the cyclic release of FSH and LH. The postulate by Garcia and David [15] that individuals with a previous history of menstrual abnormalities are more prone to develop the oversuppression syndrome than those in whom menstrual function was normal prior to the commencement of medication, has not been borne out by more recent studies [34].

## OVULATION SUPPRESSION AND OVERPOPULATION

Contraceptive techniques, particularly that depending on the suppression of ovulation by the combined Pill, are of crucial importance in the world of the 1970s as one of the methods available to mankind to mitigate one of the greatest problems affecting our planet, namely that of overpopulation [10, 26]. A few statistics will help to illustrate the gravity of the current situation.

At the end of 1969 the world population stood at 3,600,000,000, and it must be emphasized that it has taken the whole of the million years of man's existence on this planet to reach this figure. However, at the anticipated rate of increase the total number of people inhabiting the world by the year A.D. 2000 will have more than doubled and will be in the region of 7,500,000,000. But much worse is to come in the twenty-first century and beyond. One demographic projection, which may well prove to be a gross underestimate, is that by the year A.D. 2040 the world population will have reached the astronomical total of 14,000,000,000,000, while another prediction is that two hundred and fifty years from now, if the universe is still in being, the population density throughout the world will resemble that presently found in Greater London.

In 1969 we gained 2·2 people per second, 8,000 per hour, 190,000 each day. The total gain for the year was 71,000,000, 13,000,000 of these in India alone. According to a statement issued by the UNO the First World War killed some 10,000,000 people and the Second World War 55,000,000. These figures added together are equivalent to only one year's increase in the population of the world of the early 1970s. Those who seek to denigrate the steroid contraceptives as a method of birth control should bear these sombre facts in mind.

## SUMMARY

1. A large number of substances are capable of suppressing ovulation in human subjects, the most important group of these being the steroid contraceptives.
2. It is concluded that the 'classical' regime of oral contraception produces

its effect by the inhibition of ovulation; however in the case of sequential treatment alternative modes of action should be considered. Low dose progestogens have a variable effect on ovulation and inhibition of this process is probably not their major mode of action.

3. Medication by the combined Pill obliterates the midcycle LH peak, and following withdrawal of this form of treatment cycles rapidly revert to an ovulatory pattern. On the other hand, the effect of progestogens alone and of sequential contraception on endocrine function vary considerably from one woman to another.

4. The main clinical features of the so-called 'over-suppression syndrome' are described and the lack of precise information regarding its aetiology is emphasized.

5. The gravity of the world population crisis is stressed, as is the important role of ovulation suppression in combating this major problem facing the human race.

## REFERENCES

[1] Bell, E.T., Brown, J.B., Fotherby, K. and Loraine, J.A., *Lancet*, **2,** 528, 1962.
[2] Bell, E.T., Brown, J.B., Fotherby, K., Loraine, J.A. and Robson, J.S., *J. Endocr.*, **25,** 221, 1962.
[3] Bell, E.T., Herbst, A.L., Kirshnamurti, M., Loraine, J.A., Mears, E., Jackson, M.C.N. and Garcia, C.R., *Acta endocr., Copnh.*, **54,** 96, 1967.
[4] Brown, J.B., Fotherby, K. and Loraine, J.A., *J. Endocr.*, **25,** 331, 1962.
[5] Buchholz, R., Nocke, L. and Nocke, W., *Int. J. Fert.*, **9,** 231, 1964.
[6] De Feo, V.J. and Reynolds, S.R.M., *Science*, **124,** 726, 1956.
[7] Diczfalusy, E., *Am. J. Obstet. Gynec.*, **100,** 136, 1968.
[8] Diczfalusy, E., Goebelsmann, V., Johannisson, E., Tillinger, K.-G. and Wide, L., *Acta endocr., Copnh.*, **62,** 679, 1969.
[9] Dufau, M., Catt, K.J., Dulmanis, A., Fullerton, M., Hudson, B. and Burger, H.G., *Lancet*, **1,** 271, 1970.
[10] Ehrlich, P.R., *The Population Bomb*. New York: Ballantine Books, 1968.
[11] Elstein, M. In *Chlormadinone Acetate: A new departure in oral contraception*, p. 46. Eds. G.A. Christie and M. Moore-Robinson, published for Syntex Pharmaceuticals Ltd. by Excerpta Medica Foundation, 1969.
[12] Felton, H.T., Hoelscher, E.W. and Swartz, D.P., *Fert. Steril.*, **16,** 665, 1965.
[13] Fuchs, A.R., Fuchs, F. and Johnsen, S.G., *Int. J. Fert.*, **9,** 139, 1964.
[14] Garcia, C.R., Paper presented at Eighth Conference of IPPF, Santiago, Chile, April 1967 and quoted by Diczfalusy, E., *Am. J. Obstet. Gynec.*, **100,** 136, 1968.
[15] Garcia, C.R. and David, A., *Int. J. Fert.*, **13,** 287, 1968.
[16] Ham, A.W. and Leeson, T.S., *Histology*, p. 890. London: Pitman Medical, 1965.
[17] Harrington, F.E., Eggert, R.G., Wilbur, R.V. and Linkenheimer, W.G., *Endocrinology*, **78,** 1130, 1966.
[18] Harris, G.W. and Naftolin, F., *Br. med. Bull.*, **26,** 3, 1970.
[19] Horowitz, B.J., Solomkin, M. and Edelstein, S.W., *Obstet. Gynec.*, **31,** 387, 1968.
[20] Jaffe, R.B. and Midgley, A.R., Jr., *Obstet. Gynaec. Surv.*, **24,** 200, 1969.
[21] Jeffery, J. d'A. and Klopper, A.I., *J. Reprod. Fert., Suppl.* **4,** 81, 1968.
[22] Klopper, A., *Br. med. Bull.*, **26,** 39, 1970.

[23] Klopper, A., Michie, E.A. and Brown, J.B., *J. Endocr.*, **12**, 209, 1955.
[24] Larsson-Cohn, V., Johansson, E.D.B., Wide, L. and Gemzell, C.A., *Acta endocr., Copnh.*, **63**, 216, 1970.
[25] Larsson-Cohn, V., Johansson, E.D.B., Wide, L. and Gemzell, C.A., *Acta endocr., Copnh.*, **63**, 705, 1970.
[26] Loraine, J.A., *Sex and the Population Crisis*, London: Heinemann Medical Books, 1970.
[27] Loraine, J.A. and Adamopoulos, D.A., *Hormones*, **1**, 96, 1970.
[28] Loraine, J.A. and Bell, E.T., *Fertility and Contraception in the Human Female*, p. 19. Edinburgh/London: E. & S. Livingstone, 1968.
[29] Loraine, J.A. and Bell, E.T., *Fertility and Contraception in the Human Female*, p. 259. Edinburgh/London: E. & S. Livingstone, 1968.
[30] Loraine, J.A. and Bell, E.T., *Fertility and Contraception in the Human Female*, p. 303. Edinburgh/London: E. & S. Livingstone, 1968.
[31] Loraine, J.A. and Bell, E.T., *Hormone Assays and Their Clinical Application*, 3rd ed. Edinburgh/London: E. & S. Livingstone, 1971.
[32] Loraine, J.A., Bell, E.T., Harkness, R.A., Mears, E. and Jackson, M.C.N., *Lancet*, **2**, 902, 1963.
[33] Loraine, J.A., Bell, E.T., Harkness, R.A., Mears, E. and Jackson, M.C.N., *Acta endocr., Copnh.*, **50**, 15, 1965.
[34] MacLeod, S.G., Parker, A.S. and Perlin, I.A., *Am. J. Obstet. Gynec.*, **106**, 359, 1970.
[35] Martinez-Manautou, J. In *Chlormadinone Acetate: A new departure in oral contraception*, p. 18. Eds. G.A. Christie and M. Moore-Robinson, published for Syntex Pharmaceuticals Ltd. by Excerpta Medica Foundation, 1969.
[36] Mears, E., *Handbook on Oral Contraception*, p. 5. London: Churchill, 1965.
[37] Mishell, D.R., El Habashy, M.A., Good, R.G. and Moyer, D.L., *Am. J. Obstet. Gynec.*, **101**, 1046, 1968.
[38] Mishell, D.R., Jr., Talas, M. and Parlow, A.F. In *Advances in Planned Parenthood*, **6**, p. 103. Amsterdam and New York: Excerpta Medica Foundation, 1969.
[39] Morrison, R.L. and Johnson, D.C., *J. Endocr.*, **34**, 117, 1966.
[40] Noble, R.L., Plunkett, E.R. and Graham, R.C.B., *J. Endocr.*, **10**, 212, 1954.
[41] Novak, E.R. and Woodruff, J.D., *Gynecologic and Obstetric Pathology*, 5th ed., p. 291. Philadelphia: Saunders, 1962.
[42] Papanicolaou, A.D., Loraine, J.A. and Jackson, M.C.N., *Acta endocr., Copnh.*, **52**, 477, 1969.
[43] Rudel, H.W. and Kincl, F.A., *Acta endocr., Copnh.*, **51**, *Suppl.* 105, 1966.
[44] Schwimmer, W.B., Ustay, K.A. and Behrman, S.J., *Fert. Steril.*, **18**, 167, 1967.
[45] Segal, S.J. and Tietze, C., *Reports on Population/Family Planning*. Issued by Population Council and International Institute for Study of Human Reproduction, Columbia University, October, 1969.
[46] Shearman, R.P., *Lancet*, **1**, 197, 1963.
[47] Stevens, V.C. and Vorys, N., *Obstet. Gynaec. Surv.*, **22**, 781, 1967.
[48] Stevens, V.C., Vorys, N., Besch, P.K. and Barry, R.D., *Metabolism*, **14**, 327, 1965.
[49] Swerdloff, R.W. and Odell, W.D., *J. clin. Endocr. Metab.*, **29**, 157, 1969.
[50] Walpole, A.L. In *Agents Affecting Fertility*, p. 159. Eds. C. R. Austin and J.S. Perry. London: Churchill, 1965.
[51] Whitelaw, M.J., *Int. J. Fert.*, **5**, 175, 1960.

*Discussion of paper by Dr Loraine*

*Odell* We (Swerdloff and Odell, *J. clin. Endocr. Metab.*, **29**, 157, 1969) have shown that FSH levels are suppressed by both the combined contraceptives as well as the sequential variety. We (Mishell and Odell, *Am. J. Obstet. Gynec.*, **109**, 140, 1971) have information showing the effect of chlormadinone acetate in a great variety of doses from 0·5 mg to 2 mg administered daily and we found that the pattern of response depended on the administered dose. In our paper in 1969 we first speculated that the mechanism of action of sequential contraceptives might be due to suppression of the FSH rise initiating follicle growth.

*Klopper* Dr Loraine, you rather slid over the question of the unwanted side effects of the steroid contraceptives. As they very much control the pattern of usage I wonder if you would agree that the unwanted side effects of steroid contraceptives appear to reside more in the oestrogen than the progestogen moiety. I think that the only oestrogens used so far in oral contraception are those with an alkylated sidechain and I wonder about the possibility of using other oestrogens which might avoid the side effects.

*Loraine* Side effects of oral contraceptives are certainly important and at present we appear to have reached an impasse in this situation. New ideas are required and new compounds must be developed.

*Klopper* Could I ask your views about the possible usage of long-acting preparations such as the silicone linked steroids. I do not know of any particular studies in this field.

*Loraine* The literature on silicone linked steroids is at present sparse, but one can expect it to increase in the future. The technique is one which may hold promise provided that its efficacy is satisfactory.

*Newton* We can confirm that the FSH and LH peaks are obliterated using a radioimmunoassay in patients taking combined oral contraception. Could I also refer to the over-suppression syndrome which Dr Loraine has mentioned. I think that patients who have amenorrhoea or severe oligomenorrhoea following long-term oral contraception usually have a definite history of oligomenorrhoea prior to starting treatment. All our patients so far have been on the high dose combined preparations. Not one of them has failed to respond to clomiphene treatment for ovulation induction.

*Brown* With reference to the suppression of FSH production by the contraceptive pill, may I refer to a paper which we published some years ago describing experiments in which normally ovulating women were given different doses of norethisterone and its acetate (Brown, J.B., Fotherby, K. and Loraine, J.A., *J. Endocr.*, **25**, 331, 1962). On a lower dose, ovulation was inhibited as judged by the absence of a luteal phase increase in pregnanediol excretion but a definite rise and fall in oestrogen excretion still occurred showing that a follicle had developed. Follicle stimulating hormone must therefore have been produced to cause this effect. However, when the dose of norethisterone was increased, cyclical production of both pregnanediol and oestrogen was completely suppressed. We interpreted these findings as being due to suppression of the ovulatory surge of LH by the lower dose of norethisterone but not of the initial release of FSH, whereas the higher dose suppressed the release of both pituitary hormones. This evidence obtained from the response of the target organ is just as valid as that obtained from the measurement of the gonadotrophin levels, assuming that the pill operates via the pituitary.

*Loraine* I think that the major criticism of our original paper in this field was that we used the mouse uterus test to measure urinary gonadotrophins. This test is now recognized as being completely non-specific, and therefore when it is employed one cannot draw any conclusions with respect to FSH/LH ratios. I must admit that I am puzzled by the rise in FSH output at midcycle and particularly by the fact that the peaks of FSH and LH at this time may coincide. It seems to me that the role of FSH during the cycle remains to be elucidated.

*Mills* I do not agree with Dr Klopper that all the side effects of the steroid contraceptives are due to oestrogens. The progestogens are responsible for the weight gain in a number of women and they may also produce depression. This depression in a number of women goes on to ovulation suppression. I agree with Dr Newton that a number of these women have very irregular periods before treatment started. I think there is an important group that ends up depressed on the contraceptive tablets and that ovulation will not occur after stopping the tablets until the depression is treated. I think this is a matter of some importance.

*Klopper* I did not mean to imply that the progestogen was free from any side effects. I think that getting fat or feeling depressed kills comparatively few people whereas having lung emboli or alterations in carbohydrate tolerance does.

*Mills* The death rate from depression is very much higher than the death rate from thromboembolism.

*Fotherby* Once we get away from the really serious side effects we don't know the incidence of these other side effects such as depression. There are no good figures on the incidence of depression in women on oral contraceptives. I cannot agree with Dr Loraine that there are no data on biochemical changes in women on low dose progestogen treatment. There are data on at least four different progestogens used in the low dose regime. Chlormadinone acetate seems to produce rather weird effects in that you get high peaks of oestrogen excretion at times when you would not expect them. With norgestrel the effects are more predictable but the predominant picture is an absence of the luteal rise in pregnanediol. Megestrol seems to produce very little change at all and you get a normal level of pregnanediol excretion in the second half of the cycle.

*Loraine* I think that the individual compounds will have to be studied in considerable detail before any conclusions are drawn.

*Fotherby* In those studies I have mentioned LH has been measured by radio-immunoassay and although the peak might be low there is, in fact, an LH peak. Whether the size of this peak was lower than it would be in a normal cycle we don't know, but ovulation occurred in a number of these women since corpora lutea were obtained at laparotomy.

*Johansson* I agree with what Dr Fotherby has said and think that the gestagen might interfere with steroid production in the corpus luteum. Some of the compounds have luteolytic effects as measured by peripheral plasma levels of progesterone.

*Eik-Nes* I am worried about the unwanted side effects of these high levels of steroids. We have some information as far as the adrenal is concerned that the corticoids might inhibit the adrenal directly without going via the pituitary gland and I wonder if similar experiments have been performed on the ovary, i.e., progesterone or oestrogen acting directly on the biosynthetic capacity of ovarian tissue.

*Johansson* I think the effect is on the corpus luteum in the ovary and is not mediated through the pituitary centres in these cases.

*Aakvaag* I think that chlormadinone acetate inhibits 3β-hydroxydehydrogenase.

*Fotherby* I agree with Dr Aakvaag and we have found that progesterone synthesis by corpora lutea incubated *in vitro* was inhibited by extremely small doses of norgestrel.

SESSION V. GENERAL DISCUSSION

*Klopper* I am puzzled by some of Dr Brown's data on the oestrogen excretion which shows a very regular increase during the growth of the cycle. I have found that there is some degree of variation and you do not always obtain such a smooth and consistent increase. For example, in some cycles the level would rise to 15 μg of oestrogen and the next day drop to 12 μg, then rise to 20 μg and so on.

*Brown* The final rise to the oestrogen peak which occurs during the last few days of follicular development usually follows a smooth curve, more so than at any other time of the menstrual cycle. This is the period which concerns us most during gonadotrophin therapy and in concentrating on this I may have given a better picture of smooth and consistent increases than would be expected at other times of the cycle.

*Butt* I agree that oestrogen monitoring is very useful but we have also found that another index such as pregnanetriol was of value. In induced ovulation there is a rise of pregnanetriol excretion along with the oestrogen and we wondered if this might be a better index of hyperstimulation. The rise occurred before ovulation.

*Macnaughton* In the gonadotrophin induced cycle there is a general increase in the level of steroid hormones and we have noticed an increase in pregnanetriol at midcycle and also an increase in urinary testosterone levels at this time. There seems to be a general increase in ovarian steroidogenesis and we have also found that pregnanetriol was a function of the corpus luteum of pregnancy being produced from precursor 17α-hydroxyprogesterone from the corpus luteum. In early gonadotrophin induced pregnancy there is a steep rise in plasma progesterone levels due to the corpus luteum of pregnancy. These fall off at eight to ten weeks and then rise again as trophoblastic production of progesterone increases. It has also been shown that plasma 17α-hydroxyprogesterone levels rise *pari passu* with progesterone and then fall away at six to ten weeks when the corpus luteum ceases to function. This suggests that 17α-hydroxyprogesterone produced by the corpus luteum is perhaps a measure of the function of that organ in early pregnancy. Since the largest precursor of pregnanetriol is 17α-hydroxyprogesterone we have found that the level of this steroid also rises in early pregnancy and then falls to normal at about ten weeks or so whereas the level of pregnanediol and oestriol rise further as the foeto-placental unit begins to function. The pattern of pregnanetriol in the urine therefore parallels that of its precursor 17α-hydroxyprogesterone in the blood. The measurement of pregnanetriol in the urine during gonadotrophin therapy may give some idea of the degree of ovarian stimulation and the function of the corpus luteum. It is just possible that this parameter might be able to assess whether or not the ovary has been hyperstimulated and perhaps even indicate the likelihood of early abortion.

*Oakey* We agree with Professor Macnaughton that the pregnanetriol levels are associated with gonadotrophin stimulation. In a patient we studied who became pregnant without gonadotrophin stimulation the pregnanetriol level did not rise above 4 mg/24 hours.

*Griffiths* It seems possible that another pathway might be involved and pregnenolone be converted to progesterone and then 17α-hydroxyprogesterone with the reaction stopping at 17α-hydroxyprogesterone. I think that the pathway from pregnenolone to oestrogen is usually via dehydroepiandrosterone.

*Harkness* We have some data on pregnanetriol excretion after clomiphene therapy. We have found that the rise was to 4 mg/24 hours at eight to ten weeks of pregnancy and then there was a drop.

*Naftolin* I think that the pregnanetriol level might indicate that luteinization was occurring and might in fact say that the ovary was ready for stimulation with HCG. It might be possible to say that the ovary was ready when the pregnanetriol level had reached a certain height and this might be a useful index in deciding when to give LH or HCG.

*Fotherby* It should also be noted that pregnanetriol diminishes before pregnanediol in an anovular cycle.

*Brown* With reference to the over suppression syndrome, although this may affect only a small percentage of women taking the contraceptive pill, the ones who have it are concentrated in the patients attending the Endocrine and Sterility Clinics so we see a good number of them. The syndrome is quite serious for the women who have it and although the majority respond to treatment, some of our 10 per cent of failures to gonadotrophin therapy have come from this group.

*Loraine* The incidence of the over-suppression syndrome is low but it may increase with the wider use of hormonal contraception.

*Grant* I would like to turn the discussion for a short time to the problems of population control and to ask if it is not crazy to go on with fertility problems when the main problem is overpopulation.

*Loraine* Investigations on the treatment of infertile women by gonadotrophins and clomiphene are probably still justified. The number of patients treated is relatively small, and accordingly the population explosion will not be exacerbated. Many women derive great satisfaction from becoming pregnant and, in addition, this form of treament is providing useful information on the physiology of the menstrual cycle.

*Mills* Although the rapid rise of population in the developing countries is perturbing I think the problems are particularly dangerous in developed countries where the main interest is centred on pollution. This results, for example, in the increasing problem of attempted suicide. In Edinburgh 1 : 500 young women attempt suicide each year. In Cambridge the figure is 1 : 380 young women and for young men 1 : 450. I feel that the effect of population in developed countries is a dominant problem : attempted suicide now accounts for 50 per cent of cases of young women admitted to medical beds in Cambridge.

*Loraine* There are really two categories of nation with respect to population problems. Developed countries such as the UK often have a high population density. However, these are rich and technologically advanced, and it is unlikely that their food supplies will run short in the foreseeable future. On the other hand, the underdeveloped countries of Asia, Africa and Latin America present quite a different problem. In these areas starvation is rife and is likely to continue in spite of the recent much publicized 'green revolution'. In India in 1960 the population was approximately 370,000,000; in 1970 it had topped 540,000,000 in spite of the fact than an active family planning programme had been in operation for more than a decade. However, even worse is in store for India because its numbers will double in a further 28 years.

*Odell* It is interesting to note that although Egypt built the Aswan Dam the population during that time increased by 30 per cent and wiped out the advantage gained in food production by building the dam. I would like to go back to some basic facts again. There seem to be two areas in the hypothalamus controlling the ovarian cycle and it may be possible to stimulate a follicle to stimulate ovulation without giving HCG in a patient who was defective only in one of those centres.

*Crooke* We have noticed the opposite. In some patients with Simmond's disease with oestriols up to 600 μg/24 hours we cannot get pregnanediol above 2 mg/24 hours : in some women even with 72,000 i.u. of HCG.

*Naftolin* Follicle growth and ovulation occur every time a woman takes clomiphene alone and we have demonstrated that women can become pregnant on clomiphene alone or with LH.

*Stitch* I should like to remind this audience that women with amenorrhoea of several years' duration can become pregnant without other stimulation. We have a woman who was treated with FSH alone and had a classical ovulatory cycle and then became pregnant two cycles later without further stimulation.

# The Investigation of Patients with Menstrual Disturbance and the Response to Treatment with Clomiphene

I. H. MILLS
R. J. WILSON
R. E. TAYLOR *and*
S. H. H. DAVISON

Department of Investigative Medicine and Biochemical Section of the John Bonnett Clinical Laboratories
Addenbrooke's Hospital, Cambridge

¶ IN assessing the problem of menstrual disturbance it is important to treat the woman as a whole person and not just as a collection of endocrine functions. Our studies have shown that a complete history is of great importance if a diagnosis is to be arrived at. For the purposes of the present investigation all the women had had either complete amenorrhoea for more than six months or menstrual irregularity for more than a year. A very limited number of women have been investigated for infertility in spite of having fairly regular menstrual cycles.

Viewed with hind-sight the important features in the history are (1) the precise pattern of menstrual disturbance; (2) alteration in sensitivity to temperature (hot or cold); (3) any sudden changes in dietary habits or weight; (4) features of depression. Characteristically patients with the polycystic ovary syndrome described more or less regular menstrual cycles in the earlier years but with increasing irregularity as time went by. This sometimes culminated in total amenorrhoea which might be a spontaneous outcome or the result of a relatively mild psychological or depressive upset, or might follow some months on contraceptive steroids.

Recognition of depression, even in its minor degrees, is of very great importance. It is becoming increasingly obvious that this is an important feature in the endocrine control of menstruation. Relatively slight depression may be sufficient to disturb the control mechanisms. Since many women deny that they are depressed it is important to enquire about undue tendencies to cry or feeling like doing so, increased irritability especially with immediate relatives, sleep disturbance, loss of libido and headaches. Some women may have fluctuating degrees of depression so producing irregular menstrual cycles which may resemble the pattern seen in patients with the polycystic ovary syndrome.

Menstrual disturbance in patients suffering from thyrotoxicosis is well known but if, as occasionally happens, the woman has gained weight the thyrotoxicosis may not be obvious. It is less well known that amenorrhoea may be due to hypothyroidism and a history of sensitivity to cold may then be helpful.

True anorexia nervosa is a relatively uncommon condition but self-starvation to the point of producing amenorrhoea is now relatively common. The full picture of anorexia nervosa is not present in most of these young women but they are nevertheless frequently very loath to admit to the dietary changes that they have imposed on themselves. Persistent questioning from a variety of angles may be necessary to reveal the truth.

## DIAGNOSTIC INVESTIGATIONS

In the first part of this report we will outline the results of a series of endocrine investigations on 117 women. The age distribution of the women is

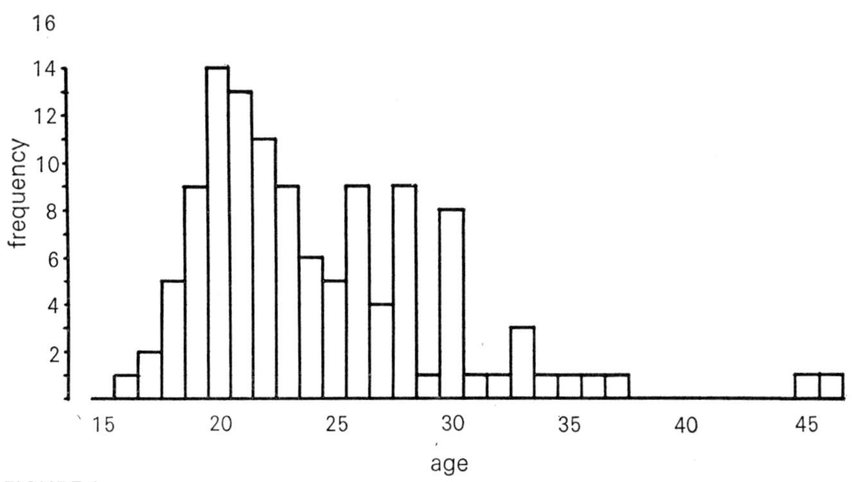


FIGURE 1
Age distribution of the 117 patients fully investigated

shown in Figure 1. The two women over 40 were investigated for infertility and were menstruating regularly.

The tests carried out were as follows:

1. Skull x-ray
2. BMR
3. Radioactive iodine uptake by the thyroid
4. Excretion of 17-oxosteroids and 17-oxogenic steroids
5. Response to metyrapone
6. Pregnanetriol excretion
7. Total gonadotrophin excretion
8. Gynaecography – the measurement of ovarian size on x-ray after induction of a pneumoperitoneum

The skull x-ray proved to be useful because two patients were found to have pituitary tumours.

*Thyroid function.* In Figure 2 is shown the relationship between the BMR and the thyroid uptake of $^{131}I$ at either 24 or 48 hr (whichever was the higher). The lower limit of normal for the latter test was taken as 20 per cent and for BMR as −14 per cent. Only three patients were hypothyroid by both tests.

There are two reasons why patients might have a low BMR with a normal thyroid uptake of radioactive iodine. It is our observation that many patients with hypopituitary hypothyroidism have a low BMR and an uptake of radioactive iodine which is in the lower part of the normal range. None of the patients studied here had clinical features of myxoedema. Thyroid stimulation with TSH for five days in a series of these women with low BMR, raised the metabolic rate to normal or above and also increased the thyroid uptake of $^{131}I$.

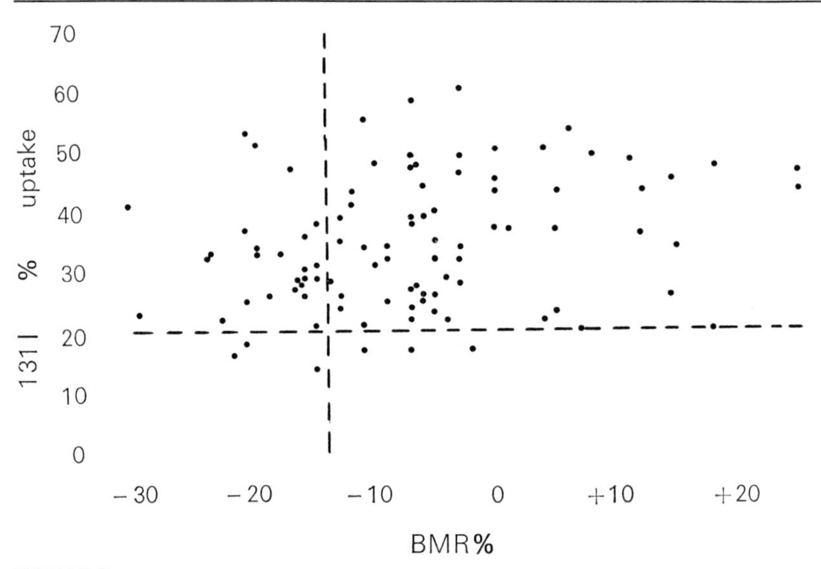


FIGURE 2
The relationship between the BMR and the neck uptake of $^{131}I$. The dashed lines represent the lower limit of the normal range

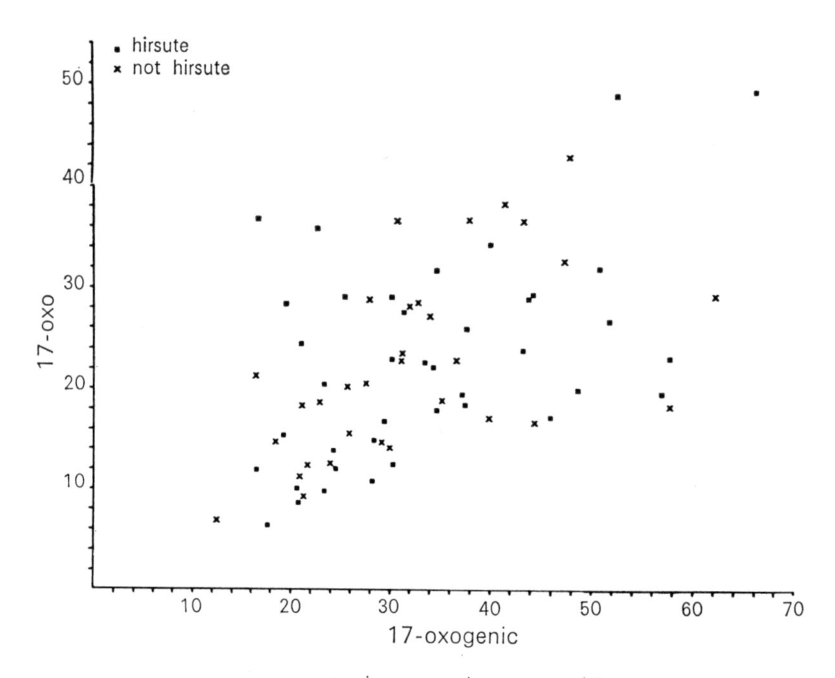


FIGURE 3
The maximum excretion of 17-oxosteroids and oxogenic steroids (mg/day) during the administration of metyrapone (metopirone) for 3 days at a dose of 1 g every 8 hours

The second reason for a low BMR and normal uptake of radioactive iodine is prolonged semi-starvation. An appreciable number of these young women had imposed on themselves a regime of drastic calorie restriction, frequently with almost no carbohydrate. It is well known that the BMR is low in patients with anorexia nervosa. In a few of these patients, when they were consuming 3,000–4,000 calories per day the BMR was measured again and values up to + 30 per cent were obtained.

*Pituitary-adrenal function.* The maximum urinary 17-oxosteroid and 17-oxogenic steroid response to metyrapone given in a dose of 1 g 8-hourly for three days is shown in Figure 3. It will be seen that five patients had a 17-oxogenic steroid response of less than 20 mg per day and also a poor 17-oxosteroid response. On further investigation only one of these proved to have partial hypopituitarism.

The hirsute women do not differ from the non-hirsute in the 17-oxosteroid response. This is of interest because it was previously shown that the response of hirsute women to exogenous corticotrophin produced a higher than normal ratio of 17-oxosteroids to 17-oxogenic steroids [1].

The two patients with pituitary tumours had a normal response to metyrapone.

No patient in this series had an elevated pregnanetriol excretion.

*Excretion of total gonadotrophins.* These were measured by the mouse uterine weight test and standardized against HMG 20A. The frequency distribution of the excretion in the various women is shown in Figure 4. The three women who were diagnosed as suffering from early menopause had excretions above 25 mg per day.

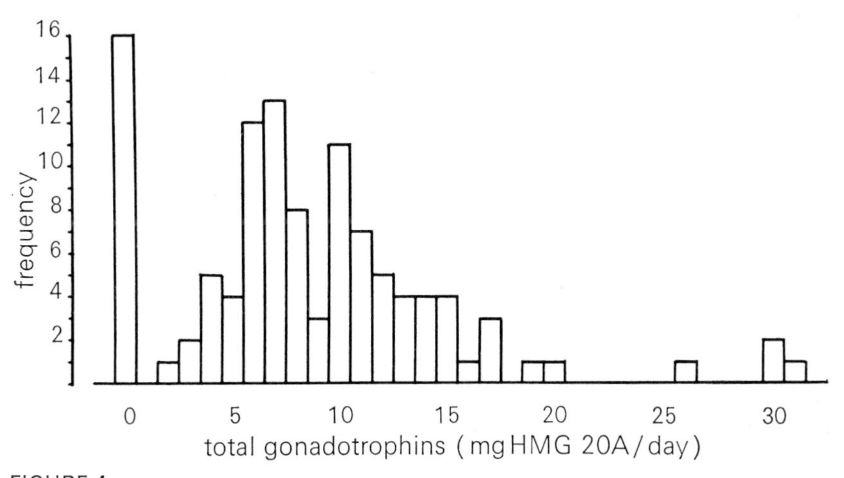


FIGURE 4
The frequency distribution of the excretion of total gonadotrophin ( as mg HMG 20A per day)

*Ovarian size.* The size of the ovaries was assessed from the x-ray film taken after inducing a pneumoperitoneum. The patient was placed prone on a tip-table and tipped head down at an angle of 45°. The x-ray beam was vertical, through the pelvis, with the film immediately under the table. The ovarian index was obtained by measuring each ovary in two directions at right angles, multiplying the measurements together, dividing by two and adding the areas for the two ovaries together.

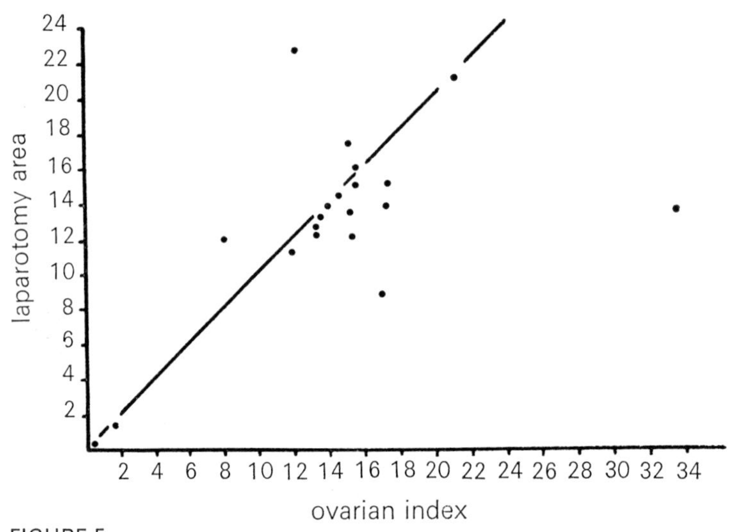


FIGURE 5
The relation between the ovarian index (sq. cm) and the area calculated from the measurements of the ovaries at operation

In Figure 5 is shown the relationship between the ovarian index and the size of the ovaries measured at operation for wedge resection in 18 patients. Although a few show appreciable discrepancy, the majority show a good correlation. Figure 6 shows the distribution of ovarian size and what we regard as the normal range. The ovarian index used by Ferriman and Purdie [2] is twice the index used here but if their values are halved, their normal range is approximately the same as the range shown here.

*Diagnosis.* From the various criteria a diagnosis was arrived at in 105 of the 117 patients referred because of menstrual irregularity. These are shown in Table 1. It will be seen that the polycystic ovary syndrome is by far the largest group, making up 50 per cent of the total cases. The next largest group is classed as psychological, which includes depression and self-imposed starvation. In the latter category there were 20 patients (17 per cent) so that this is the second largest cause of menstrual disturbance in this series.

The girl with chromosomal mosaicism is of interest because some menstrual periods had occurred.

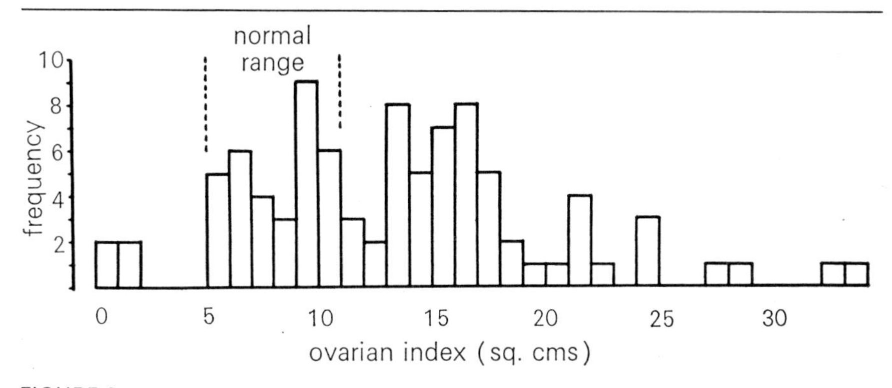


FIGURE 6
The frequency distribution of the ovarian index. The normal range is considered to be 5–10·5 sq. cm

TABLE 1. The diagnoses in 117 women with menstrual disturbance

| | |
|---|---|
| Polycystic ovaries | 58 |
| Psychological (including 20 with self-starvation) | 26 |
| Hypothyroidism | 7 |
| Ovarian hypoplasia | 3 |
| Early menopause | 3 |
| Obesity amenorrhoea | 2 |
| Pituitary tumour | 2 |
| Partial hypopituitarism | 1 |
| Cushing's syndrome | 1 |
| Thyrotoxicosis (with weight gain) | 1 |
| Chromosomal mosaic (XX/XO) | 1 |
| Uncertain | 12 |
| Total | 117 |

TABLE 2. Response to thyroxine in patients with hypothyroidism

| Type of menstrual disturbance | Response | | | |
|---|---|---|---|---|
| | Irregular periods | Regular periods | None | Total |
| Amenorrhoea | 2 | 2 | 7 | 11 |
| Irregular periods | – | 3 | – | 3 |
| Total | 2 | 5 | 7 | 14 |

*The response to treatment*

*Hypothyroidism.* The response in 14 patients to treatment with thyroxine is shown in Table 2.

*Wedge resection of ovaries.* Of 21 patients treated by this operation 16 developed regular periods, four had periods for some months and then they ceased and in one there was no response. Six had successful pregnancies.

*Self-starvation.* Of the 20 patients in this group, seven patients successfully increased their weight and it remained stable. In eight patients menstruation returned and one had a successful pregnancy.

## RESPONSE TO CLOMIPHENE

Twenty-two of the patients in the above series and 96 other patients have been treated with clomiphene. This is a selected group of patients. All those diagnosed as having polycystic ovaries (ovarian index $>$ 10·5 sq. cm) were treated with clomiphene. Those with starvation amenorrhoea were only treated after weight gain. The diagnoses in the treated women and their response to treatment are given in Table 3. A positive response in terms of menstruation is taken as regular ovulatory cycles in those who had irregular cycles or menstruation occurring (even irregularly) in those who had complete amenorrhoea. In some the response is unknown because they failed to attend for follow-up or moved from the district. It will be seen that in three the diagnosis was primary amenorrhoea. All three had appreciable ovarian enlargement and it is assumed that they had polycystic ovaries. Although it is not usually considered that primary amenorrhoea occurs with this syndrome, it would appear that assessment of ovarian size in patients with primary amenorrhoea could be useful in both diagnosis and treatment.

TABLE 3. Diagnoses in patients treated with clomiphene and the response to treatment

| Diagnosis | Total number | Menstrual response | | | Pregnancies | | |
|---|---|---|---|---|---|---|---|
| | | Positive | Negative | Unknown | At risk | No. | % |
| Polycystic ovaries | 71 | 55 | 3 | 7 | 48 | 24 | 50 |
| Uncertain | 16 | 9 | 4 | 3 | 10 | 3 | 30 |
| Depression | 14 | 8 | 5 | 1 | 3 | 1 | 33 |
| Starvation amenorrhoea | 8 | 3 | 3 | 2 | 1 | 0 | 0 |
| Infertility | 4 | – | – | – | 4 | 2 | 50 |
| Primary amenorrhoea | 3 | 3 | | | 0 | | |
| Pituitary tumour | 1 | 1 | | | 0 | | |
| Early menopause | 1 | | 1 | | 0 | | |
| Total | 118 | 79 | 15 | 13 | 66 | 30 | 45 |

The relationship between response to clomiphene and the excretion of total gonadotrophins is shown in Table 4. In general terms there is a greater incidence of response to clomiphene in those women with the higher excretion of total gonadotrophin.

From Table 3 it is obvious that the highest incidence of menstrual response to clomiphene occurs in women who have been diagnosed as having polycystic ovaries (78 per cent positive responses). If one groups all those with normal sized ovaries together, 51 per cent of the patients had a menstrual response to clomiphene and 33 per cent of those at risk became pregnant.

In conclusion, therefore, response to clomiphene is greatest in these women with larger ovaries and excreting higher quantities of total gonadotrophins.

TABLE 4. Relationship between response to clomiphene and the excretion of total gonadotrophin (as mg HMG-20A)

| Total Gonadotrophin excretion | Menstrual response | | | |
|---|---|---|---|---|
| | Positive | (%) | Negative | Total |
| Undetectable | 5 | (55) | 4 | 9 |
| 3–12 | 37 | (80) | 9 | 46 |
| 12–34 | 23 | (96) | 1 | 24 |
| Total | 65 | (82) | 14 | 79 |

TABLE 5. Relationship between depression and response to clomiphene

| | |
|---|---|
| No response to clomiphene until after depression treated | 4 |
| Depression impaired response to clomiphene, i.e., response lost or higher dose needed | 3 |
| Depression treated but no response till clomiphene given | 15 |
| Response to clomiphene in spite of depression | 6 |
| Unknown if treatment of depression affected clomiphene response (both treatments given together) | 6 |
| No response to clomiphene even after treatment | 2 |
| Total | 36 |

*Depression.* In Table 3 it is indicated that depression was thought to be the cause of the menstrual irregularity in 14 patients. Some other patients were depressed but had another reason for the irregular menses. This was particularly true of the patients with polycystic ovaries. In all there were 36 patients in whom depressive features were noted. The relationship between depression and the response to clomiphene is shown in Table 5.

The data are not extensive enough to draw firm conclusions but it is suggestive that the presence of depression may impair the response to clomiphene. The degree of depression was such that it was frequently not obvious without direct questioning but in many cases it had impaired or even totally abolished the woman's libido and her ability to respond (by vaginal secretion) to sexual stimulation.

## CONCLUSIONS

The results are presented of endocrine investigations in 209 women with menstrual disturbance and four women with regular menstruation but complaining of infertility. In the unselected series of 117 women the diagnosis of polycystic ovaries was made in 50 per cent as a result of measurement of ovarian areas from the x-ray films taken after induction of a pneumoperitoneum. It seems probable that at the upper limit of normal (10·5 sq. cm) there is no sharp distinction between the size of normal and polycystic ovaries. The second most common cause of menstrual disturbance was self-starvation amenorrhoea : the incidence was 17 per cent. In seven cases (6 per cent) the diagnosis made was hypopituitary hypothyroidism. The criteria used were a low BMR (less than −14 per cent) in a patient who had no evidence of self-starvation and in whom (in most cases) the radioactive $^{131}$I uptake was within the normal range.

Skull x-ray revealed a pituitary tumour in two patients.

Response to clomiphene was assessed in 118 patients. In 78 per cent of the women with polycystic ovaries the menstrual pattern was restored either to normal or, in some of those with complete amenorrhoea, to irregular menstruation. Three patients with primary amenorrhoea were found to have polycystic ovaries and all three responded to clomiphene.

The highest incidence of pregnancy (50 per cent) was in the polycystic ovary group. In general terms response to clomiphene was best in those with large ovaries and a high normal excretion of total gonadotrophins.

Depression in some patients appears to interfere with their ability to respond to clomiphene.

## REFERENCES

[1] Mills, I.H., Brooks, R.V. and Prunty, F.T.G., *The Human Adrenal Cortex.* p. 204. Eds. A.R. Currie, T. Symington and J.K. Grant. Edinburgh: E. & S. Livingstone, 1962.

[2] Ferriman, D. and Purdie, A.W., *Br. med. J.*, **2,** 69, 1965.

*Discussion of paper by Professor Mills*

*Prunty* What happened to the patients with Stein-Leventhal's syndrome on follow-up?

*Mills* As far as we were able to ascertain they continued to have regular menses on clomiphene except for the ones who became pregnant.

*Naftolin* I have some information which fits with Professor Mills' thesis. We have studied nine women with 'weight-loss' amenorrhoea. We found that all except one had very low levels of LH in their plasma, in a range nearly as low as that of a patient who had had a complete surgical removal of the pituitary. Only one patient had levels consistent with the follicular phase of the menstrual cycle.

*Mills* It might be of interest to do LH assays in people who have lost their libido. I suspect that it would be low.

*Gemzell* Professor Mills, how do you treat these women with self-starvation amenorrhoea?

*Mills* If you get them within a year of onset you can bring the power of personality to bear on them. A high percentage will return to a normal diet and their periods will return within the second year. If you get them later than a year after the onset you have progressively greater difficulty in getting a response. We bring them in to hospital if we get no response to treatment as an outpatient. We give them massive doses of chlorpromazine. We also give them insulin and have well-trained nurses who see to it that they eat. We have a high success rate in restoring their weight but the relapse rate in those who have had the condition for some years is as bad as anybody else's.

*Newton* Our experience in over a hundred cases of secondary amenorrhoea has been the same as Professor Mills'. In the first hundred we found 30 of these patients with self-starvation amenorrhoea. All had low LH and FSH levels and very low levels of urinary oestrogens. The five patients with full-blown anorexia nervosa sent to us from the Maudsley hospital also had extremely low levels of LH and FSH.

We have performed a pituitary function test by giving these patients 100–200 mg of clomiphene over a five-day period and monitored their LH and FSH output and oestrogen excretion. Figure 1 shows a patient with secondary amenorrhoea for six years. Both LH and FSH rose during treatment and thereafter the oestrogen excretion rose to 400–500 μg per 24 hours. We have carried out this test in 26 patients with secondary amenorrhoea and in all but two we have seen a similar response. It is possible that this may be a useful pituitary function test and we are evaluating it in males and females with hypopituitarism.

*Odell* Since 1967 (Odell, Ross and Rayford, *J. Clin. Invest.*, **46**, 248, 1967) we have routinely used clomiphene as a test in males and it works very well. Furthermore my colleagues Dr Ross, Dr Hertz and I have done gonadotrophin assays by the mouse uterine weight method in normal women in order to test this bioassay technique. In approximately a hundred urines collected daily, 15 per cent of normal women had no detectable gonadotrophin and 10 per cent of the time the gonadotrophins fell in the postmenopausal range (Hertz, Odell and Ross, *Ann. intern. Med.*, **65**, 800, 1966). I would like to ask Professor Mills whether his findings are based on a single collection and by what criteria did he place patients in the hypopituitary or the postmenopausal range?

*Mills* We mostly analyzed only a single 48-hour urine. In perhaps 10 per cent we did serial estimations.

*Odell* Possibly that explains the response of the postmenopausal patient. I also wanted to ask you whether any of your patients with low BMR were treated with thyroxin. Did you do thyroxin measurements on your patients? Did you treat any with placebos to see whether the response was due to thyroxin or placebo?

*Mills* We did a lot of PBI's and in our hands there was no correlation with either the uptake of radioiodine, or with the BMR. We have now stopped doing PBI's since they are so inaccurate. The answer therefore is that we don't know the thyroxin level. Nor did we test the effect of treatment with placebo.

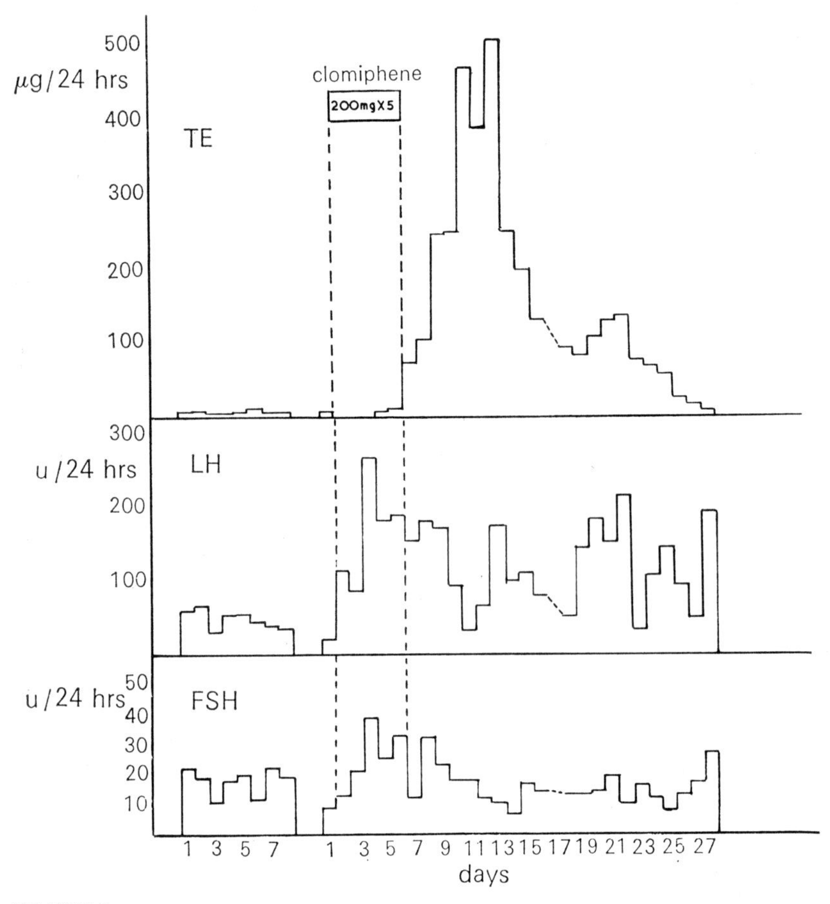


FIGURE 1
Secondary amenorrhoea P.R.T.S.

# The Polycystic Ovary Syndrome

S. L. JEFFCOATE

Department of Chemical Pathology
St Thomas's Hospital Medical School
London

¶ THE apparently well-circumscribed syndrome described by Stein and Leventhal in 1935 [1] has, in recent years, been the source of much controversy. This has covered its clinical, pathological and biochemical aspects to such an extent that many have been led to doubt its existence as a single disease entity [2–5]. Because of the variability of the reported features, the more vague term 'polycystic ovary syndrome' has been widely used. Since different authors have adopted different criteria upon which to base a diagnosis of the polycystic ovary syndrome it is important to state what I mean by this term before considering its biochemical aspects.

*Clinical features.* All patients with this syndrome have enlarged polycystic ovaries and some degree of menstrual irregularity. The absence of either of these two features excludes the diagnosis. Ovarian enlargement may be demonstrated either clinically, by pneumoperitoneum X-ray, by culdoscopy or laparoscopy, or at laparotomy. The menstrual upset is characteristically progressive, a normal menarche being followed by a few years of regular cycles then increasing oligomenorrhoea culminating in amenorrhoea. Patients may be seen at any time in this progression. In addition the majority (over 90 per cent in our experience) of patients have hirsutism, though this is often only mild. Infertility is also a frequent complaint, though this may be secondary and corpora lutea are sometimes seen in the ovaries (about 20 per cent of cases).

There has been an enormous amount of biochemical research into this syndrome. Two main aspects will be discussed here : the nature and source of the secreted androgens and possible abnormalities in control mechanisms.

## ANDROGEN SECRETION IN THE POLYCYSTIC OVARY SYNDROME

*Testosterone production.* Since testosterone (T) is the most biologically active androgen, an increase in the concentration of T in plasma is the best index of an increased androgen stimulus to peripheral tissues. There is a mean threefold increase in plasma T in the polycystic ovary syndrome (Fig. 1) though there is a wide scatter of values about this mean [6–9]. The raised plasma T is an underestimate of the increase in the blood production rate of T since there is also an approximate doubling of the metabolic clearance rate [6, 7, 9] and thus a sixfold increase in T production, from a mean of 270 μg/day in normal women to a mean of 1,500 μg/day in the polycystic ovary syndrome (Fig. 1).

The plasma T concentration is probably also an underestimate of the circulating level of biologically available T since it has been shown recently [9] that the percentage of the total plasma T that is free (i.e., not protein-bound) and thus available to the tissues, is increased from 6 per cent in normal women to about 12 per cent in the polycystic ovary syn-

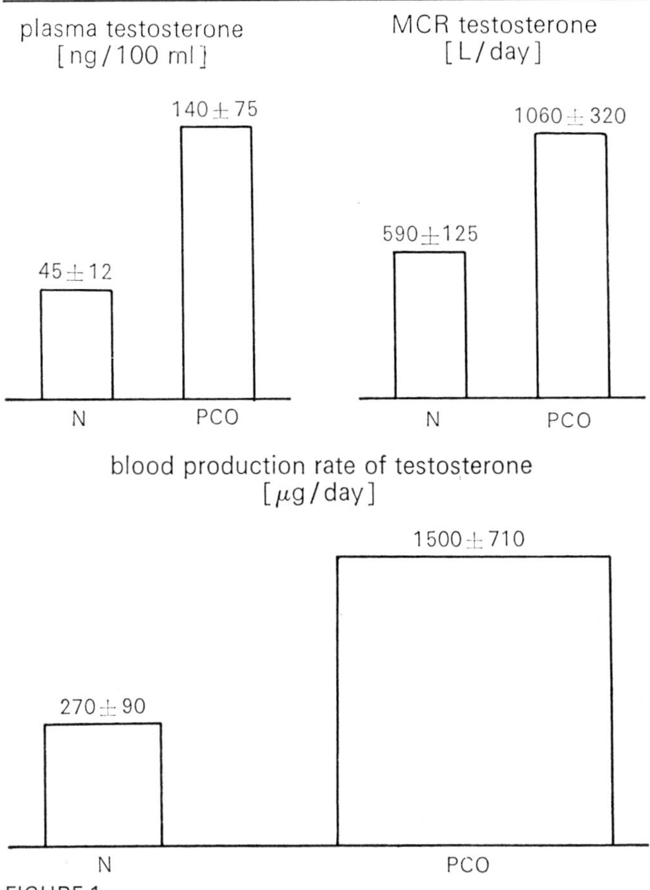


FIGURE 1
Plasma concentrations (ng/100 ml); metabolic clearance rates (MCR) (litres/day); and blood production rates (μg/day) of testosterone in normal women (N) and patients with the polycystic ovary syndrome (PCO). Means ± SD calculated from [6–9]

drome. If the results of these *in vitro* experiments can be translated to the physiological state this suggests a sixfold increase in the levels of biologically available T.

In normal women part of the plasma T is secreted as T and part is converted from secreted androstenedione (Δ); furthermore each of these fractions has two possible sources, the ovary and the adrenal. Thus the increased plasma T in the polycystic ovary syndrome could originate from any one or more of these four sources.

*Androstenedione production and conversion to testosterone.* As shown in Figure 2 there is a mean twofold increase in the production rate of Δ [6–9] but no change in the fraction that is converted to T. The converted portion of the plasma T is increased from about 140 μg/day (50 per cent of total) in normal women to about 300 μg/day (20–25 per cent of total) in the

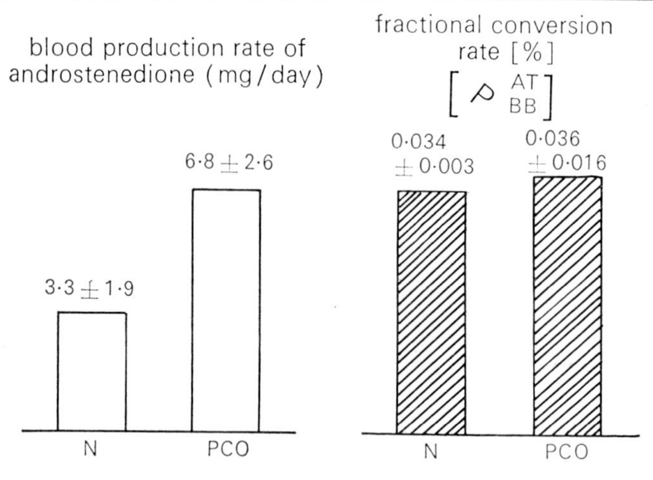


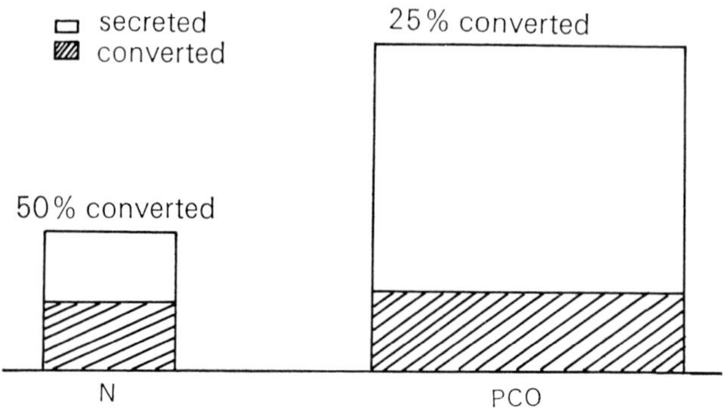


FIGURE 2
Blood production rates (mg/day) of androstenedione; fractional conversion rates of androstenedione to blood testosterone; and secreted and converted portions of total blood testosterone production in normal women (N) and patients with the polycystic ovary syndrome (PCO). Hatched areas of the blood testosterone represent portions converted from androstenedione. Means ± SD calculated from [6–9]

polycystic ovary syndrome. Thus the major part of the increase in plasma T is due to T secreted as such, this fraction being increased about eight times.

*In vivo differentiation of ovarian and adrenal androgen.* The differentiation of adrenal androgen from ovarian androgen *in vivo* has been the subject of many studies in the past using a variety of parameters of androgen secretion. The procedures used have included ovarian suppression (with oestrogen) and stimulation (with gonadotrophin); the effect of wedge resection of the ovaries; and adrenal suppression (with corticosteroids) and stimulation (with ACTH). The results obtained have been variable and conflicting and have been well reviewed recently [3–5].

Our results [10] and those of Mahesh and Greenblatt [11] appeared to indicate two main groups of patients with polycystic ovaries. Patients of the '*ovarian*' type showed a relatively poor decrease of androgen production when the adrenals were suppressed and a big decrease on ovarian suppression or following wedge resection. Other patients, the '*adrenal*' type, showed the opposite pattern. Some patients however were difficult to classify. The variability in response to short-term adrenal suppression may be more apparent than real since it has been shown that continuing corticosteroid administration for one month produces a consistent suppression of plasma T almost to normal (unsuppressed) levels [8].

Two further considerations apply to the interpretation of adrenal suppression tests. Firstly, there is the possibility of extra-adrenal effects. Corticosteroid administration has been shown to produce increases in the excretion of both oestrogen and gonadotrophin in the polycystic ovary syndrome [12, 13]. Secondly, there is evidence that part at least of the adrenal androgen secretion is not ACTH-dependent and thus may not be suppressible with corticosteroids (see later).

*Ovarian androgen secretion.* A variety of techniques has been used to establish that polycystic ovaries are secreting increased amounts of Δ. High concentrations are found in the cyst fluid and large amounts are synthesized by ovarian tissue *in vitro*; at the same time the synthesis of oestrogen appears to be relatively low with a high Δ : oestrogen ratio as a result (Table 1 : data from [10, 14, 15]). These findings and those of many other studies [3–5, for reviews] suggested the possibility of ovarian enzyme defects analogous to those of congenital adrenal hyperplasia. The apparent block can readily be overcome by FSH administration however (Table 1); there is a rise in Δ production but a much larger rise in oestrogen production.

TABLE 1. Ratio of androstenedione synthesis and secretion relative to oestrogen in normal women and patients with the polycystic ovary syndrome, as judged by urine production rates; concentrations in cyst fluid; conversion from progesterone *in vitro*. Data calculated from [10, 14, 15]

| | | Polycystic ovary syndrome | | |
|---|---|---|---|---|
| | Normal | Untreated | +FSH | After W.R. |
| Urine production rates (during adrenal suppression) | – | 48 | 15 | 20 |
| Cyst fluid | 0·6 | >50 | 1·5 | – |
| Biosynthesis from progesterone *in vitro* | 3 | >500 | 30 | – |

The most direct indication of ovarian steroid secretion is given by measurement of steroids in ovarian venous plasma but these studies [11, 15–18] are few because of the technical difficulties. Very little T is secreted by normal ovaries and the levels of Δ suggest that less than 25 per cent of Δ secretion is from the ovary [16]. In blood from polycystic ovaries there are normal levels of oestradiol indicating a normal rate of secretion in contrast to the cyst-fluid and *in vitro* results. There are increased concentrations of Δ confirming that secretion of this androgen is increased. The secretion of T does not appear to be high however, suggesting that the ovary is not the source of the major part of the secreted T in this syndrome. Since increased T secretion forms the bulk of the increase in plasma T, as discussed earlier, this again suggests that the adrenal gland may be implicated.

*Adrenal androgen secretion.* Though there are no direct measurements of steroid secretion by the adrenal glands in the polycystic ovary syndrome there is a lot of indirect evidence suggesting that adrenal overactivity is present [3–5]. Some have pointed to an association between adrenal lesions and polycystic ovaries though it is doubtful if typical polycystic ovaries are found [5]. Several studies have shown the effectiveness of corticosteroid therapy which may be as effective as other forms of therapy in restoring menstruation and fertility [3–5]. The chemical results of adrenal suppression have been discussed earlier; there is also a tendency to an increased response to ACTH. The raised excretion of 11-oxopregnanetriol in the polycystic ovary syndrome [3] also points to adrenal overactivity since 11-hydroxylation is only found in the adrenal.

In adrenal vein plasma from normal women levels of about 1 μg per 100 ml for T and 20–40 μg per 100 ml for Δ have been reported [18–20]. These are more than ten times the corresponding levels in normal ovarian vein blood. Though no data have been reported in the polycystic ovary syndrome, in idiopathic hirsutism there is an increased adrenal secretion of T [21].

*Source of testosterone production in the polycystic ovary syndrome.* Although the data are incomplete and some of the conclusions speculative the probable source of the circulating T in normal women and in the polycystic ovary syndrome is shown in Figure 3. In normal women less than 10 per cent of secreted T and less than 25 per cent of converted T is ovarian; thus over 80 per cent of the circulating T is adrenal in origin. In the polycystic ovary syndrome 75 per cent of the plasma T is secreted and ovarian T secretion can only account for a small part of this; the increase in converted T is probably both adrenal and ovarian in origin.

## PITUITARY CONTROL OF OVARY AND ADRENAL

The involvement of both the ovary and the adrenal in the polycystic ovary syndrome suggests that the condition originates from a disruption of the normal hypothalamic-pituitary-ovary-adrenal control system. This view is supported by other, indirect, evidence.

There are for instance the experimental polycystic ovary syndromes in

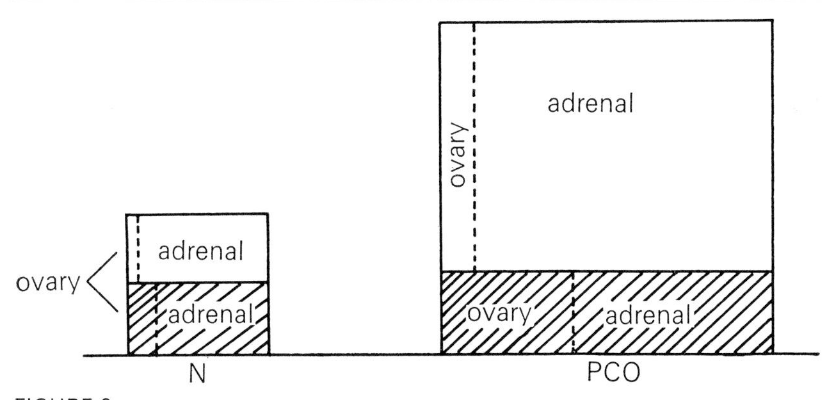


FIGURE 3
Origin of blood testosterone in normal women (N) and patients with the polycystic ovary syndrome (PCO). Hatched areas represent the fraction converted from secreted androstenedione. 'Ovary' and 'adrenal' indicate those portions that were secreted by the ovary and adrenal gland, respectively. See text for discussion

rats which can be induced by a variety of procedures [22]. These include neonatal androgen administration, lesions in the hypothalamus, pinealectomy and a constant light environment; all these affect the hypothalamus. It is however hazardous to extrapolate from these experimental lesions in the laboratory rat to the situation in human polycystic ovarian disease. Clomiphene for instance, which is effective in inducing ovulation in a high proportion of patients, is ineffective in relieving persistent oestrus in rats and the rat polycystic ovaries do not show the biochemical defects found in the human [22].

As clomiphene acts via the hypothalamus, stimulating the release of LH and FSH, its effectiveness in the polycystic ovary syndrome suggests an abnormality of gonadotrophin release or secretion. One case treated with clomiphene is shown in Figure 4; there was a rise in serum LH during treatment followed by an ovulatory LH peak five days after ceasing treatment.

Finally, the ready response of the ovaries to administered FSH has suggested to some that there may be a relative lack of FSH with an increased LH : FSH ratio.

*Gonadotrophin assays.* A few studies using specific bioassays for the urinary excretion of FSH and LH have been reported but have not been helpful. For LH, irregular fluctuating levels and a lack of an ovulatory peak have been described; the mean was higher than normal [23, 24]. Normal FSH levels have been reported [12].

Some of our recent data (Dr J. S. M. Hutchinson) are shown in Figure 5. Eight of 11 patients had low (<1 i.u./day) FSH levels; for LH, two had very high, two normal, and two low levels.

Longitudinal studies using radioimmunoassays of LH and FSH in blood

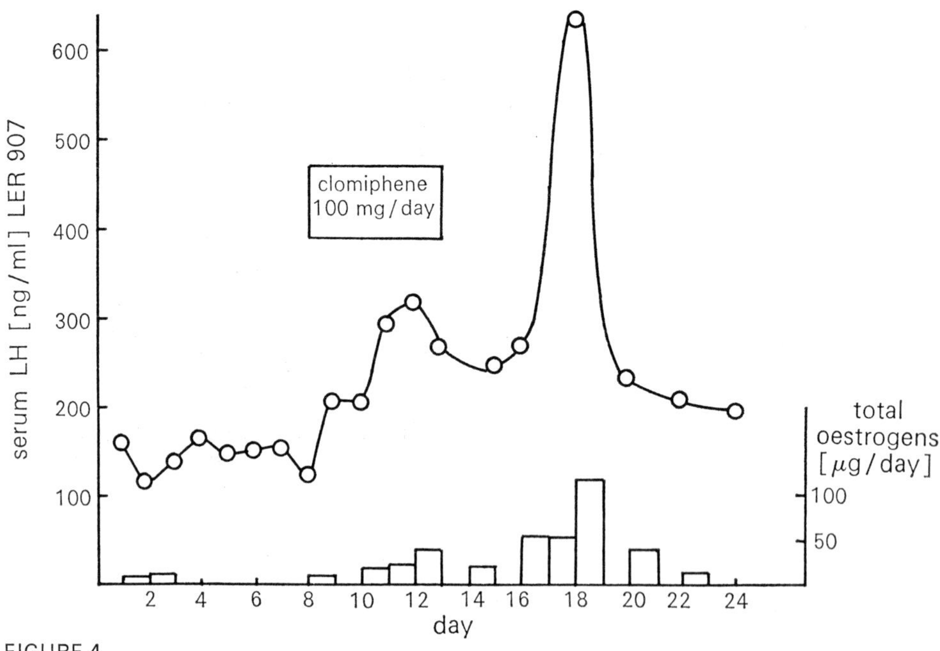


FIGURE 4
Serum LH (ng/ml LER 907 standard) measured by radioimmunoassay and urine oestrogen excretion in a patient with the polycystic ovary syndrome before, during and after treatment with clomiphene (100mg/day)

should provide a more useful tool but no meaningful data have yet been reported. The availability in the near future of gonadotrophin releasing hormones should also help to establish whether the pituitary or hypothalamus is at fault.

*Control of adrenal androgen secretion.* Although at least 80 per cent of plasma T in normal women appears to be non-ovarian and presumably adrenal in origin, adrenal suppression with corticosteroids in normal women only reduces plasma T levels by about 25 per cent when cortisol secretion and, by inference, ACTH secretion are almost completely suppressed [7]. This is thus evidence for a non-ACTH-dependent adrenal androgen secretion and is in favour of a long-held view [25–27] that there is a pituitary hormone which acts synergistically with ACTH in the control of adrenal androgen secretion. There is, for example, an increase after puberty in the excretion of 17-oxosteroids relative to 17-oxogenicsteroids in response to ACTH stimulation. After hypophysectomy there is a reversion to the prepubertal pattern. Some [e.g., 28] consider that this factor is LH but there is no direct evidence for this.

In the polycystic ovary syndrome larger falls (about 50 per cent) in plasma T can be induced by adrenal suppression though this is variable [7, 8, 17, 18]. This, again, is less than the calculated adrenal contribution

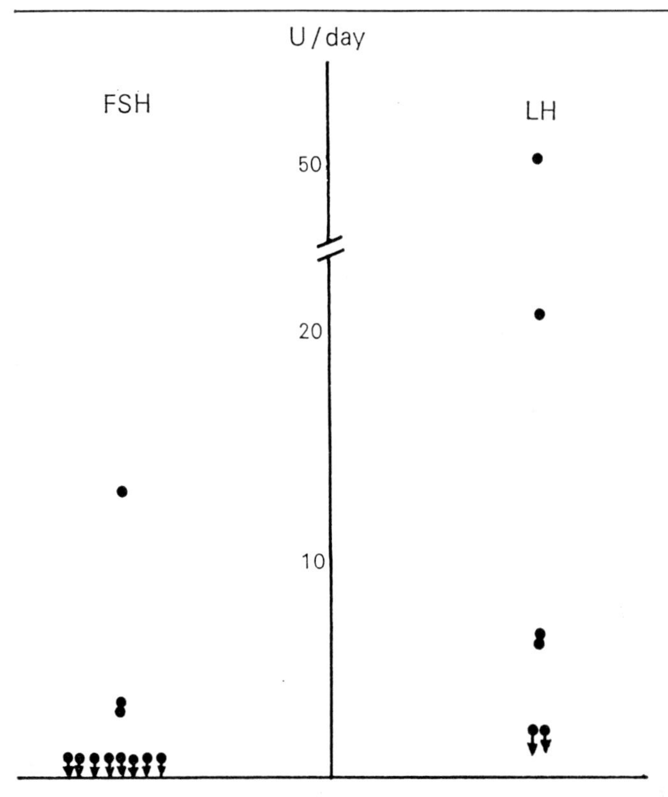


FIGURE 5
Urine excretion of FSH (P.S. Brown modification of Steelman-Pohley assay) and LH (OAAD assay) in patients with the polycystic ovary syndrome.

to plasma T and suggests a possible abnormality in the non-ACTH-dependent secretion of T by the adrenal in the polycystic ovary syndrome.

## CONCLUSIONS

Despite the variable and often controversial findings in the polycystic ovary syndrome it is possible to draw some conclusions at this time. Firstly, there are abnormalities of androgen secretion by both the ovary and adrenal and the adrenal gland is the source of the major part of the increased circulating T. Secondly, there is strong circumstantial evidence implicating abnormalities of the control of androgen secretion by the hypothalamus and pituitary though this is not adequately supported yet by data. It is not possible however to state how the vicious circle begins nor how it is interrupted by wedge resection, corticosteroids, clomiphene or other therapeutic procedures.

REFERENCES

[1] Stein, I.F. and Leventhal, M.L., *Am. J. Obstet. Gynec.*, **29,** 181, 1935.
[2] Goldzieher, J.W. and Green, J.A., *J. clin. Endocr. Metab.*, **22,** 325, 1962.
[3] Shearman, R.P. and Cox, R.I. *Obstet. Gynec. Surv.*, **21,** 1, 1966.
[4] Goldzieher, J.W. In *Advances in Obstetrics and Gynecology*, p. 354. Eds. S.L. Marcus. and C.C. Marcus. Baltimore: Williams and Wilkins, 1967.
[5] Prunty, F.T.G., *J. Endocr.*, **38,** 203, 1967.
[6] Bardin, C.W. and Lipsett, M.B., *J. clin. Invest.*, **46,** 891, 1967.
[7] Bardin, C.W., Hembree, W.C. and Lipsett, M.B., *J. clin. Endocr. Metab*, **28,** 1300, 1968.
[8] Horton, R. and Neisler, J. *J. clin. Endocr. Metab.*, **28,** 479, 1968.
[9] Southren, A.L., Gordon, G.G., Tochimoto, S., Olivo, J., Sherman, D.H. and Pinzon, G., *J. clin. Endocr. Metab.*, **29,** 1356, 1969.
[10] Jeffcoate, S.L., Brooks R.V., Londn, D.R., Smith, P.M., Spathis, G.S. and Prunty, F.T.G., *J. Endocr.*, **42,** 213o 1968.
[11] Mahesh, V.B. and Greenblatt, R.B., *Recent Prog. Hormone Res.*, **20,** 341, 1964.
[12] Butt, W.R., Crooke, A.C., Cunningham, F.J. and Palmer, R., *J. Endocr.*, **26,** 303, 1963.
[13] Barlow, J.J., *J. clin. Endocr. Metab.*, **24,** 586, 1964.
[14] Short, R.V. In *Proceedings of Second International Congress of Endocrinology*, London, 1964, p. 940. Excerpta Medica Foundation I.C.S. No. 83, 1965.
[15] Jeffcoate, S.L., Brooks, R.V., London, D.R., Prunty, F.T.G. and Rhodes, P., *J. Endocr.*, **42,** 229, 1968.
[16] Horton, R., Romanoff, E. and Walker, J., *J. clin. Endocr. Metab.*, **26,** 1267, 1966.
[17] Lloyd, C.W., Lobotsky, J., Segre, E.J., Kobayashi, T., Taymor, M.L. and Batt, R.E., *J. clin. Endocr. Metab.*, **26,** 314, 1966.
[18] Gandy, H.M. and Peterson, R.E., *J. clin. Endocr. Metab.*, **28,** 949, 1968.
[19] Wieland, R.G., de Courcy, C., Levy, R.P., Zala, A.B. and Hirschmann, H., *J. clin. Invest.*, **44,** 159, 1965.
[20] Weinheimer, B., Oertel, G.W., Leppla, W., Blaise, H. and Bette, L. In *Androgens in Normal and Pathological Conditions*, Ghent, 1965, p. 36. Excerpta Medica Foundation I.C.S. No. 101, 1966.
[21] Burger, H.G., Kent, J.R. and Kellie, A.E., *J. clin. Endocr. Metab.*, **24,** 432, 1964.
[22] Singh, K.B., *Obstet. Gynec. Surv.*, **24,** 2, 1969.
[23] Ingersoll, F.M. and McArthur, J.W., *Am. J. Obstet. Gynec.*, **77,** 795, 1959.
[24] Taymor, M.L. and Barnard, R., *Fert. Steril.*, **13,** 501, 1962.
[25] Prunty, F.T.G., *Br. med. J.*, **2,** 673, 1957.
[26] Mills, I.H., Brooks, R.V. and Prunty, F.T.G. In *The Human Adrenal Cortex.*, p. 204. Eds. A.R. Currie, T. Symington and J.K. Grant. Edinburgh: E. & S. Livingstone, 1962.
[27] Segre, E.J., Klaiber, E.L., Lobotsky, J. and Lloyd, C.W., *Ann. Rev. Med.*, **15,** 315, 1964.
[28] Pauerstein, C.J. and Solomon, D., *Obstet. Gynec.*, **28,** 692, 1966.

*Discussion of paper by Dr Jeffcoate*

*Loraine* I presume that your FSH assays were in fact single determinations by bioassay. It will be very interesting when one can conduct serial FSH assays in this condition. My impression is that original work on LH assay by Janet McArthur using the hypophysectomized rat prostate test has now been confirmed by the more modern immunoassay techniques.
*MacDonald* I think that your evidence for the secretion of testosterone by the adrenal is tenuous. There may be precursors other than adrenal androstenedione. I agree concerning the difficulties of interpretation of *in vivo* suppression experiments. It is not possible to separate the effects of one gland from all the other steroid-producing organs.
*Jeffcoate* There is evidence for some conversion of androstenediol to testosterone *in vivo* but no evidence that this hormone is secreted in sufficient amount to contribute significantly to the blood production rate of testosterone.
*Gemzell* Have you studied the effect of FSH stimulation in these patients?
*Jeffcoate* Yes. There is an increased production of both androgens and oestrogens, more marked in the case of the latter.
*Baird* I must contest again your statement concerning the proportion of the blood production rate of androstenedione which arises from adrenal secretion in normal women. We discussed yesterday the difficulty in obtaining glandular venous effluent undiluted by peripheral venous blood and also the problem of estimating adrenal and ovarian blood flow. There is, however, indirect evidence that the ovary produces more than 25 per cent of the blood production rate of androstenedione. In the castrated or postmenopausal woman the blood production rate of androstenedione is about half that in women during the normal menstrual cycle (Abrahams, Lobotsky and Lloyd, *J. clin. Invest.*, **48**, 696, 1969). Measurements of androstenedione in adrenal venous effluent of normal women are very hard to come by. In the best documented series including four reasonably normal women (Weinheimer et al., 1966, in *Androgens in Normal and Pathological Conditions*, Excerpta Medica Foundation), the mean concentration of androstenedione in adrenal venous plasma was 9·2 μg/100 ml (range 6·2–14·2). By comparing the ratio of androstenedione to cortisol in both adrenal and peripheral plasma, it is possible to calculate an adrenal secretion of androstenedione of about 1·2 mg/day, i.e., about 40 per cent of the total secretion rate of androstenedione in the follicular phase of the cycle (Baird, 1970)*. I have done a similar calculation in a series of 18 normal women in whom ovarian venous blood was collected at various stages of

* Baird, D. T. In *Reproductive Endocrinology*, p. 95. Ed. W. J. Irvine, Edinburgh: Livingstone, 1970.

the menstrual cycle (Lloyd et al., 1971)*. Assuming that circulating oestradiol is secreted uniquely by the ovary, the secretion rates of androstenedione from the active ovary were calculated to range from 0·5 to 2·56 mg per day with a mean of 1·2 mg (Baird, 1970) which is about the same quantity as adrenal secretion. As I discussed yesterday, the inactive ovary also secretes significant quantities of androstenedione, making the combined ovarian secretion on average greater than the adrenal. Validity is given to these calculations by the fact that the sum of these calculated ovarian and adrenal secretions corresponds closely to the value for the secretion rate of androstenedione of 2·8 mg calculated by subtracting the contribution of dehydroepiandrosterone from the blood production rate of androstenedione. So I suggest that you have underestimated the ovarian contribution to the blood production rate of androstenedione in normal women.

*Jeffcoate* Are you basing the adrenal calculations on the ratio of androstenedione to cortisol multiplied by the cortisol secretion rate?

*Baird* Yes.

*Jeffcoate* Taking the data available in the literature the levels of testosterone in adrenal vein blood are about one per cent of those of cortisol. If one takes the figure of 15 mg for daily cortisol secretion you are in the case of testosterone dealing with 150 μg per day but it becomes very difficult to do accurate estimations.

* Lloyd, C. W. et al. *J. clin. Endocr. Metab.*, 32, 155, 1971.

# Ovarian Tumours and Steroid Hormone Biosynthesis

K. GRIFFITHS
D. FAHMY
W. J. HENDERSON
A. C. TURNBULL *and*
C. A. F. JOSLIN

Tenovus Institute for Cancer Research
Welsh National School of Medicine, Cardiff

¶ In recent years, there have been impressive advances in our understanding of the biochemistry of steroid hormone biosynthesis in ovarian tissue. Despite the complex nature of the ovary with its interrelated cell types undergoing cyclical changes of structure and secretory activity, *in vitro* experimentation has been particularly valuable in defining the biosynthetic role of the individual cells [1]. Studies *in vitro* with ovarian tumours of histologically homogeneous cell type have also been of value, but in relating these data to the function of the normal cell, it should always be recognized that the neoplastic cell may possess different biosynthetic characteristics. Indeed, such studies are really of greater importance in relation to theories of tumour histogenesis providing more biochemical parameters to the problems of ovarian tumour classification [2–4]. There is now a considerable amount of information on the steroid biochemistry of ovarian neoplasms, which generally can be related to the associated endocrine disturbance of the patient, although morphology still remains the essential basis by which such tumours are identified and classified. Even then, tumour classification on a reasonable histogenetic basis is difficult because of the diversity of cell types usually observed in these tumours, and consequently, a confusing nomenclature has evolved.

A generally accepted form of ovarian tumour classification, that of Morris and Scully [3], is concerned principally with the 'functional' tumours, and divides these into (*a*) the 'sex cord–mesenchyme' type which includes the oestrogen-secreting granulosa-theca cell and the virilizing Sertoli-Leydig cell tumours. The latter group, composed of the 'testicular' elements Sertoli cells and Leydig cells in various stages of maturity, are normally referred to as arrhenoblastomas. A non-specific name 'lipoid cell tumours' is given to that group of neoplasms (*b*) which are composed of large polyhedral cells containing lipid. In this group are the 'adrenal-like tumours', hilus cell tumours, 'masculinovoblastomas' and luteomas, whereas group (*c*) includes the germ cell neoplasms, the germinomas and teratomas and (*d*) a variety of tumours which appear to be associated with what is referred to as 'functioning stroma'.

Granulosa-theca cell tumours constitute approximately 10 per cent of all primary ovarian carcinomas [5]. The clinical symptoms, precocious puberty, menstrual disorders or postmenopausal bleeding, are attributed to the secretion of oestrogen by the tumours, and increased urinary excretion of oestrogen has been observed in patients with these tumours [6, 7]. It was not unreasonable therefore that the studies of Marsh and his colleagues [8] showed a very high capacity of luteinized granulosa cell tumour tissue from a 26-month-old girl, to convert *in vitro*, testosterone to oestrone and oestradiol-17β. Although similar studies with luteinized granulosa-theca cell tumour tissue [9] also demonstrated the conversion of androstenedione to oestrogen, no $C_{19}$- or $C_{18}$-steroids were formed from progesterone incubated with this tissue, 20α-hydroxypregn-4-en-3-one being the principal metabolite in this experiment. It is interesting that similar patterns of steroid metabolism have been observed with closely related tissue : luteinized ovaries of pseudopregnant rats [10], corpus luteum of the mare [11], cow [1], and man [12], and also porcine granulosa cells [13].

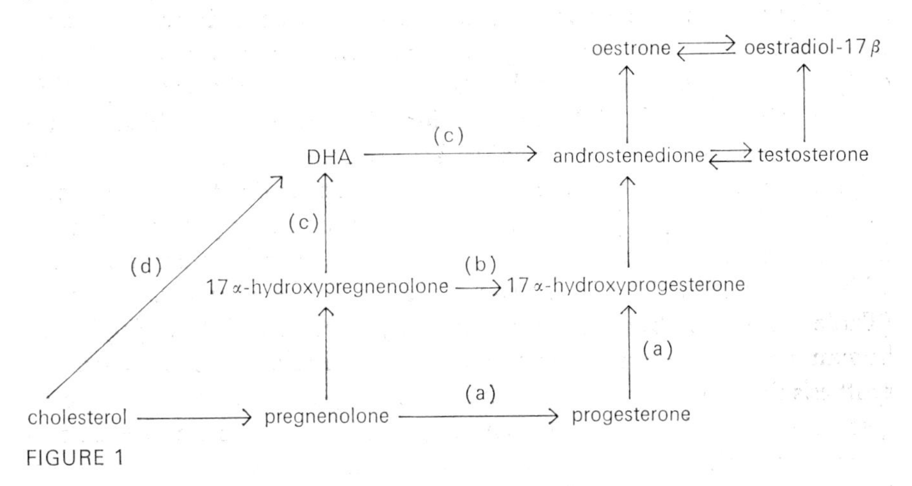


FIGURE 1

It was suggested at this time [9] that the 'alternative pathways' (b) or (c) (Fig. 1) which exclude progesterone, may be involved in the synthesis of oestrogen from pregnenolone by this type of luteinized granulosa cell. Probably dehydroepiandrosterone (DHA) would then become the major intermediate. Evidence for such a pathway in the granulosa cell tumour tissue was provided by Kase [14] who incubated homogenates with radioactive pregnenolone and progesterone. Of interest, although difficult to explain, was the formation of DHA and oestrone from pregnenolone, whereas there was no conversion of progesterone to oestrogen despite the synthesis of androstenedione. Furthermore, other investigations [15] in which [4-$^{14}$C] DHA and [7α-$^{3}$H] pregnenolone were incubated simultaneously with tissue from a granulosa cell tumour, also provided evidence that DHA may have a major role as a precursor of oestrogen in this tissue. These experiments showed that whereas approximately 25 per cent of the DHA was converted to oestrone and oestradiol-17β, only 0·16 per cent of the pregnenolone was similarly transformed, and MacAulay and Weliky [16] have also provided evidence that the 'alternative pathway' was of particular importance in cells of a similar tumour investigated in their laboratories. Such studies *in vitro*, on pathways for the biosynthesis of steroid hormones, do however require care in interpretation when attempting to define the role of the cells *in vivo*, especially with regard to tumour cells. Sampling of tumour tissue, often with its heterogeneous cell types, together with varying degrees of anoxia or necrosis of the tissue, must all have some bearing on the experimental results. The limitations of the rather arbitrary *in vitro* experimental systems employed to study these pathways must also be recognized. However, it is noteworthy that the steroid biosynthetic activity of the luteinized granulosa cell of the human corpus luteum of pregnancy, resembles in many respects the patterns shown by tissue from the granulosa-theca cell tumours [17, 18]. Chopped tissue from corpora lutea of early human pregnancy was incubated simultaneously with [$7\alpha$-$^{3}$H] DHA sulphate and [4-$^{14}$C] pregnenolone in Krebs-Ringer bicarbonate glucose medium in the absence of co-factors. Under these conditions DHA sulphate, but not pregnenolone, was converted to androstenedione, testosterone and oestrogen (Table 1). Furthermore a similar pattern of metabolism was obtained when the same radioactive steroids were incubated with homogenates of this luteal tissue in the presence of various co-factors (Table 1). These observations are contrary to results of Ryan [19] with human corpus luteum of pregnancy, which indicated that oestrogen synthesis from pregnenolone occurred via progesterone, $17\alpha$-hydroxyprogesterone and androstenedione. DHA appeared not to be concerned in oestrogen synthesis in these experiments which did however utilize different incubation conditions, again emphasizing the difficulties inherent in *in vitro* studies.

TABLE 1. Incubation of 4-$^{14}$C pregnenolone and $7\alpha$-$^{3}$H DHA sulphate with minced and homogenized luteal tissue. Percentage of the incubated radioactivity which was isolated in the carrier steroids is shown

| Compound isolated | Minced tissue $^{14}$C | $^{3}$H | Homogenized tissue $^{14}$C | $^{3}$H |
|---|---|---|---|---|
| Pregnenolone | 42·4 | – | 38·6 | – |
| Progesterone | 46·0 | – | 27·9 | – |
| DHA sulphate | – | 76·1 | | 51·7 |
| DHA | – | 6·2 | | 6·1 |
| Androstenedione | – | 6·2 | | 4·0 |
| Oestrone | – | 0·4 | | 0·1 |
| Oestradiol-17β | – | 0·5 | | 11·3 |

Tissue was homogenized in 0·25 M sucrose/0·12 M nicotinamide and incubated in tris buffer (pH 7·4) containing KCl, potassium fumarate, MgS04, NADP, ATP, glucose-6-phosphate and glucose-6-phosphate dehydrogenase.

Enzyme specificity may decide the relative activities of these pathways and such *in vitro* experiments may indeed reflect the true *in vivo* state. On the other hand, the presence of DHA sulphate, or DHA, within the incubation system may exert some inhibitory concentration effect on the metabolism of pregnenolone. The possibility that DHA sulphate may have an intracellular role in regulating steroid metabolism should however be considered,

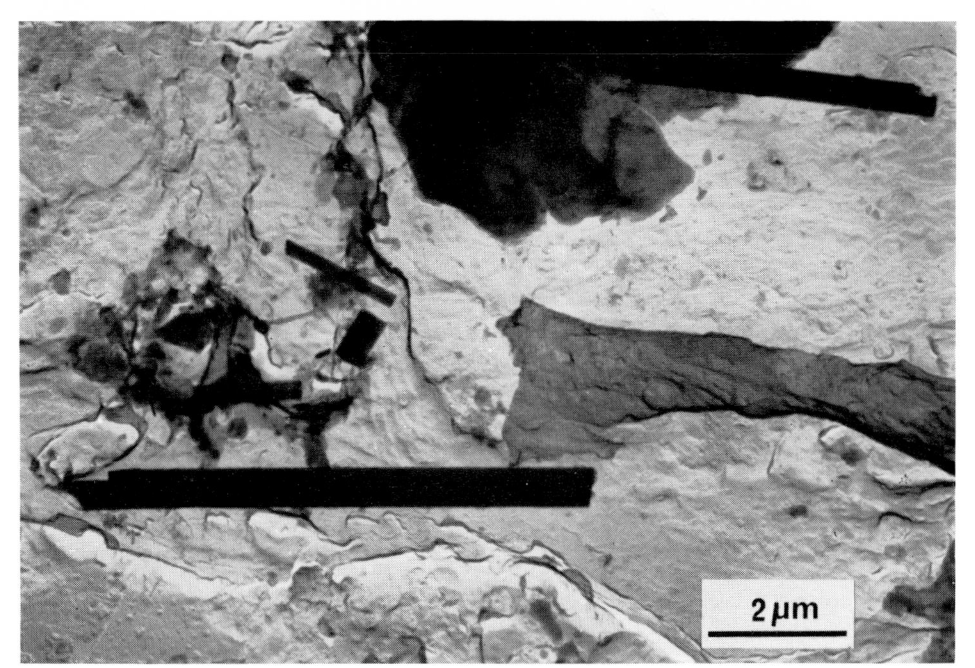


FIGURE 2
Asbestos particles extracted from the tissue of a Mesothelioma (x10,000)

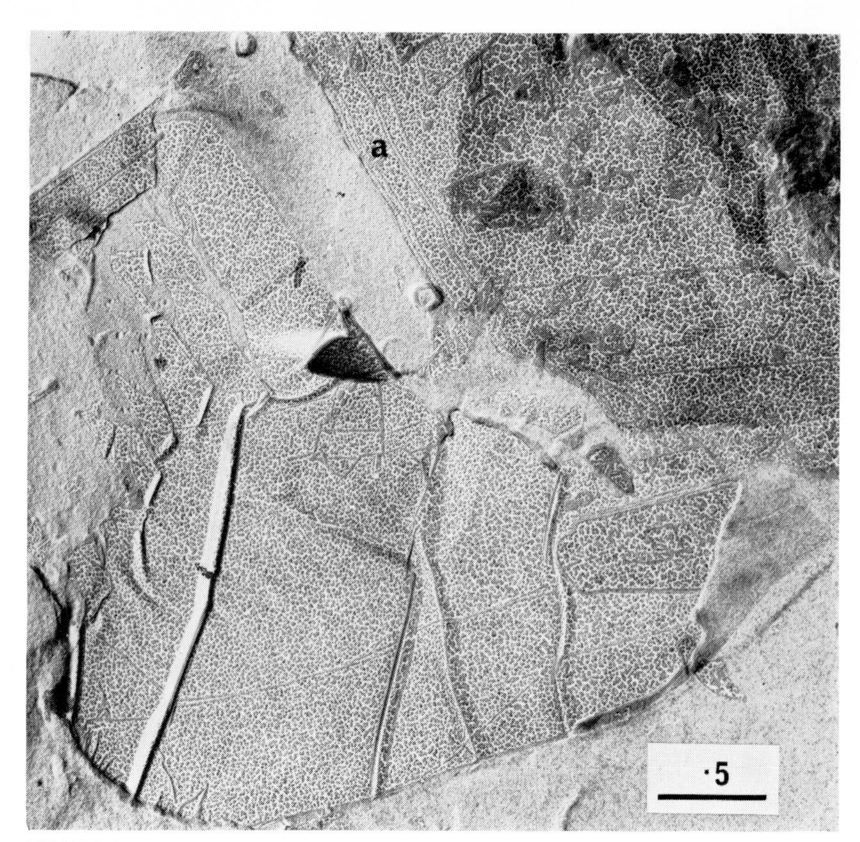


FIGURE 3
A particle of *natural* talc exhibiting the 'decoration pattern' (x30,000)

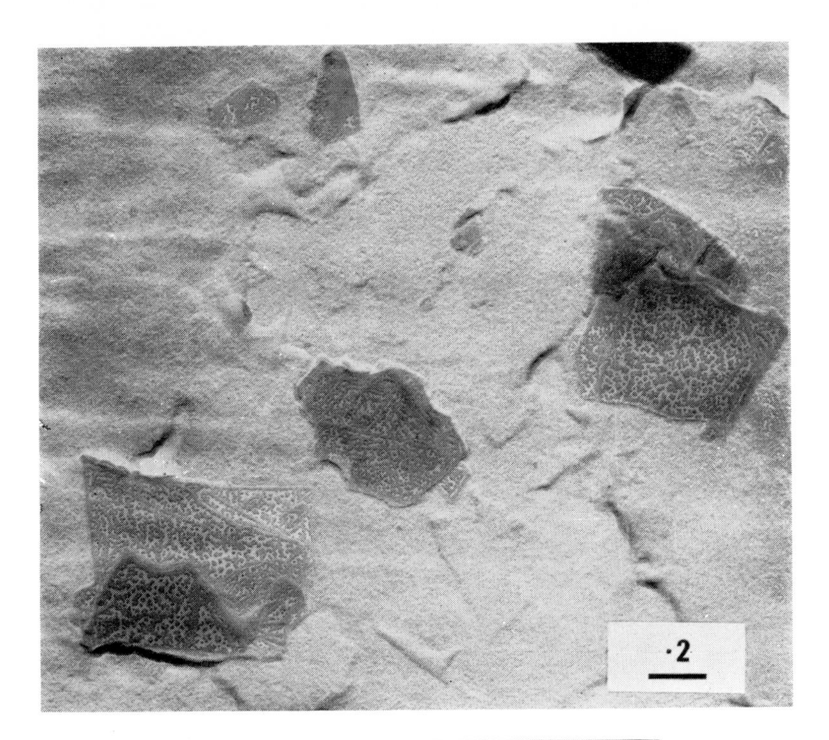


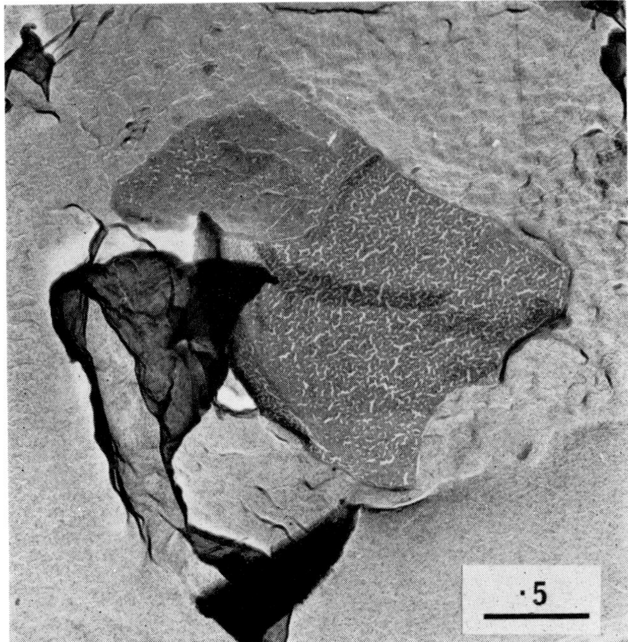


FIGURE 4

A number of talc particles (from a cosmetic preparation) displaying the 'decoration pattern' (x40,000)

FIGURE 5

A typical talc particle in tissue from a serous papillary cystadenocarcinoma of the ovary, removed from a 27-year-old female, with no previous abdominal operation (x30,000)

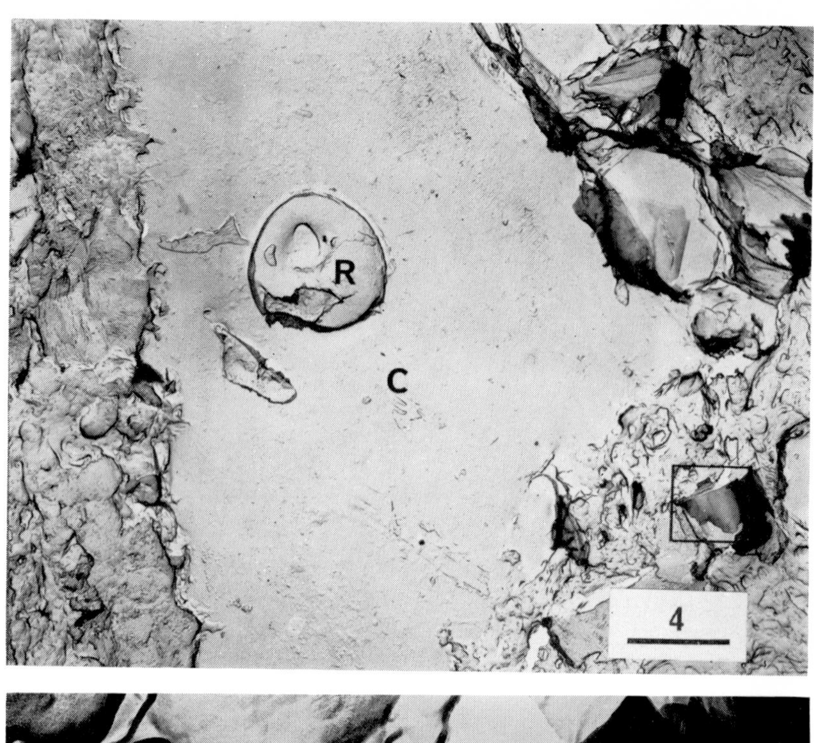


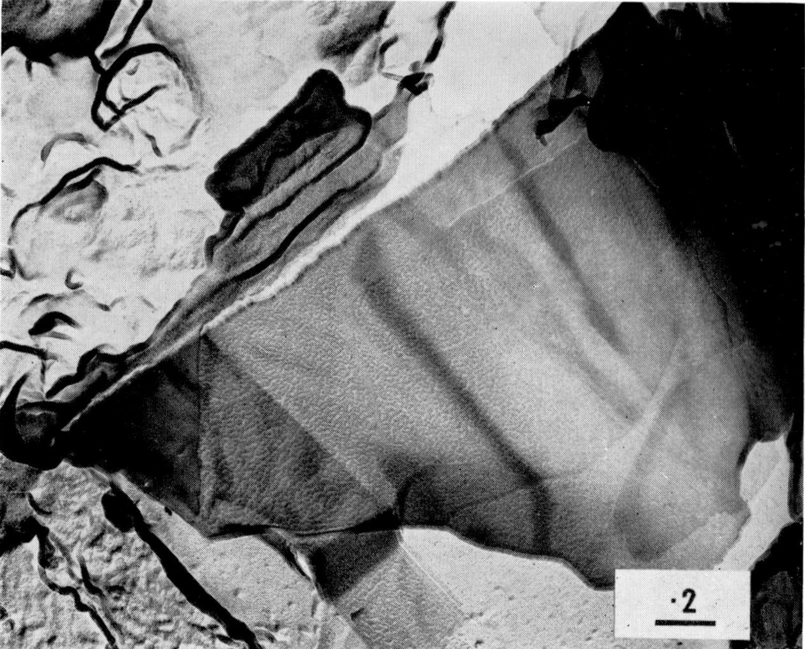


FIGURE 6

Tissue from a squamous cell carcinoma of the cervix from a 62-year-old female. The micrograph shows a capillary – C., red blood cell – R. and a talc particle embedded deep in the capillary wall (x3,500)

FIGURE 7

The talc particle outlined in Figure 6 is shown at a higher magnification to display the 'decoration pattern' (x40,000) and has been previously suggested [20, 21]. As a preliminary experiment, [7α-$^3$H] 17α-hydroxypregnenolone was incubated with chopped tissue from an early corpus luteum of pregnancy in the presence of varying concentrations of DHA sulphate. Table 2 shows the results of this experiment. Oestrogens were formed from 17α-hydroxypregnenolone, and DHA sulphate was an obvious controlling factor. Of interest however, in this regard, was the increased metabolism of 17α-hydroxypregnenolone in the presence of higher concentrations of DHA sulphate, and it would seem that further studies to determine the products of the metabolism are obviously in order. DHA sulphate, present in the plasma in relatively high concentrations [22], may then be the precursor of testosterone or oestradiol-17β in certain of these endocrine tumours, or alternatively influence the metabolism of steroids within the cell. On the other hand, the relatively efficient conversion of DHA to oestrogens compared to that of $C_{21}$-steroids by such tissues, might indicate that the pathway cholesterol – DHA which excludes pregnenolone [23] could be of significance and the investigations of Hammerstein, Rice and Savard [24] on the metabolism of acetate by the corpus luteum are noteworthy in this respect.

TABLE 2. Incubation of 7α-$^3$H 17α-hydroxypregnenolone with luteal tissue in the presence of varying concentrations of DHA sulphate. Percentage of incubated radioactivity which was isolated in the carrier steroids is shown

| | % radioactivity | | | | | | | |
|---|---|---|---|---|---|---|---|---|
| | mμMoles DHA sulphate added | | | | | | | |
| Compound Isolated | 0 | | 25 | | 50 | | 100 | |
| 17α-hydroxypregnenolone | 27·5 | | 25·4 | | 18·7 | | 6·3 | |
| 17α-hydroxyprogesterone | 48·9 | | 52·7 | | 52·4 | | 50·1 | |
| Androstenedione | 2·1 | | 2·3 | | 2·7 | | 3·1 | |
| DHA | 0·6 | | 0·5 | | 0·9 | | 1·2 | |
| Oestrone | 5·6 | 14·1 | 4·8 | 10·7 | 4·3 | 9·7 | 3·6 | 8·8 |
| Oestradiol-17β | 8·5 | | 5·9 | | 5·4 | | 5·2 | |

It has been recognized for a number of years that the hilus of the ovary contains nests of cells which are morphologically similar, if not identical with the Leydig cells of the testis [25, 26]. Hyperplasia, or more particularly neoplasia of such cells forming a hilus cell tumour, is generally associated with the clinical symptoms of virilization. (The hilus cell tumour is a tumour of pure Leydig cells, distinct from the Sertoli-Leydig cell tumour, or arrhenoblastoma, which contains a mixture of Sertoli and Leydig cells.) Although approximately 50 cases of hilus cell tumours have been described in the literature [27, 28] little was known regarding their metabolism of steroids until recent biochemical studies were reported [29–31]. The concept that the hilus cell tumour, by analogy with the Leydig cell,

TABLE 3. Incubation of [4-$^{14}$C] pregnenolone and [7α-$^{3}$H] DHA sulphate with minced tissue from a variety of 'nonfunctional' ovarian tumours, and also with ovarian stromal tissue. Figures show the percentage incubated radioactivity isolated in the carrier steroids

| Steroid investigated | Papillary Adenocarcinoma | | Fibroma | |
|---|---|---|---|---|
| | $^{14}$C | $^{3}$H | $^{14}$C | $^{3}$[illegible] |
| Pregnenolone | 100·0 | – | 90·14 | – |
| Progesterone | – | – | 0·07 | – |
| DHA sulphate | – | 97·85 | – | 79·[illegible] |
| DHA | – | 1·63 | – | 2·[illegible] |
| Androstenedione | – | 0·17 | – | 0·[illegible] |
| Testosterone | – | – | – | – |
| Androstenediol | | | – | 0·[illegible] |
| Oestrone | – | 0·13 | – | 0·[illegible] |
| Oestradiol-17β | – | 0·22 | – | 0·[illegible] |

actively synthesizes androstenedione and testosterone was supported by these studies, two groups [30, 31] showing active conversion of pregnenolone to $C_{19}$-steroids and two [29, 31] the formation of these steroids from progesterone. In addition, two of these studies [29, 31] also demonstrated the 11β-hydroxylation of androstenedione, an observation which, together with the report of Nocke [32] on the presence of an 11β-hydroxylase in a 'gynandroblastoma' (an arrhenoblastoma associated with androgen and oestrogen secretion [3]), indicate that the identification of the presence of the 11β-hydroxylase, an adrenal enzyme system, therefore provides little evidence of the adrenal origin of the tumour.

It was also demonstrated that DHA sulphate was extensively metabolized (41·4 per cent conversion to androstenedione) by hilus cell tumour tissue [30] and contrasts with the small formation (0·1 per cent) of androstenedione from DHA sulphate by an arrhenoblastoma [34]. Some evidence for oestrogen synthesis was also obtained [30, 31] and it is interesting that Novak and Mattingly [34] have described the association between endometrial hyperplasia and virilization in a number of patients with these hilus cell tumours.

Sufficient comparative studies have not yet been made on ovarian tumours to establish any definite relationship between a particular cell type and an exclusive steroid biosynthetic pathway, although generally the results obtained from the biochemical studies do tend to correlate with the clinical condition. Virilizing symptoms in patients have been associated with *in vitro* testosterone synthesis in a number of arrhenoblastomas [35–37] and also with lipoid cell tumours [38–40].

There is a striking morphological resemblance of certain virilizing lipoid cell tumours to the zona fasciculata of the adrenal cortex [40, 41]. The

| ondary granulosa cell tumour | | Benign mucinous cystadenoma | Stroma | |
|---|---|---|---|---|
| $^{4}$C | $^{3}$H | $^{3}$H | $^{14}$C | $^{3}$H |
| ·85 | – | | 99·0 | – |
| ·24 | – | | | |
| – | 56·29 | 80·42 | – | 53·70 |
| – | 29·21 | 7·42 | – | 9·02 |
| – | 0·38 | 0·30 | – | 0·08 |
| – | 0·02 | – | – | – |
| – | 0·42 | – | – | – |
| – | 0·46 | – | – | – |
| – | 0·85 | – | – | – |

histology, together with the marked responsiveness of the tumour to ACTH and HCG, and also the presence of some of the symptoms of Cushing's Syndrome [40–43] have been considered good evidence in favour of an adrenal origin for these tumours. Taylor and Norris [44] believe these tumours to be derived, however, from the ovarian stromal cells. *In vitro* studies have yet to provide evidence of a specific adrenal steroid biosynthetic pattern, although Dorfman [7] described high urinary 11-oxy-17-oxosteroid levels associated with a lipoid cell tumour. Perhaps the most interesting biosynthetic pattern was described recently by O'Malley and his colleagues [45] for a luteoma of pregnancy which caused virilization of mother and child. Their experiments suggested that the predominant pathway for testosterone synthesis involved pregnenolone–17α-hydroxypregnenolone–17α-hydroxypregnenolone sulphate–DHA sulphate–androstenediol sulphate–androstenediol–testosterone.

Over the past twenty years, a considerable amount of evidence has been obtained to indicate that endocrine effects can occur in association with the presence of ovarian tumours which are not of the group classically referred to as 'functional tumours' [3, 46]. Hormonal activity has been observed with secondary ovarian neoplasms, many derived from gastrointestinal tumours, and with no evidence that the primary tumour synthesizes steroids, it has been assumed that the metastatic cells also lacked this biosynthetic capacity [47, 48]. A number of Krukenberg ovarian tumours of this type have been described [49, 50]. It was suggested that there is a localized stromal reaction to the presence of either metastatic tissue, or the primary neoplasm, with the formation from the stromal cells surrounding the tumour of 'theca-lutein' type cells. These cells, which have been identified in close relation to the tumour, have been considered responsible for the hormone secretion, 'the stroma treating the expanding tumour as if it were a ripening follicle' [52].

Endocrine changes, generally manifested in an endometrial response, have been associated with a number of different types of neoplasms, pseudomucinous cystadenomas, cystadenofibromas, serous cystadenomas and primary and secondary ovarian carcinomas [52, 54, 55] and Plotz and his colleagues [56] have demonstrated the presence of steroid metabolizing enzymes concerned in androgen and oestrogen synthesis from $C_{21}$-steroids in homogenates of certain of these 'nonfunctional' tumours.

Results from some of our studies with tissue from such tumours from patients who presented without any endocrine disturbance, are shown in Table 3. On simultaneous incubation of [4-$^{14}$C] pregnenolone and [7α-$^{3}$H] DHA sulphate, it was shown that the various tissues metabolized DHA sulphate with the formation of androstenedione, oestrone and oestradiol-17β. There was, however, only limited metabolism of the [4-$^{14}$C] pregnenolone by this tissue, and none of the carrier $C_{19}$- or $C_{18}$-steroids were labelled. The stromal tissue studied did not synthesize oestrone or oestradiol-17β from DHA sulphate as might be expected [1]. Again interpretation of such *in vitro* observations is difficult. The results do however confirm the presence of these enzyme systems within this type of tumour tissue, although whether this activity is only associated with the theca-lutein cells present within the tissue remains a problem, and the possibility that the tumour cells themselves are concerned in steroid metabolism must also be borne in mind. Circulating DHA sulphate may be utilized by the tissue, the relative amounts of testosterone or oestradiol-17β produced determining whether there is a marked endocrine effect and secondly whether the effect is androgenic or oestrogenic.

Of interest is the possibility that such *localized* oestrogen formation by the 'theca-stroma' cells may influence the growth of the neoplastic tissue. Relevant in this respect are the studies of Gricouroff [57], who has stated that since the ovary can be the site of primary tumours which histologically resemble tumours found in the endometrium of the uterine corpus, and endometriosis of the ovary is quite frequent, it is therefore reasonable to suppose that endometrioid tumours originate in such an endometriotic lesion. Since endometriosis can show the same cyclic changes seen in the uterus, it would appear to be functional endometrial tissue responding normally to hormonal stimulation. Furthermore, irrespective of whether the histogenesis of endometriosis is due to metaplastic change in the ovary, or to endometrial tissue migrating to the ovary, the possible stromal reaction caused by the presence of this tissue with subsequent oestrogen synthesis, may be concerned in the development of the neoplastic tissue.

Induction of primary cancers of the ovary has been associated with asbestos. Graham and Graham [58] suggested that the increasing incidenceof ovarian carcinoma in modern society must be related to some factor of 'civilization' which is lacking in undeveloped countries, but which has a steadily developing influence in the Western world. With the reported association between asbestosis and ovarian cancer [59], together with the similarity in histological appearance between certain ovarian carcinomas and mesotheliomas, it was suggested that asbestos may be the factor to which attention should be directed.

The development in our laboratories of an extraction-replication technique [60] for the study of foreign particles within tissues has allowed the *in situ* identification of crocidolite asbestos within the tissues of various mesotheliomas [61] (Fig. 2). However, application of this technique to a series of ovarian carcinoma and also to tissue removed from tumours of the cervix showed that no asbestos particles could be found in the tissue studied. Noteworthy, however, was the identification of talc particles deep within the tumour tissue, in approximately 75 per cent (10 from 13) of sections from the ovarian neoplasms studied. Talc, a magnesium silicate, recognizable because of the characteristic 'decoration pattern' induced by evaporation of platinum *in vacuo* on the crystal surface (Figs. 3 and 4), is known to be converted *naturally* from anthophyllite asbestos. This is the only crystalline material at present known to be indistinguishable from talc using the extraction-replication technique. The observation that talc particles found in the ovarian tissue (Fig. 5) were much smaller (1,000 Å–2 nm) than those found in cervical tissue (as large as 4 μ) may be relevant (Figs. 6 and 7 ). Application of the technique to normal ovarian tissue showed talc particles in 4 from 12 sections studied.

There have been a number of reports concerning the relationship between asbestos and carcinogenesis [62], and although it remains to be established whether talc is present in *all* tissues of the body, its possible localization in ovarian tissue, and an acknowledged relationship with asbestos, suggest that this material is worthy of further consideration in relation to ovarian tumour induction.

ACKNOWLEDGMENTS

The authors wish to record their sincere appreciation for the generous financial support of the Tenovus Organization.

## REFERENCES


[1] Savard, K., Marsh, J. and Rice, B.F., *Recent Prog. Hormone Res.*, **21** 285, 1965.
[2] Teilum, G., *Acta path. microbiol. scand.*, **23**, 252, 1946.
[3] Morris, J.M. and Scully, R.E., *Endocrine Pathology of the Ovary*, St. Louis: The C.V. Mosby Company, 1958.
[4] Santesson, L. and Kottmeier, H.L. In *Ovarian Cancer*, UICC Monograph Vol. II. Berlin: Springer-Verlag, 1968.
[5] Novak, E., *Gynecology and Obstetric Pathology*, p. 416. Philadelphia: W.B. Saunders Co., 1952.
[6] Bruk, I., Dancaster, C.P. and Jackson, W.P.U., *Br. med. J.*, **2**, 26, 1960.
[7] Dorfman, R.I. In *Biological Activities of Steroids in relation to Cancer*. Eds. G. Pincus and E.P. Volmer, London: Academic Press, 1960.
[8] Marsh, J.M., Savard, K., Baggett, B., Judson, J., Van Wyk, J.J. and Talbert, L.M., *J. clin. Endocr. Metab.*, **22**, 1196, 1962.
[9] Griffiths, K., Grant, J.K. and Symington T., *J. Endocr.*, **30**, 247, 1964.
[10] Huang, W.Y. and Pearlman, W.H., *J. biol. Chem.*, **237**, 1060, 1962.
[11] Mahajan, D.K. and Samuels, L.T., *Fed. Proc. Fedr. Am. Soc. Exp. Biol.*, **22**, 2214, 1963.
[12] Huang, W.Y. and Pearlman, W.H., *J. biol. Chem.*, **238**, 1308, 1963.
[13] Bjersing, L. and Cartensen, H., *Biochim. biophys. Acta*, **86**, 639, 1964.
[14] Kase, N., *Am. J. Obstet. Gynec.*, **90**, 1262, 1964.
[15] Griffiths, K., Grant, J.K., Browning, M.C.K., Cunningham, D. and Barr, G., *J. Endocr.*, **35**, 299, 1966.
[16] MacAulay, M.A. and Weliky, I., *J. clin. Endocr. Metab.*, **28**, 819, 1968.
[17] Fahmy, D., Griffiths, K. and Turnbull, A.C., *Eur. J. Steroids*, **2**, 483, 1967.
[18] Fahmy, D., Griffiths, K. and Turnbull, A.C., *Biochem. J.*, **107**, 725, 1968.
[19] Ryan, K.J., *Acta endocr., Copnh.*, **44**, 81, 1963.
[20] Neher, R. and Kahnt, F.W., *Experientia*, **21**, 310, 1965.
[21] Notation, A.D. and Ungar, F., *Can. J. Biochem.*, **46**, 1185, 1968.
[22] Baulieu, E.-E., Mauvais-Jarvis, P. and Corpechot, C., *J. clin. Endocr. Metab.*, **23**, 374, 1963.
[23] Jungman, R.A., *Biochim. biophys. Acta*, **164**, 110, 1968.
[24] Hammerstein, J., Rice, B.F. and Savard, K., *J. clin. Endocr. Metab.*, **24**, 597, 1964.
[25] Berger, L., *C. r. hebd. Seance. Acad. Sci., Paris*, **175**, 498, 1922.
[26] Sternberg, W.H., *Am. J. Path.*, **25**, 493, 1949.
[27] Boivin, T. and Richart, R.M., *Cancer, N.Y.*, **18**, 231, 1965.
[28] Dunnihoo, D.R., Grieme, D.L. and Woolf, R.B., *J. Obstet. Gynaec. Br. Commonw.*, **27**, 703, 1966.
[29] Corral-Gallardo, J., Acevedo, H.A., Perez de Salazar, J.L., Loria, M. and Goldzieher, J.W., *Acta. endocr., Copnh.*, **52**, 425, 1966.
[30] Fahmy, D., Griffiths, K., Turnbull, A.C. and Symington, T., *J. Endocr.*, **41**, 61, 1968.
[31] Jeffcoate, S.L. and Prunty, F.T.G., *Am. J. Obstet. Gynec.*, **101**, 684, 1968.
[32] Nocke, W. In *Proceedings Second International Congress of Endocrinology*, Amsterdam, 1965. Excerpta Medica Foundn., p. 1304.
[33] Sandberg, E.C., Jenkins, R.C. and Trifon, H.M., *Steroids*, **8**, 249, 1966.
[34] Novak, E.R. and Mattingly, R.F. *Obstet. Gynaec., N.Y.*, **15**, 425, 1960.
[35] Wiest, W.G., Zander, J. and Holmstrom, E.G., *J. clin. Endocr. Metab.*, **19**, 297, 1959.

[36] Savard, K., Gut, M., Dorfman, R.I., Gabrilove, J.L. and Soffer, J.L., *J. clin. Endocr. Metab.*, **21**, 165, 1961.
[37] Kase, N. and Conrad, S.H., *Am. J. Obstet. Gynec.*, **90**, 1251, 1964.
[38] Brysson, M.J., Dominguez, O.V., Kaiser, I.H., Samuels, L.T. and Sweat, M.L., *J. clin. Endocr. Metab.*, **22**, 773, 1962.
[39] Sandberg, A.A., Slaunwhite, W.R., Jackson, J.E. and Frawley, R.F., *J. clin. Endocr. Metab.*, **22**, 929, 1962.
[40] Rosner, J.M., Conte, N.F., Horitz, S. and Forsham, P.M., *Am. J. Med.*, **37**, 638, 1964.
[41] Scully, R.E. In *The Ovary*, 1st ed., p. 143. Eds. H.G. Evady and E.C. Smith, Baltimore: Williams and Wilkins Co., 1963.
[42] Morrow, L.B., Thompson, R.J. and Millinger, R.C., *J. clin. Endocr. Metab.*, **28**, 1756, 1968.
[43] Osborn, R.H., Bradbury, J.T. and Yannone, M.E., *Obstet. Gynec.*, **33**, 666, 1969.
[44] Taylor, H.B. and Norris, H.J., *Cancer*, **20**, 1953, 1967.
[45] O'Malley, B.W., Lipsett, M.B. and Jackson, M.A., *J. clin. Endocr. Metab.*, **27**, 311, 1967.
[46] Novak, E. and Woodruff, E.R. In *Gynecologie and Obstetric Pathology*, 4th ed., p. 402. Philadelphia/London: W.B. Saunders Co., 1958.
[47] Pfeiderer, A. and Teufel, G., *Am. J. Obstet. Gynec.*, **102**, 997, 1968.
[48] Kondstaal, J., Bossenbroek, B. and Hardonk, M.J., *Am. J. Obstet. Gynec.*, **102**, 1004, 1968.
[49] Scott, J.S., Lumsden, C.E. and Levell, M.J., *Am. J. Obstet. Gynec.*, **97**, 161, 1967.
[50] Connor, T.B., Ganis, F.M., Levin, H.S., Migeon, C.J. and Martin, L.G., *J. clin. Endocr. Metab.*, **28**, 198, 1968.
[51] Turunen, A., *Acta endocr., Copnh.*, **20**, 50, 1955.
[52] Hughesdon, P.E., *J. Obst. & Gynaec. Br. Emp.*, **65**, 702, 1958.
[53] Scully, R.E. and Richardson, G.S., *Cancer*, **14**, 827, 1961.
[54] Wren, B.G. and Frampton, J., *Br. med. J.*, **2**, 842, 1963.
[55] Fox, M., *Cancer*, **18**, 1041, 1965.
[56] Plotz, E.J., Wiener, M., Stein, A.A. and Hahn, B.D., *Am. J. Obstet. Gynec.*, **97**, 1050, 1967.
[57] Gricouroff, G. In *Ovarian Cancer*, UICC Monograph Vol. II. Berlin: Springer-Verlag, 1968.
[58] Graham, J. and Graham, R., *Environ. Res.*, **1**, 115, 1967.
[59] Keal, E.E., *Lancet*, **2**, 1211, 1960.
[60] Henderson, W.J., *J. Micr.*, **89**, 369, 1969.
[61] Henderson, W.J., Harse, J. and Griffiths, K., *Eur. J. Cancer*, **5**, 621, 1969.
[62] Wagner, J.C., Sleggs, C.A. and Marchand, P., *Br. J. ind. Med.*, **21**, 304, 1960.

*Discussion of paper by Dr Griffiths*

*Odell* Is it possible that some of these effects could have resulted from talcum off the surgeon's gloves?

*Griffiths* None of the patients had undergone operation previously.

*Naftolin* If talcum powder was the cause, there would have been an epidemic of ovarian pathology at the time when talc was still used on surgeons' gloves.

*Griffiths* Endometriosis is also a phenomenon very little studied in this context. Apparently you get fragments of endometrium carried to the ovary by retrograde tubal menstruation and these could be the focus of malignant change. Professor Gricouroff in Paris has some very nice pictures of endometrial tissue in the subperitoneal uterine lymphatics.

*Van der Molen* Coming back to steroids, is anything known about sulphatase in the tumours you discussed?

*Griffiths* These enzymes as such were not studied. We incubated DHA sulphate, as I described, and some metabolism to oestrogen occurred.

*Van der Molen* What about sulphokinase?

*Griffiths* We did not study this enzyme system in the tumour tissue.

# Pituitary, Adrenal and Ovarian Hormones in the Aetiology and Clinical Course of Breast Cancer

R. D. BULBROOK *and* D. Y. WANG

Imperial Cancer Research Fund
Lincoln's Inn Fields, London

¶ In reviewing the role of the hormones in human breast cancer, it is convenient to consider the aetiology and the clinical course of the disease separately. This may not be an artificial division. It is generally believed that the hormones do not initiate cellular events but control and regulate reactions that would occur in their absence. The broad conception is that an unknown agent, which might be viral or chemical, transforms the normal cell into a malignant one. The behaviour of the transformed cell is then controlled or modified by hormones, at least for a time. The degree of hormonal control may be so powerful that the cell is totally dependent upon the hormonal environment but, with the passage of time, dependence is replaced with responsiveness to alterations in the hormonal milieu and this phase is followed by total independence of the cell [1]. Another possibility is that the malignant transformation of the normal breast cell does not occur without pre-existing hormonal abnormalities making the cell susceptible to such a change.

These processes are of fundamental interest to the biologist but they may turn out to be only of academic interest to the clinician. Irrespective of the initiating events, it is already apparent that hormonal control of the cell may be so powerful in some instances that manipulation of the endocrine environment may reduce the incidence of breast cancer to very low levels or bring about a considerable delay in the time at which the tumours appear in laboratory animals. If similar results could be obtained in man, many of the present clinical problems would disappear.

The problem that now arises is to decide which hormones may be of the greatest importance in controlling the growth of normal and neoplastic breast cells in man. This is a situation of great complexity since it is now clear that in animals deprived of the secretions of pituitary and adrenal glands and of the ovaries, maximal breast growth is best achieved by administration of almost all of the known active hormones. The most important of these are the oestrogens, the progestins, growth hormone and prolactin. However, the actions of these hormones may be profoundly modified by other hormones which themselves may have no direct effect on the growth of breast cells. Such secondary hormones include the androgens, the corticosteroids, insulin and thyroid hormones. In tissue culture, breast cells will not survive, nor does prolactin have any effects, in the absence of insulin and corticosteroids. That secondary hormones may be important in the aetiology of human breast cancer is indicated by reports of changes in incidence in hypo- and hyperthyroid patients and in diabetics.

It may very well be that the oestrogens, progestins, growth hormone and prolactin have a major influence on the rate of tumour cell growth during the pre-clinical phase of the disease but since this period may be from ten to twenty years, a marginal synergistic or antagonistic effect of other subsidiary hormones may have important bearing on the time in the life span of the patient at which the tumour becomes clinically manifest.

In general terms, therefore, it may be unwise to investigate the role of the hormones in human breast cancer in terms of one or two hormones but to consider the disease as one involving the entire endocrine system.

*Direct evidence that endocrine abnormalities precede the clinical appearance of breast cancer*

Investigations of the involvement of the endocrine system in breast cancer have been carried out almost invariably in patients with overt breast cancer, and evidence that the hormones are involved at an earlier stage in the disease has been indirect, stemming either from epidemiological studies or from fortuitous observations of the effects of hormones given for other diseases on the incidence of breast cancer. The results of investigations of hormonal status in patients with established breast cancer have generally been so inconclusive that there has been no stimulus to undertake the formidable task of looking for endocrine abnormalities before the disease is diagnosed. This applies particularly to the oestrogens. However, in 1962, Bulbrook, Hayward, Spicer and Thomas [2] reported that patients at the time of mastectomy excreted less androgen metabolites in their urine than normal women and it was then shown that these patients had a more rapid recurrence rate after mastectomy than women with normal ratios of androgens to corticosteroids [3]. These authors suggested that the abnormal steroid ratios might have preceded the clinical appearance of the disease.

A prospective study was then set up to test this suggestion. One 24-hour specimen of urine was collected from each of 5,000 ostensibly normal women between 30 and 55 years of age. The 17-hydroxycorticosteroids (17-OHCS) and the androgen metabolites (dehydroepiandrosterone, androsterone and aetiocholanolone) were determined. The population had an incidence of breast cancer of 1 / 1,000 per year and it was thus possible to see whether the urinary steroid excretion was abnormal before a clinical diagnosis of breast cancer was made.

In an initial report based on 17 cases of breast cancer [4] it was shown that the pre-diagnosis excretion of androgens and corticosteroids differed significantly from that of appropriate controls without breast cancer. The main tendency was for women who subsequently developed breast cancer to exhibit a low excretion of urinary androgen metabolites but a speculative case could be made for describing the steroid excretion pattern of the pre-cancer cases as 'multidirectional'. That is to say, that either high or low amounts of 17-OHCS might be associated with high or low values of androgen metabolites.

A subsequent analysis based on 24 patients (Dr C.C. Spicer, personal communication) showed that the pre-clinical levels of the androgen metabolites are significantly lower than those of normal controls.

The reality of the multidirectional abnormalities originally suggested [4] remains to be determined. Since these cases are in a minority, it would be necessary to accumulate a large number of cases for formal proof for this hypothesis. Nevertheless, the concept that there may be several endocrine states associated with a high risk of subsequent breast cancer should be borne in mind. Some of the discrepancies in the literature concerning hormonal status in the established disease could be reconciled on this basis and there is some clinical evidence that would support this thesis.

The present results of the prospective study are based on relatively small numbers of cases but some support for the validity of the results has been obtained by studying the steroid excretion of sisters of patients with breast cancer. The bulk of the evidence suggests that sisters of such patients have an increased risk of developing the disease by a factor of three or four. A preliminary investigation showed that the steroid excretion of unaffected sisters was more like that of the pre-cancer cases than of the normal controls [5] and a recent analysis based on more subjects has shown that the androgen excretion of the sisters is midway between that of the pre-clinical cases and the normal controls (Dr C.C. Spicer, personal communication).

The main finding, therefore, in the present prospective trial is that hormonal abnormalities precede the clinical appearance of breast cancer in some women. From a consideration of the normal distribution of the androgen metabolites with age, the most likely explanation of the results is that women whose androgen excretion lies at the bottom of the normal range have an increased risk of subsequent breast cancer. It is possible that the low excretion is due to a sudden drop in the production of their precursors but it seems much more probable that a 'normal' secretion of androgen metabolite precursors was never attained at puberty. The only way to check this would be to carry out a prospective study in normal females from the age of the menarche onwards but this would then entail waiting for thirty years for the first clinical results. In advanced breast cancer, the short survival of many of the patients often is a problem to the investigator; in a forward study of the influence of pubertal hormone changes on the subsequent development of breast cancer, the survival of the investigators would be the main difficulty.

The results of the present prospective study fit either the hypothesis that malignant transformation occurs in breast cells that have been exposed to an abnormal environment or, alternatively, that such a transformation is a random event occurring equally in any member of the population but that the growth rates of tumours in women with a low androgen excretion are such that the tumours occur earlier in the life span of these women, compared with women with normal or high androgen levels. It might be possible to distinguish between these alternatives if the population under study is followed up for a sufficient length of time.

*Hormones and the clinical course of breast cancer*

Once a diagnosis of breast cancer has been made, a host of uncontrolled factors makes the interpretation of the results of investigation of the patient's hormonal status difficult. These factors include the profound stress of the diagnosis itself and the subsequent disruption of normal life by the disease process and by treatment. It is often difficult to decide whether a particular hormone pattern is due to a long-established endocrine abnormality or to the disease itself or to treatment. For example, 17-OHCS excretion before diagnosis appears to be marginally below that of normal controls; after diagnosis it tends to be slightly higher than normal and in the late stages of the disease it may be very high indeed (see Bulbrook, 1970). In other words, endocrine measurements made once the disease is clinically apparent may give an entirely misleading picture of the environment before diagnosis. On the other hand, although such measurements may not be useful in terms of the aetiology of the disease, they may be extremely important in terms of the subsequent clinical course. If the rate of growth of a particular type of tumour cell is dependent to a marked extent upon the peripheral levels of a hormone, then apparently adventitious events may have a profound influence on growth rates through alterations in the secretion rates of key hormones.

The relationship between the hormones and the clinical course of breast cancer has been recently reviewed [6, 7]. The main findings can be briefly stated as far as the urinary steroids are concerned:

(1) There is no agreement about oestrogen excretion by patients with breast cancer. The amounts of oestrogens in the urine have been variously reported as high, low, or normal. The most persuasive evidence is that of Lemon [8] who found a subnormal excretion of oestriol in patients with early breast cancer.

(2) The weight of the present evidence supports the view that about half the patients with advanced breast cancer excrete subnormal amounts of androgen metabolites but there is some doubt concerning the proportion of patients with early breast cancer who show the same abnormality.

(3) The 17-OHCS are within the normal range or slightly above it (especially in patients with advanced breast cancer).

As far as the plasma levels of the precursors of these urinary steroids are concerned:

(4) There is no information about the plasma oestrogens in breast cancer.

(5) Plasma testosterone (which would give rise to a minor fraction of the urinary androgen metabolites) is reported to be within the normal range [9]. Plasma total 17-oxosteroids tend to be at the lower end of the normal range [10]. Plasma dehydroepiandrosterone and androsterone sulphates (which give rise to the bulk of the urinary androgen metabolites) are at the lower end of the normal range in patients with early breast cancer but are significantly subnormal in patients with the advanced disease [11]. There is a good correlation between the amounts of 17-oxosteroids in plasma and their metabolites in urine.

Benard et al. [12] have claimed that patients with breast cancer have abnormally high levels of plasma 17-oxosteroids in the free (unconjugated) form but Garnham et al. [13] have been unable to confirm this.

(6) Plasma 17-OHCS tend to be at the upper end of the normal range [10]. The blood production rate of cortisol is normal in the majority of the patients with early breast cancer although a high production rate is found in the occasional patient. In the advanced disease, the majority of patients have an elevated production rate and this rate is greater than would have been expected from the values of the urinary 17-OHCS [14]. The correlation between cortisol production rates and peripheral levels of plasma cortisol is good but both these parameters are poorly correlated with the urinary 17-OHCS values [14]. This may be due to differences in protein binding [15].

There is little information about the pituitary hormones. Urinary gonadotrophins are said to be raised in some patients [16] and plasma growth hormone levels appear to be marginally higher than normal [17]. Now that so many new methods for the analysis of pituitary hormones are available, a thorough investigation of this field would be desirable.

This meagre amount of information may seem a poor return for the amount of work carried out in the last decade but one important fact has emerged. This is that in at least half the patients investigated, no hormonal abnormalities have been discovered. In no single reported study has there been a clear-cut difference between the endocrine status of the patients with breast cancer and that of their controls. The patients in whom no endocrine abnormalities can be found appear to be those with the best prognosis. This finding means that it is often difficult to interpret the results of endocrine assays without prior knowledge of the clinical course of the disease.

The finding of endocrine abnormalities in patients with a poor prognosis and apparently normal endocrine status in patients with a good prognosis may be linked with the results so far obtained in the prospective study described previously. In this trial, at least half the women in the pre-clinical stage of breast cancer excreted subnormal amounts of urinary androgen metabolites. Unless there is a change in their excretion, these should be the patients who have a poor prognosis when the disease is eventually diagnosed. If this proves to be so, then the clinical course of the disease may be determined many years before actual diagnosis takes place.

*The physiological implications of endocrine abnormalities in patients with breast cancer*

The finding of a low excretion of urinary androgen metabolites in women before a diagnosis of breast cancer is made is one thing; a physiological explanation of the results is another. Androgens administered in large doses are inhibitors of breast tumour growth, acting either directly on the tumour cells or via the pituitary gland. It would be an attractive hypothesis that endogenous androgens acted in the same way and that the low androgen excretion found in the pre-clinical phase of the disease therefore represented a net over-stimulation by oestrogens. However, there is at least an indication that this may not be the case. Adlercreutz et al. [18] have shown that in normal premenopausal women, urinary androgen excretion is correlated with urinary oestrogen excretion. Our own results are in agreement; high amounts of oestriol, oestradiol-17β and oestrone are associated with high amounts of urinary androsterone, aetiocholanolone and dehydroepiandrosterone (Bulbrook, Guillebaud and Lewis, unpublished observations).

The question now is whether the same relationship holds for women with breast cancer, either in the pre-clinical phase of the disease or when the disease is manifest. If this were so, the low androgen excretion found in the pre-clinical phase of the disease would also indicate a subnormal oestrogen production. This possibility would run contrary to the concepts of the last forty years since it has usually been assumed that a high oestrogenic stimulus was a key factor to the genesis of breast cancer.

If the excretion of oestrogens were indeed low in the pre-clinical phase of breast cancer, a direct action of pituitary hormones upon breast tissue might be postulated to be of first importance in breast cancer. In the rat, pituitary hormones can induce breast growth in the absence of steroid hormones, and recently Boot [19] has shown that implanted pituitary glands have a marked luteotrophic effect (thereby reducing the amount of oestrogen secreted) and increase the incidence of breast cancer in the mouse. This effect is almost certainly due to prolactin.

All the emphasis so far has been placed on the relationship between the endocrine environment and the tumour. However, if the endocrine abnormalities discussed above are indeed important, then other biochemical parameters should be affected and we have recently investigated several of these.

One end point of androgen activity is the production of sebum. Krant et al. [20] reported that postmenopausal women with breast cancer produced more sebum than normal controls and postulated that their patients had an excessive androgen production. Wang, Bulbrook, Guillebaud and Lewis (unpublished observations) have confirmed the findings of a higher sebum production in patients with breast cancer and have also shown that sebum production is correlated with plasma levels of dehydroepiandrosterone and androsterone sulphates (DS and AS) in normal women. However, in the patients with breast cancer, more sebum was produced for a given plasma level of DS or AS than in the controls. Since pituitary prolactin or growth hormone is also involved in the control of sebum production [21] these factors may account for the large amounts of sebum produced by patients with breast cancer.

As far as the physiological effects of cortisol are concerned, Mackay and Baum [22] found that the immune response of patients with breast cancer was depressed and that there was a relationship between immunological incompetence and prognosis. Plasma DS, AS and cortisol, and the patient's immune response have now been measured simultaneously. Surprisingly, there was a better correlation between plasma DS and AS levels and immune response than with the plasma cortisol [23].

Finally, Rose [24] found that tryptophan metabolism was abnormal in patients with breast cancer. The activity of liver tryptophan pryollase is markedly affected by administration of cortisol. Preliminary results indicate that abnormalities in tryptophan metabolism correlated with the ratio of the urinary androgen metabolites to the urinary 17-OHCS in premenopausal women (Bell, Bulbrook, Mainwaring, Tong and Hayward, unpublished observations).

It is not suggested that the plasma DS and AS levels have a direct effect on immune response or that tryptophan metabolism is necessarily influenced by the androgen/corticoid ratio. What these results do show is that the abnormalities in androgen production are associated with profound alterations in homeostasis in some patients. In other words, four major abnormalities are detectable; defective steroidogenesis [25] leading to low plasma DS and AS levels and a low urinary excretion of their metabolites; excessive sebum production; diminished immune response; and an abnormal metabolism of tryptophan. It seems highly probable that all these abnormalities are associated with a poor prognosis.

There can be little doubt that hormones from the pituitary, the adrenal glands and from the ovaries are of cardinal importance in the aetiology and in the clinical course of human breast cancer. So much remains to be investigated that it seems likely that the role of the hypothalamus in this disease will have to await the attentions of the next generation.

## REFERENCES

[1] Furth, J., *Cancer Res.*, **25,** 117, 1965.
[2] Bulbrook, R.D., Hayward, J.L., Spicer, C.C. and Thomas, B.S., *Lancet*, **2,** 1235, 1962.
[3] Bulbrook, R.D., Hayward, J.L. and Thomas, B.S., *Lancet*, **2,** 1238, 1964.
[4] Bulbrook, R.D. and Hayward, J.L. *Lancet*, **1,** 519, 1967.
[5] Bulbrook, R.D., Hayward, J.L. and Allen, D.S. In *Dutch Year Book of Cancer*, p. 163. Ed. J.H. De Bussey. Amsterdam, 1969.
[6] Bulbrook, R.D., *Vitam. Hormones.*, **23,** 329, 1965.
[7] Bulbrook, R.D. In *Advances in Steroid Biochemistry and Pharmacology*, vol. 1, p. 387. Ed. M.H. Briggs. London/New York: Academic Press, 1970.
[8] Lemon, H.M., *Cancer*, **23,** 781, 1969.
[9] Wang, D.Y., Hayward, J.L. and Bulbrook, R. D., *Eur. J. Cancer*, **2,** 373, 1966.
[10] Desphande, N., Hayward, J.L. and Bulbrook, R.D., *J. Endocr.*, **32,** 167, 1965.
[11] Wang, D.Y. In *The human adrenal gland and its relationship to breast cancer*, p. 71. Eds. K. Griffiths and E.H.D. Cameron. Cardiff: Alpha Omega Alpha Press, 1969.
[12] Benard, H., Bourdin, J.S., Saracino, R. and Seeman, A., *Eur. J. Cancer*, **5,** 239, 1969.
[13] Garnham, J.R., Bulbrook, R.D. and Wang, D.Y., *Eur. J. Cancer*, **5,** 239, 1969.
[14] Jensen V., Deshpande, N., Bulbrook, R.D. and Doouse, T., *J. Endocr.*, **42,** 425, 1968.
[15] Bell, E., Bulbrook, R.D. and Deshpande, N., *Lancet*, **2,** 395, 1967.
[16] Loraine, J.A., Strong, J.A. and Douglas, M., *Lancet*, **2,** 575, 1957.
[17] Greenwood, F.C., James, V.H.T., Meggitt, B.F., Miller, J.D. and Taylor, P.H. In *Prognostic factors in breast cancer*, p. 409. Eds. A.P.M. Forrest and P.B. Kunkler. Edinburgh/London: E. & S. Livingstone, 1968.
[18] Adlercreutz, H., Luukkainen, T. and Svanborg, A., *Ann. Med. Exp. Fenn.*, **45,** 277, 1967.
[19] Boot, L.M., *Int. J. Cancer*, **5,** 167, 1970.
[20] Krant, M.J., Brandrup, C.S., Green, R.S., Pochi, P.E. and Strauss, J.S., *Nature*, **217,** 463, 1968.
[21] Ebling, F.J., Ebling, E. and Skinner, J., *J. Endocr.*, **45,** 245, 1969
[22] Mackay, D. and Baum, M. In *Prognostic factors in breast cancer*, p. 319. Eds. A.P.M. Forrest and P.B. Kunkler. Edinburgh/London: E. & S. Livingstone, 1968.
[23] Mackay, D., Wang, D.Y. and Bulbrook, R.D., *Proc. Ass. Surg.* (in press, 1970).
[24] Rose, D.P., *Lancet*, **1,** 239, 1967.
[25] Deshpande, N., Jensen, V., Bulbrook, R.D. and Doouse, T.W., *Steroids*, **9,** 393 1967

*Discussion of paper by Dr Bulbrook*

*Griffiths* We have also studied DHA sulphate levels in the plasma of normal women and in those with benign breast disease and primary and advanced breast cancer, and can confirm your findings that in advanced breast cancer the DHA sulphate levels are lower than normal. We find little difference in DHA sulphate levels when comparing early primary breast cancer with the benign state.

*Bulbrook* The puzzling feature of these findings is that the patients were in a state of stress when the blood was taken, having just come into hospital and had the diagnosis made. Yet in the early stage of the disease they have normal levels of DHA sulphate. I suspect that the effect of breast cancer in lowering DHA sulphate may be much larger than we think and that it is their stress reaction which has brought them back up to normal. We are going to get our patients back into hospital three months after diagnosis and see what the levels are in a less stressed state. Don't you find it surprising that the early breast cancer patients should be the same as normal?

*Griffiths* We found it disappointing. I am not sure that they are as much stressed as you imply.

*Brown* In the early studies showing the relationship between androgens and oestrogens in the premenopausal women, at what stage of the cycle did you measure the oestrogens?

*Bulbrook* We took the mean of five urine collections as nearly as possible in the middle of the cycle. Of course this gives rise to some difficulty as you don't know whether any result refers to the pre-ovulatory oestrogen peak or to the post-ovulatory drop. A further problem with premenopausal patients is that they often do not re-establish menstruation at all after the mastectomy.

*Naftolin* What happens to the hormone levels after removal of the tumour? Are prolactin-secreting cells ever identified in the pituitaries of those women who have a hypophysectomy? One wonders how far the steroid differences can cause differences in the production of prolactin and what effect this might have on tumour growth.

*Bulbrook* The effects of removal of the tumour are very difficult to evaluate. There is a well-documented drop caused presumably by any operation but in some of our cases going on for as long as a year. So I can't really give a direct answer concerning the effects of removing the tumour. As regards pathological examinations of the pituitaries removed, I do not think these are very reliable. Pituitaries from cancer patients show all sorts of bizarre effects like excessive thyrotropic cells although the patients themselves seldom show thyroid malfunction. Greenwood found very little change in

the growth hormone content. It would be distressing if you were right about the prolactin changes being caused by the steroids as it would mean that there is no primary pituitary effect; it is all mediated by the steroids.
*Naftolin* Does lactation have any effect on the subsequent development of breast cancer? In other words, is there a prolactin effect in breast cancer?
*Bulbrook* The effects of both pregnancy and of lactation are very small. I suspect the woman most liable to breast cancer is the one with long periods of amenorrhoea whose prolactin has not been opposed by adequate oestrogen.
*Grant* I think you have deliberately made the rather sweeping statement that low urinary androgens equals low urinary oestrogens and therefore under-production of oestrogens. Have you any studies on plasma oestrogens or any observations on the dynamics of oestrogen production such as those Professor MacDonald has been discussing? Is it not possible that although urinary oestrogens may be low, plasma oestrogens need not be so?
*Bulbrook* We were relying on Dr Brown's paper defining the relationship between injected oestrogens and the urinary excretion. I think it is fair comment that urinary oestrogens may not be always a reliable reflection of endogenous oestrogens. We are going to have to set up proper production rate studies but it will be a terrible job *de novo*.
*Strong* To what extent is plasma DHA sulphate affected by stress? Can you equate stress with corticotropin secretion and will this profoundly affect DHA sulphate levels? If such stress effects do happen with DHA sulphate, what would be the effect of suppressing their adrenals with, say, dexamethazone? You would then presumably get basal levels of DHA sulphate. You have emphasized the stressful effect of admitting people to hospital but have you any data to compare people at home with those in hospital? I do not think it is necessarily true that changes will relate to the environment alone and not to the effect of anaesthetics and surgery or to the anticipation of these stresses.
*Bulbrook* As far as stress is concerned we have not done any plasma studies but are relying entirely on the urinary results. In urine the androgens go up quite considerably, admittedly only a third as much as do the corticoids, so we have assumed that the same thing happens in blood. I think there is a fair amount of data in the literature to support that admission to hospital is a potent stress stimulus as far as steroid production is concerned. The only controls we have are in the Guernsey experiment where the women were admitted to hospital. I do not think that as stressful stimuli, admission to hospital with breast cancer or with, say, varicose veins can be compared.
*MacDonald* Plasma levels of DHA sulphate are very resistant to change by alterations in the production rate. One may get a considerable change in production rate by the adrenal without much change in the plasma level.

The reason is that there is a buffer system between DHA sulphate and DHA, such that with increasing production in DHA sulphate there is an exponential rise in the urinary excretion so that the blood levels are not substantially altered. Conversely, if the production rate decreases, there is a fall in urinary excretion and the blood levels stay unchanged.

*Bulbrook* In the early days we tried injections of radioactive DHA and this led us to the view that our results really did arise from the low secretion of DHA.

*Mills* Since the patients with the polycystic ovary syndrome have high androgens – and you are relating low androgens to breast cancer – do you know of any data on the incidence of breast cancer in patients with polycystic ovaries?

*Bulbrook* No, I do not know of any.

*Van der Molen* I know that it is dangerous to make comparisons with animal experiments but I think that in animals simple administration of oestrogens can increase prolactin concentration. I think you are implying that lower endogenous oestrogens may raise prolactin levels. I know that some people feed their animals with oestrogens to stimulate prolactin-producing tumours.

*Bulbrook* But if you look at the affected strains of mice you will find they come into oestrus very rarely and in animals with implanted pituitaries there is very little oestrogen or progesterone floating around.

*Van der Molen* I was thinking of experiments where oestrogen is put into the drinking water and stimulates the prolactin-producing cells.